FERRAMONTI

Salvation behind the barbed wire

by

David Henryk Ropschitz

Editor: Yolanda Ropschitz-Bentham

TEXIANER VERLAG

FERRAMONTI
by
David Henryk Ropschitz (1913-1986)
Edited by
©2020 Yolanda Ropschitz-Bentham
SECOND EDITION
Published by Texianer Verlag
www.texianer.com

ISBN: 978-3-949197-12-3

DEDICATION

To Jacob and Sophia Ropschitz of Lvov and Vienna and their four children, Amalia Merkel, Klara Todt, Eduard Ropschitz and Roza Rauch, whose lives were so brutally terminated. Their names live on.

PREFACE

My father wrote this book towards the end of his life. This is his story, based on his recollections. I have simply given it wings.

Yolanda Ropschitz-Bentham
Somerset, England, 2020

Contents

Introduction

Galicia-born David Henryk Ropschitz, like other east European Jews in the early 1930s, was barred from university study in his birth country of Poland and adopted country of Austria, due to prevailing anti-Semitic laws, known as *numerus clausus*. Determined to follow the family medical tradition, he re-located to the more tolerant Italy, as did many of his contemporaries in pre-war Europe. There he qualified in medicine at the University of Genoa in 1937. As the situation in Europe worsened he became stateless and in July 1940, with only a few hours' warning, was sent on one of the first transports to Italy's newly established Ferramonti di Tarsia *Campo di Concentramento*. Apart from a short period in *confino libero* in Abruzzo, he remained in Ferramonti until its liberation by Allied forces in September 1943.

This autobiographical novel, describes the prevailing conditions and attitudes under Fascist rule in Ferramonti during the three years of internment; it tells how the lives of its internees unfurled, their joys and sorrows, their humour and stoicism against the backdrop of World War II. Names have been changed to preserve confidentiality and inevitably there will be some embellishments, omissions and chronological lapses. I hope this will not diminish the authenticity of the memories, my father, David Ropschitz, carried with him for over 40 years.

Prologue

It was in Calabria, in the middle of the Crati valley not far from the Busento, that legendary river which guards the submerged tomb of Alaric the Goth, where this history unfolds.

Greeks, Carthaginians, Romans, Goths, Normans, Moors and Albanians all trod this soil, though in its present desolation there was little to suggest its turbulent past and remote glories. The valley was almost bowl-shaped, surrounded by the barren hills, generally arid, a dust-bowl except for patches of bog and morass by the river Crati, where the Anopheles larvae bred in great profusion: a notoriously malaria-infested zone.

Trees were scarce but those that did manage to wrest a living from this inhospitable soil were astonishingly large and robust. With no help from pruning hands they grew into almost perfect spheres, which shape afforded the best protection from a merciless sun. Mainly locust, mulberry, fig and olive, with an occasional oak, they were sturdy, tall and impressive. Most of them were old, with something time-defying, archaic about them. Firmly entrenched they sent their moisture-seeking roots deep down into mother earth tapping her subterranean springs to mock the scorching sun which threatened to suck them dry.

In the middle of this valley, by 1943, on a bare stony patch were a great many Nissen-type huts, teeming with a multi-national population. Walls were fashioned from triple barbed wire, with sentry boxes at regular intervals. Viewed from above, at a distance, one could take this conglomeration of huts for a densely populated village with its inhabitants constantly on the move.

But in July 1940, when first the 'Triumvirate' arrived, things were very different. Then there was only one barrack, *una camerata,* and the rest of the desolate expanse was filled with heaps of sand and shingle, mortar and cement, planks and iron bars. Italian strategists hoping for a quick and successful campaign had put off any further construction of concentration camps. They saw the war ending in no time.

The first bunch to arrive, in the first week of July, was a random selection of twenty-three bewildered, worn out and profusely perspiring individuals from all walks of life, among them three young doctors soon referred to as the Triumvirate. Ossi Gerber, Dino Fuhrman and Henry Raupner became an inseparable trio, although their backgrounds and personalities differed widely. They would hardly have taken much notice of each other had not Fate thrown them together into this uncertain venture.

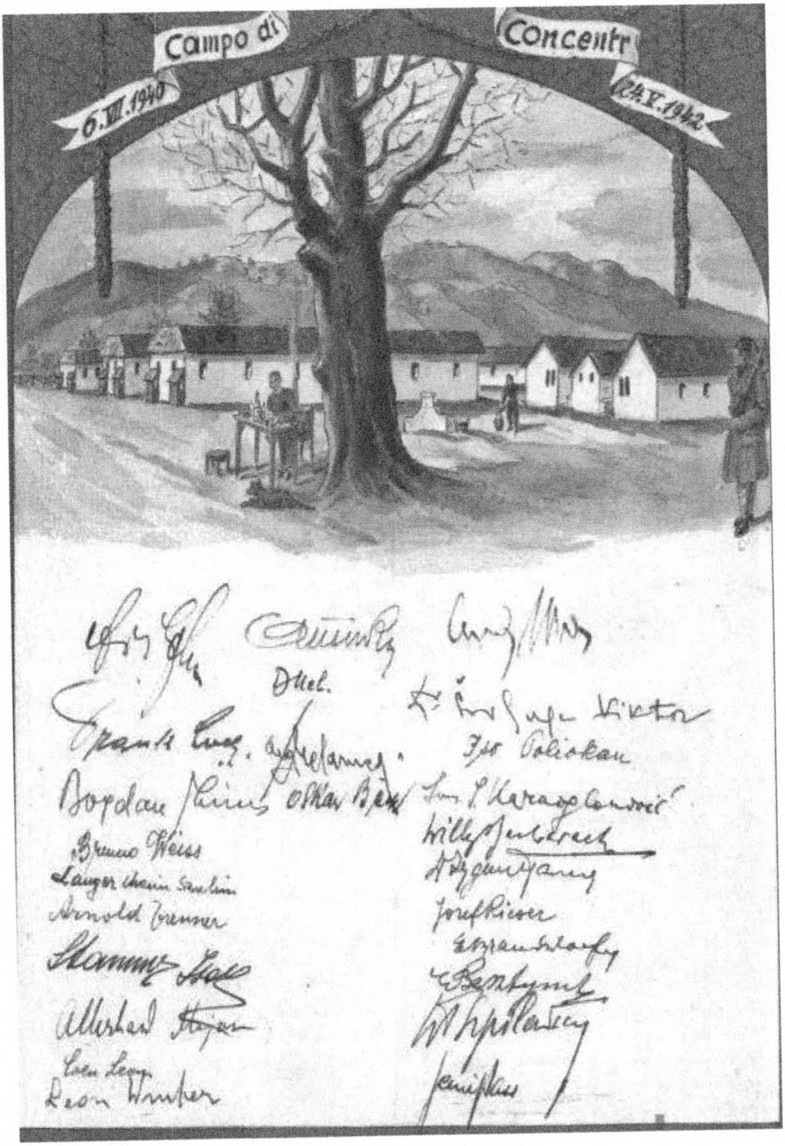
Campo di
Concentr
6.VIII.1940
24.V.1942
Bruno Weiss
Arnold Brenner
Leon Winter

Book One

July 1940–October 1941

Part One

Chapter 1

The Triumvirate

Ossi Gerber and Henry Raupner had known of each other in Genoa for some time but somehow never made close contact. They had been introduced and re-introduced several times, pretending each time to be complete strangers. The reason for this mutually reluctant acknowledgement was obscure, unless it was rooted in some vague masculine rivalry.

Ossi Gerber was a polished and extremely handsome young man. Though his looks were somewhat delicate, he could be very firm and authoritative when the need arose. He was an aesthete, much interested in the Muses as well as the art of good living. A pallid complexion contrasted sharply with raven-black hair which he wore to one side, revealing a forehead of marmoreal pallor. His dark, penetrating eyes had a sharp, vivid expression, in harmony with a sensitive aquiline nose. He was always impeccably dressed. Any superficial observer could have taken him for a bit of a dandy, but there was a lot more to him than his sophisticated exterior suggested.

He came from the provincial town of Bochnia in Poland. His father, a wealthy textile industrialist, had entertained great expectations of his only son. Like most Jewish parents who have acquired any measure of wealth, they wished their son to enter one of the professions, preferably the one most honoured by Jewish hearts: medicine. Ossi was a sickly child who at the age of fourteen had contracted rheumatic fever, which reputedly left him with some mitral valve damage. Being an only child, he was wrapped in parental cotton wool, but Ossi's independent spirit protested against their smothering. Although he had to abandon the more strenuous forms of sport on doctor's orders, he nonetheless took up soccer's less taxing position as a goalkeeper.

After matriculation his parents decided to send him abroad. Their choice fell on Montpellier, which had a renowned medical faculty. It was hard to send their only son away from home, but *numerus clausus*, that unofficial limit on the number of Jewish students, as well as the sickening anti-Semitism in Polish universities, helped them in their resolve.

Papa Gerber was an intelligent man. He'd sensed the excessive attachment between mother and son, and his own life experience had taught him the importance of stamina and moral toughness. It was imperative for the 'young *loshak*', the colt—as he called him affectionately—to escape his mother's over-protectiveness. Besides, there was also the question of prestige. It would be very agreeable to say casually, "My son? Oh yes! He's studying medicine in the South of France. At Montpellier, the town of Nostradamus."

Young Ossi enjoyed his student days in France immensely. There he'd acquired an extra polish of charm and urbanity. His French became fluent, losing its textbook flavour. To Mamma Gerber it was a source of pride to listen to her son's French chatter during the summer holidays when she paraded him in the '*mondaine*' circles of their small native town.

In those pre-war days, provincial towns with a minimum of 'high life', a modicum of vice and some cultural interests regarded themselves as a 'Little Paris' which made them feel superior, sophisticated and worldly. French was the second tongue of the Polish nobility and intelligentsia so proficiency in it was a hallmark of refinement.

To complete his education, both medical and general, Ossi decided to take the second half of his medical training in Italy, dividing the three remaining years between Florence and Genoa. He qualified in 1939, barely nine months before Italy's declaration of war and when his native Poland had already been invaded by German and Russian forces. There was nowhere else to go, so he'd stayed in Italy hoping for the best.

In complete contrast to Ossi's elegance, **Dino Fuhrman** was 'all hair'. Even with the closest shave his black stubble was not to be suppressed so that a bluish tinge suffused his sunburnt face. It was quite common for strands of curly hair to creep up from under Dino's collar. Considering the hairiness of his chest this was not surprising but, in the opinion of some fellow-students, this was deliberate and for the benefit of the girls. Dino was a well-developed athletic specimen, muscular and firm, a sports-addict who loved to give his competitive spirit full rein.

On top of his magnificent physique, nature had also bestowed on him a good brain. He was a clever student as well as an excellent chess and bridge player; this latter skill he shared with Ossi, a bridge expert in his own right. In spite of his hairy masculinity and sharp wit there was a lovable childish streak in him which made him revere the heroes of the Wild West, occasionally adopting the slang of gunmen and cowboys.

Dino was born in Brody; his parents were of Jewish Russo-Polish stock. His father served in the Imperial Austrian army in World War One, was taken prisoner on the Italian front and after several years of confinement came to love his adoptive country. After the war Fuhrman senior decided to stay on and soon became a naturalised Italian. He sent for his wife and 7 year old son to join him in Italy and so young Dino grew up in Genoa. Dino's father was a shrewd and hardworking man and in spite of the proverb '*Un Genovese vale sette Ebrei*' – one Genovese is worth seven Jews – he had established a chain of small shops in the thickly-populated neighbourhood of the port. Gradually, when his garment business began to pay, he ventured out into the more up-market districts of Genoa. So his son Dino was never subjected to the humiliating experiences of anti-Semitism to which Jews in central and Eastern Europe were exposed. There was practically no anti-Semitism in Italy before World War Two and Dino grew up uninhibited, self-assured and free, having been deprived of that catalyst of suffering, which so often produces a natural cautiousness of spirit and behaviour.

Unaffected by the constraints of *numerus clausus*, Dino was able to enter the medical faculty of Genoa University and joyously plunged into the gay, silly initiation rites of the '*Matricola*' as the freshmen were called. During the '*Festa della Matricola*' he was up in front among the craziest, noisiest and most daring. Dino was a 'natural' in every respect; he took whatever came his way unburdened by inner conflicts, inhibitions or introspection. This gave him an instant charm and charisma.

Dino was in many ways a refreshing and outgoing personality; an extravert able to communicate vitality and optimism in times of crisis or gloom. He and Ossi had been in the same stream at University and had qualified simultaneously.

At the outbreak of war, when the rounding up of foreign Jews began, Dino realised that in spite of his almost complete assimilation and Italian nationality, his fate was nonetheless linked with the rest of Jewry, for better or for worse.

Henry Raupner was born in 1913 in Lvov, Galicia, which at that time was still part of the Austro-Hungarian Empire and called Lemberg. His father, Jacob, born in 1865 into a poor Orthodox Jewish family had made his way by hard work, good brains and an extraordinary expertise in precious stones. Although Jacob held his own father David, in loving esteem, he would not follow in his footsteps because Papa Raupner, a tailor, could barely scrape a living, which wasn't surprising given his other-worldly, impractical disposition.

But his son, Jacob, was not out for Talmudic honours; he could not forget the humiliations and deprivations of his poverty-stricken youth and he vowed he would go hungry no more. By the time he was forty he had a large family, a beautiful home and a thriving jewellery business. Henry's birth embarrassed his 42 year old mother, but father Jacob beamed with masculine pride as he proudly displayed his 10th child. 'Many a fine tune is played on an old fiddle,' he quipped.

Henry was a sturdy and lively baby but soon his peaceful life was to be abruptly unsettled by the outbreak of World War One. The Russian steamroller pushed towards Lemberg and mindful of Cossack atrocities, Jacob took his family to Vienna. In their haste the family packed only bare essentials, leaving their beautiful home and jewellery shop behind. For days the family had to endure the crowded waiting rooms of the *Ostbahnhof,* before Jacob succeeded in finding a tiny flat in a dismal district of Vienna. The lavish life they had left behind in Galicia was no more than a distant memory.

However, life went on and just before Henry's third birthday Papa Jacob somehow contrived to get hold of a live chicken, a rare luxury in wartime Vienna. Little Henry was overjoyed. Trapped in the overcrowded flat in Vienna, his knowledge of zoology was limited to cockroaches, bedbugs and flies. A chicken was something out of this world. He insisted his new playmate should sleep in a box by his bedside and made mother Sophia promise that it would stay with him 'for ever and ever'. For two whole days he played with the chicken to his heart's delight, but on the morning of his birthday it had vanished. He was heartbroken.

"It must have flown up the chimney," said Sophia, "and perhaps it will come back one day." Little Henry sobbed all morning, but his tears eased at the delicious family lunch until his father absentmindedly remarked, "Mmm, fine chicken soup."

At first he did not grasp the implications of his father's comment, but his youngest sister Anna who could not control her spite, or her laughter, made clear the fate of the poor bird.

"It's on your plate, you Dummkopf!"

The 3 year old's realisation that he had enjoyed eating his pet created a profound and enduring sense of betrayal and disgust.

Henry was the youngest of ten, but only four of his siblings played a major role in his life. Izhio, his eldest brother, was the 'poet' of the family. Endowed with a rich vein of imagination and a fluent tongue, his recitals and declamations fascinated little Henry and resulted in a lifelong appreciation of poetry and drama. His second brother, Leon, was of a different mettle. An introvert and a loner, Lonek was a passionate fisherman who, using only the merest of fishing gear, caught fish by the score. He gave his brother a lasting enthusiasm for angling.

Anna played first a negative and later an ambivalent role, for she held a grudge against the late arrival, who had usurped the baby status she had relished for seven years. But Henry's closest bond was with his brother, Mundek, 12 years his senior.

After the war, when Henry was five, the family made a short-lived return to Lemberg, but soon the persistent political instability and a longing for the cultural and intellectual refinements of the ex-Hapsburg capital, drove them back to Vienna. There then followed a strange pattern, a kind of family neurosis, resulting in periodic shuttling between Lemberg and Vienna. This frequent disruption and changes of language and schools took its toll on young Henry and caused him great stress and mental confusion.

From a sheltered Hebrew kindergarten he went to Polish and then German schools where he made his first acquaintance with anti-Semitism and ridicule. That was when his brother, Mundek, proved worth his weight in gold. Mundek's own studies had been so disrupted that, unlike his brothers Izhio and Leon, he was unable to matriculate. The continual to and fro of the 'Fools Brigade' – as he called his family —had left him a misfit, a deeply displaced person, and he wanted to protect his little brother from a similar unhappy fate. Mundek taught him to swim, to kick a ball around, initiated him into the world of chess and showed him how to care for the pigeons he kept in the loft.

Mundek conveyed his love of nature to young Henry who enjoyed walking beside the Danube with his big brother and visiting the city's beautiful parks, Schonbrunn, Stadtpark and the Prater. As they walked Mundek would explain things to him and Henry avidly drank in every word. It was easy to learn from a teacher he adored.

When Henry was eleven, the family finally settled in a top-floor apartment in Vienna's Grosse Schiffgasse, and at Mundek's suggestion Henry was sent to the Chajes Gymnasium, a Jewish grammar school with Zionist leanings and a reputation for producing high-achievers. He found it a struggle at first, not only because of the rigorous academic standards required but also the school's focus on character-formation and arts appreciation. It was here that Henry first came to study the history of the Jewish people.

The school was co-educational and there was one particular girl, named Golda, to whom Henry took an immediate liking. She had long blonde plaits, blue eyes and a very sensitive face.

Permanently settled now for the first time in his life, he made friends and familiarised himself with the different districts of Vienna, its theatres, concert halls and opera houses. His adolescent mind expanded gradually for there was hardly a city in Europe in those days to rival Vienna as a source of artistic and intellectual inspiration. The teachings of Freud and Adler were in vogue with far-reaching effects on literature, education and the understanding of man.

As for Mundek, suspended in no man's land, he was eventually apprenticed to the diamond trade although his heart was not in it. He made heroic efforts to get away from the soul-destroying atmosphere of hard-boiled businessmen by taking singing and piano lessons, studying the theory of chess and exploring biology. An avid reader and deeply interested in the sciences, Mundek continued to influence young Henry, discussing and explaining to him the natural phenomena of the universe. Mundek had become not only his mentor but also his Maecenas, and whatever he suggested was gladly carried out even when it went against the grain. For example he persuaded him to shave his head during the summer holidays, "to invigorate the hair roots," just when Henry was becoming keen to impress girls. "It's better to shave off your hair when you are young instead of losing it altogether like Papa."

Meantime a very delicate romance was budding between Henry and Golda, spinning its silken threads around them. It was on a beautiful spring afternoon in March 1930 that Henry, aged 17, his head still in the clouds after saying goodbye to Golda, got home from school. The house porter gave him a strange glance, but as was his custom, Henry ran up the several flights of stairs to their top floor apartment. Anna opened the door. She was as pale as death, her red-rimmed eyes streaming with tears. With a loud sob she threw her arms about Henry. "Mundek is dead! He shot himself!"

Henry's heart thumped violently as an iron hand seemed to close around it. He tried to steady himself, his legs weak, feeling sick to the stomach. Mundek dead? How could this be? Everybody around him was sobbing, hanging on to each other in grief. He was frozen, unable to cry. He was trying to make sense of what was happening and could not. He wandered around the apartment in a daze unable to comprehend anything he was seeing or hearing.

Why Mundek, at 29, had taken his life, remained a mystery. Theories were explored: disappointment in love, financial worries, but none fitted. The most important single factor was his suspension in mid-air, the feeling that he had lost his way and was drifting aimlessly. Later in life, when Henry became more involved in psychology, he learned that those who commit suicide have usually embarked on a gradual process of self-destruction many years before.

The loss of his adored brother was a trauma from which he would never fully recover. Every member of the family suffered, but none of them owed Mundek a greater debt than Henry. All he was, all he knew, was because of his brother. On the day of Mundek's death something died in him too. He was no longer an adolescent school boy. It was a miracle that he continued his studies, but he did, like an automaton. Concentration on his books even helped to divert his attention from that constant pain, the endless inquisition within. Could Henry have prevented it? Did Mundek not realise how much he was loved? The only way out of the interminable sadness was to devote himself to his exams; this would be Henry's lasting gift to his big brother.

Eventually he got through his matriculation and so in 1931 he moved to Genoa, to study medicine. At that time Mussolini welcomed foreign students, Jews and gentiles alike. At Vienna University, even before the Anschluss, anti-Semitism had become unbearably offensive and so Henry had chosen to study on the Italian Liguria coast. His married brother, Izhio, had a medical practice in Alassio; his sisters Helena and Anna, married to Polish doctors, also resided in the region, in Bordighera and Viareggio, so he was surrounded by family and felt at home for several years.

But now that Mussolini had jumped on Hitler's bandwagon, things were very different. His siblings had left Italy because of the racial laws whereas Henry, made stateless by the Polish authorities, was stranded in Genoa without a passport, caught in the net, unable to leave, unsure of where to call home anymore. Several of his colleagues had already been arrested. Now Henry expected to share their fate.

Chapter 2

"All aboard!": July 1940

S o that was it. Passing through the *questura* gate, suitcase in hand, rucksack on back, Henry was taken into a courtyard where amidst great confusion and noise he was enveloped by the crowd. Some stood in groups while others kept apart. Henry noticed one young man perched on his case and he did the same as there was nobody there he knew. People were still arriving, some carrying hastily improvised bundles, others lugging heavy trunks. Those in groups were families, huddled together around a father, brother or son. They were talking, gesticulating, and embracing one another in tears. As far as Henry could make out, only the men were to be taken away.

He wished he had somebody by his side, but he no longer had any relatives in Italy. The order to report to the *questura* had come so suddenly, out of the blue, there had been no time even to inform any friends. As he sat on his suitcase he let his gaze wander. That solitary young man, crouching on his luggage, did seem vaguely familiar, but at that distance he couldn't be sure.

"*Appello!*" The shriek of an official in uniform reverberated suddenly around the courtyard. "*Appello!*" he yelled again above the confusion. The roll call began. "Dvorak!" "Here!" "Wolf!" "Here!" "Altman!" "Here!" "Gerber!" "Here!"

Henry nodded in recognition. So it was Gerber, Dr Ossi Gerber. No wonder the young man on the suitcase had seemed familiar. The official's rasping voice called out name after name, but Henry was not interested, although slightly amused by the comically mangled way these foreign names emerged from Italian lips.

"Fuhrman!" the official snapped.

"Here!" came a deep baritone. Henry smiled to himself. So Dino Fuhrman is here too. That makes three doctors. He had not been able to see Dino before, lost as he was behind a wall of parents, well-wishers and friends.

The moment of departure was drawing near. A sudden unrest and agitation pervaded the crowd and then loud sobbing rose above the din. People fell into each other's arms, children clung to their fathers, women moaned into their handkerchiefs. Henry and Gerber remained seated in the general commotion, but now, made aware of each other's presence, they exchanged glances and tentative smiles.

"*In fila da tre!* Three in a row!" yelled the official.

Those to be deported were segregated from the rest and formed into ranks. Ossi Gerber came over to join Henry and at the last moment Dino Fuhrman hastened to complete the trio. "*Avanti*" thundered the official. They passed through the gates of the *questura* and, flanked by militiamen, were marched to the waiting lorries, to be carried off to their unknown destination. The presence of the militia and the way they pushed and shoved their load into the lorries was a brutal awakening to the sudden loss of freedom and dignity.

A short journey later they were bundled out at Genoa Principe, the main railway station. The same silly marching manoeuvre was repeated, and like criminals, they were escorted to a train. Theirs was a sealed coach, which looked very forbidding with its iron shutters and special security locks. The three doctors entered the same compartment. Apart from the degrading escort in full view of an astonished crowd, there had been nothing vicious or inhuman in their treatment—so far.

Dino Fuhrman was the first to break the silence.

"Well, well! A sealed coach! Like the one the Germans used for Lenin to hatch the revolution!" He seemed excited, beaming all over his face—it smelled of adventure. Slapping Henry on the shoulder he exclaimed, "Don't you find it exciting John?"

"My name is Henry!"

"What's the odds? Everyone is John to me," said Dino, grinning, as the train pulled away.

Ossi Gerber remained rather quiet and aloof; Henry pensively studied the dim electric bulb, which barely illuminated the compartment. Gradually the tension and strain of the day seemed to ebb. Outside it was a beautiful midsummer's day and it was such a pity to sit in semi-darkness with the iron blinds down.

Dino's temperament did not allow him to sit still for long. He got up and tried to open the door of the compartment, but it was locked. So, out of boredom, he opened a small case and began to eat. One could see at a glance that the food was prepared by loving hands; *focaccia*, fruit and sweets, all nicely wrapped in multi-coloured soft tissue paper. Serviettes were carefully folded, dainty forks and knives, a shining thermos flask, all impeccably arranged and packed, proclaimed the thoughtfulness and care that lay behind their preparation. Mamma Fuhrman idolised her son; she had prepared a picnic with tender foresight.

A militiaman unlocked the door and looked in.

"Come to collect our tickets?" asked Dino jokingly.

He only got a blank look.

"Anybody for the toilet?"

They shook their heads. As the Black-shirted militiaman was about to retrace his steps, Dino had a sudden inspiration. He grabbed the Chianti flask from his case and offered it to the Italian, who accepted a drink. Dino engaged him in conversation, remarking after a while, "It's very hot in here. *Molto caldo*. Could you open the window?"

"*Proibito*! Forbidden!" replied the Blackshirt dryly.

But Dino was not taking 'No' so easily. He knew his Italians.

"But why? We could not escape if we wanted to."

"It's not that," said the Italian with some hesitation, "you are not supposed to look and ..."

"To look at what?" Dino interrupted him, "at the tomatoes? *I pomodori*?"

The militiaman seemed to lose patience.

"Don't play the fool!"

He did not know whether to be annoyed or amused, but looking into Dino's friendly eyes and reassured by that impeccable Genoese accent, he relented and pulled up the metallic blind a little way. Then he left the compartment, locking the door behind him.

The crack was only a few inches wide, but what a difference it made when the bright Italian sun began to flood the compartment. Dino sank to his knees to peer through the glass pane, which could not be opened.

"Rapallo!" he exclaimed. They were going south. Taking turns at the space they watched the landscape flitting by: peach trees bending under ripening fruit, vineyards, scattered villas, palm trees, cypresses — a typically bucolic Italian scene.

After a while they grew tired of crouching and sank back into their seats. The sealed compartment was too stuffy and hot to think, which was a blessing, for the less one thought, the better.

"Hey John! Let's play cards!" Dino suggested suddenly.

"My name is Henry."

"Never mind. Let's play."

Ossi, familiar with Dino's mannerisms, smiled at Henry's annoyance. A pack of cards was quickly whipped from Dino's pocket. Henry was non-plussed; had he not known otherwise, he might have mistaken him for a professional gambler, so dexterously did he shuffle the pack.

This is one of his juvenile exhibitions, Henry thought. They played, but their hearts were not in it. Time seemed to drag and they did not know what to do with themselves. So Dino began to reminisce about his student pranks in the dissecting room and during exams. Gradually, via his exploits at sport, bridge and chess, he came upon his pet topic: his mother, and her culinary prowess. He described in minute detail the *borscht* and *cholent* at which she excelled.

Henry also enjoyed a strong bond with his mother. She wasn't a mean cook either, especially with roast duck and *Apfelstrudel* and so he joined in the eulogy in praise of Jewish mothers.

As all three continued to extol their mothers' virtues it dawned on Henry that this had not arisen by chance but came from a deeper craving in their hour of need; a need for nourishment both physical and maternal.

Peering through the narrow slit Henry noticed that the day was drawing to its end. *L'heure bleue,* he whispered to himself, that fine bluish mist-shrouded sundown, so typical of Italian summer evenings. Scattered lights began to glow. What a pity the window would not budge! How he longed to inhale the fresh evening air!

As they sped through a station, Henry's eye caught the name and he announced loudly, "Forte dei Marmi!" Neither Dino nor Ossi paid much attention to this name, but it made Henry's heart beat faster for the next station was Viareggio. *Oh! If Mona only knew I am passing so close to her!* Henry had spent many glorious hours on its sandy beaches, first with sister Anna and husband Frederico, later with Mona. How he would long for his holidays there after the exhausting cramming for his medical exams!

Dino suddenly got up. "Was that Forte dei Marmi just now?"

Henry nodded.

"Well then we are past La Spezia by now."

"What of it?" asked Ossi.

"Don't you see? That Blackshirt said we shouldn't look. Most likely he meant the naval base of La Spezia." Then, laughing contemptuously, he added, "They are afraid we might catch sight of the Italian Fleet, the mighty Armada."

"So what?"

"Well, he might open the shutters and window now at least."

This said, he started banging on the compartment door. After a while the same militiaman appeared. "What do you want now?" he barked.

"It's hot and stuffy here. We can hardly breathe! Besides it's getting dark so one can't see a damn thing anyway."

As the militiaman seemed unmoved, Dino quickly changed his tactics. "You know the Geneva Conventions on Prisoners of War? They have to be treated humanely. Now, we are not even prisoners, just civilian internees."

"You are Jews," the militiaman observed with a shrug.

Dino ignored this remark.

"It is against all the rules to lock people up in a confined space, especially in such heat, without a breath of air."

The Blackshirt seemed undecided whether to take Dino's remarks seriously or just brush them aside. So Dino, sensing the man's hesitation, continued to press his point.

"Look here, all three of us are doctors and we are telling you it is unhealthy and against the Geneva Conventions!" Then, indicating Ossi, he continued, "See my friend here? He has heart trouble, *malattia di cuore*, and needs plenty of air!"

Italians are not generally dogmatic; one can usually argue with and appeal to them. Whether it was Dino's Genoese accent that disarmed him, or the Geneva Conventions bit, was immaterial; he pushed up the metal blind completely and opened the window as well. Having done so, he left the compartment without a word, locking them in.

Dino was triumphant and beat his chest Tarzan fashion. "Ah!" he grunted. "It's all psychology!"

Amazing how quickly Dino can switch from child to adult and vice versa, thought Henry. All three rushed to stick their heads out of the window. The fragrance in the air was overwhelming; a mixture of salt, oleander and rosemary. From their window only the *campagna* was visible. The sea lay on their blind side, hidden from view by the shutters in the corridor.

"What a shame we can't see the sun sinking into the sea," Ossi said, wistfully.

"Listen to him!" laughed Dino. "Give him a finger and he wants the whole arm!"

When the novelty of the open window had worn off, Dino became bored and restless again. "Let's have some food. What do the eggheads call it? Oral gratification?" Down came his suitcase. Out came the parcels in their many-coloured wrappings. He began to eat, or rather devour, the savoury delicatessen Mamma Fuhrman had prepared for her beloved son.

Ossi lit himself a cigarette in his urbane manner. First he selected a cigarette from his engraved silver case. Then he tapped the end lightly to level off any roughness, and placing it gently in the corner of his mouth, he lit it adroitly with his pretty silver lighter. Inhaling deeply, he blew the smoke through his nostrils. The coordination of his movements was immaculate, yet neither studied nor affected, like a high priest performing some ceremonial rite.

Henry, sitting next to the open window, enjoyed the sweet evening breeze and closed his eyes. Even though he was tired and drained emotionally after the strenuous events of the day, his mind still worked overtime. How quickly it had all come about! How brutal his awakening from wishful thinking!

Surely, after nine years of unblemished residence in Italy they will leave me in peace? As soon as he'd seen his landlady's swollen eyes that morning, he'd known his luck had run out.

"A man from the *questura* left this note for you." She had passed the note with trembling hand and great trepidation.

The instructions, in German, were terse. He had to present himself on 7th July at the Genoa *questura* at 11 a.m. "Punktlich." Punctually. Only one suitcase was permitted. It was not the alien they were after, but the Jew. There was nothing he could do about it. At least he had been spared the humiliation of an arrest. There was so much to do or to be taken care of that he didn't even attempt to put his affairs in order. All he did was to pack the barest of essentials, leaving the rest of his belongings with his landlady, and the host of undealt with personal affairs to Fate.

The train rattled its way along the coast.

"Sleeping or brooding?" asked Ossi suddenly.

Henry opened his eyes. "Just reviewing the day," he replied with a deep sigh.

"Why didn't you leave Italy before?" Ossi asked.

"I couldn't. I'm stateless. They took my passport. You?"

"I had to finish my studies first. By the time I got my medical degree, Poland was already invaded. I had nowhere to go and very little money. So I stayed put, hoping for the best."

Both fell silent. Only Dino's snoring broke the stillness.

"Why does he call me John?" Henry asked all of a sudden.

Ossi smiled. "His mannerism. He still inhabits the world of cowboys and Indians. To him 'John' or 'Bill' are synonymous with trappers, buffalo hunters."

"But he can be so sensible at times."

"I know. That's where his special charm comes from." With these words Ossi reclined and closed his eyes.

It was getting dark. Henry tried to sleep, but his brain couldn't rest. Why had he not bothered to write to anyone, not even Mona, about the gradual change in his circumstances? He had known he was on borrowed time. On reflection this peculiar apathy had been with him for some time now. But alongside that apathy there had been another sensation, a kind of curiosity and expectation, which gradually began to surface; an inquisitiveness about the sort of experiences life now had in store for him. At this stage of his development Henry did not believe that there existed 'good' or 'bad' experiences *per se*; all depended, he thought, on being able to find some meaning, some spiritual essence, from whatever experience came one's way. And now that he came to consider it, his apathy was not the paralysing kind; it was more like a detachment from things, a disengagement from passionate involvement as preached by *Siddhartha Gautama*, the Christ of the Far East. Ever since Mundek's death, and possibly much earlier, he had experienced a relative ease of detachment from objects of love, from friends and possessions too, whenever the need arose.

He must have fallen asleep while contemplating these matters for when he opened his eyes the electric bulb in the compartment was out and both his companions were fast asleep. Dino's grunting noises filled the air as he ran the gamut of the snoring scale. Ossi's head, resting on his palm, seemed petrified in pallid immobility, to which the moonlight lent a ghostly appearance. He hardly seemed to breathe at all. Henry watched him closely. Yes, Ossi had a finely chiselled face, delicate yet strong, with an aquiline nose that lent an aristocratic air to his countenance.

The night was still, and only the rhythmic rolling and clanging of the wheels could be heard. Scrutinising the landscape in the moonlit summer night, he tried to identify the location by some prominent characteristics but without success. Aqueducts, pinewoods, occasional castles, more pinewoods; these could be found in most provinces of Italy.

He lit a cigarette as silently as possible so as not to waken the others. This was as good a time as any to go through the balance sheet of his life. He was twenty-seven years old and like historians, who divide time into BC and AD, Henry separated two epochs in his existence: before, and after, Mundek's death. Many a time he had dwelt on the golden epoch preceding Mundek's suicide, so he did not feel the need to review it now; but the second period had lasted a decade, and he had seldom felt the need to examine it. Its first years were too painful and nebulous, and later when his life began to revive he'd been too busy living it to bother. Now the time was ripe to take stock of those last ten years.

With Mundek's death his adolescence had come to an abrupt end. It had taken a very long time for the wound to heal and when it eventually did it left a deep scar. He had grown harder, sterner and too introspective for his age. By the time he graduated from high school he was starting to break through the cocoon of emotional stagnation; when it was decided that he should study in Italy, his heartbeat had at last quickened. Once captivated by the loveliness of the Italian scene, the taste of freedom, the glorious Liguria, the crazy antics of medical students, he gradually came back to life. Back then he was barely eighteen; everything was new — the dazzling Italian sun, the sea azure as picture postcards, the palm trees, the sparkling wines and the ravishing Italian beauties. All this went to his head, like the *Chianti* and *Barbera* which were served freely with his meals. He enjoyed the comradeship and fraternity of foreign students, learned to play the guitar and to roll yard-long pasta on his fork. Life was wonderful; he blossomed until there was frequently a roguish sparkle in his eyes as well as in his blood.

The first few months were largely taken up with learning Italian but he had become adept at switching from one language to another; besides he had been a frequent visitor to his older brother Izhio in Alassio. To get the hang of colloquial Italian he chatted with his landlady's daughter and then with other girls. He seemed to attract them easily, with his well-cut suits, bow ties and ready smile.

A shrill whistle from the locomotive brought him back to the present. Henry looked out of the window. The night was unusually clear and bright and the sky was suffused with a strange pinkish glow yet it was far too soon for sunrise. He resumed the reflections which had been interrupted by the train's whistle. Yes, those had been wonderful times. After a year or so he spoke fluent Italian, and passed all his exams; the

family took pride in his achievements. It all helped to dull the
ache of losing Mundek.

Then, about five years ago, he had met Mona in Viareggio.
At that time she had been a slip of a girl, barely seventeen. He
had taken an immediate liking to her, for although a bit of a
dreamer, she was unusually wise and mature for her age. Her
parents called her 'Wise Old China'.

Through her father, a Sicilian artist, Henry had been introduced to Theosophy, to the concepts of Karma and the importance of direct experience over learning. At first he saw Mona
only after long intervals, during summer holidays when he
stayed with Anna in Viareggio. Gradually they drew closer
and he presented Mona to his sister and her good friends the
Weismanns, a Jewish couple, both pharmacists, who knew
how to enjoy life, introducing Henry to Pisa, Florence and the
splendours of Tuscany. As his relationship with Mona grew
deeper and more loving they developed a tacit understanding
that they were as good as engaged.

As he glanced casually through the window Henry was
struck by a reddish hue in the firmament. Even the clouds
seemed to be bathed in red. A strange phenomenon, for only
the *aurora* could produce such a colourful display, but now
they were still deep in the night. Intrigued by this unusual
spectacle he leaned right out of the window, and there it was:
Vesuvius in all its majesty and splendour. The famous 'Penone',
the permanent canopy hovering over the crater, kept the sky
above it in darkness but the edges of the black umbrella were
fiery as were the heavens surrounding them, a symphony of
red, gradually paling outwards to a glory of crimson and fine
rosy pink. This was a sight of such singular beauty that he had
to wake the others. He shook them by their shoulders and, still
drunk with sleep, they stumbled towards the window. The
magnificence of this natural wonder sobered them instantly.

"Napoli!" murmured Ossi in awe.

"Nabule!" corrected Dino, using the Neapolitan dialect.

"It is extraordinary!" Ossi muttered to himself.

"And to think we get it all free," added Dino, who had
meantime regained his sobriety and humour. His voice sounded hoarse and dry. He opened his mouth wide in an endless

yawn, stretched his arms in all directions and then, pointing at Vesuvius he said, "I wouldn't mind a drop of the *Lacrima Christi* that grows on yonder slopes. My tonsils feel parched, my tongue is like sandpaper."

"I'm not surprised your throat is dry," remarked Henry, "you could have brought down the walls of Jericho with that snore!"

Dino picked up the Chianti flask, up-ended it and shook it.

"Hopeless! Not a drop!"

Automatically he put his hand on the door handle. It was no use. The compartment was locked.

"Going to the restaurant car?" Ossi asked in a sudden excess of hilarity but his eyes still rested on Vesuvius. He was fascinated, unable to tear himself away. "I have been to Naples many times," he said after a while, "but never have I seen so much fire in the sky."

"It all depends on the volcano's mood. He may be more active just now."

"Well John! As long as he does not erupt over our heads," remarked Dino, and then yawning at full stretch he muttered, "we'd better get back to sleep and save some energy for tomorrow."

The train was slowing and came to a halt in Naples. By the time it resumed its journey all three of them were fast asleep. But in his present frame of mind and tired as he was, Henry's mind would not be lulled into slumber for long and at the next jolt of the train he woke up again. Outside the early dawn played tricks, peopling the rising mist with strange, ghostly mirages and as the day broke, those nebulous wraiths gradually dissolved, as objects regained their outlines and shapes. Rose-fingered Eos was painting everything pink.

Dino began to stir and opened his eyes.

"This blasted throat! I've got to have something to moisten it!"

Without hesitation he began banging at the compartment door. There was no response.

"They will still be asleep at this hour," remarked Ossi.

"So what?" retorted Dino, "let them wake up! They're supposed to look after us, aren't they?" And undeterred he went on banging. Eventually a different militiaman appeared. This one was short, olive-skinned with a thin black moustache; a southern type.

"Why are you making this *fracasso* at this infernal hour?"

"We need some water," and extracting some coins from his pocket Dino added, "*Vino* would be even better."

The smallish man looked searchingly at Dino, shifting his cunning eyes from Dino's face to his outstretched palm, smiling significantly. Apparently there were not sufficient lire in it, for he stood in silence, motionless. Dino's hand dived quickly into his pocket, fishing for more coins. The little Blackshirt in his ill-fitting uniform took all the money without uttering a word, turned on his heels and soon reappeared with a half empty bottle in his hand and a sly grin on his face.

"*Vino Siciliano di Catania. Buono!*"

Dino took the bottle, raised it over his open mouth and poured the wine from above. Then he passed the bottle to his colleagues, who drank likewise.

"Where are we going?" asked Ossi.

The little man in his comic opera outfit shrugged his shoulders and brushed his chin with a sweeping movement of his fingertips.

"*Ma, non saccio,*" he said in local dialect, "I don't know." He eyed the bottle and Dino let him have it. With one mighty gulp he emptied the rest of it, wiped his mouth with the back of his hand, spat on the floor, lifted the shutter and glass pane in the corridor and threw the empty bottle out of the window. Then he left, without bothering to lock the compartment.

"African!" exclaimed Dino.

This was the usual derogatory way in which the North Italians referred to their brethren south of Rome. They also accused them of laziness and sponging off the industrious north. Moreover they criticised southern passivity, fatalism, ignorance, lack of manners and even their poverty and slums, which they ascribed to all these shortcomings. Many of them worked for the police as informers, although some allegedly pulled in the opposite direction, being deeply involved with the *Mafia* and *Camorra*.

To the unbiased foreigner these southerners made an interesting subject of study. Ethnologically they derived from a vast mixture of races and nationalities, including Greeks, Normans, Arabs, Albanians and Spaniards, beside their Latin ancestry. Psychologically they were the outcome of centuries-long oppression by foreign rulers, local barons, feudalism and their great expanse of barren soil. Their fatalism stemmed largely from their frequent earthquakes and their three volcanos: Etna, Stromboli and Vesuvius. Major catastrophes were a constant threat and so they reacted to this with passive submission, fatalism and extreme adoration of the Madonna, with local saints providing additional insurance.

This militiaman's neglecting to lock the door could have various explanations, but the most likely was '*Menefreghismo*', the legendary 'couldn't care less' attitude of southerners. Whatever the motive, the three doctors were grateful for this act of providence. Dino was the first out of the compartment. With his extravert nature and outdoor habits, enforced confinement in the narrow space of a railway compartment must have been very hard to bear. He began to exercise his limbs, bending his knees, throwing his arms about and finally bursting into a brief trot along the corridor. As he did so he became aware that all the other men were still incarcerated in their compartments.

"Hey John!" he called over, "these poor devils have been travelling all the way with their shutters closed. They could have suffocated in that heat."

"We'd better find that Sicilian and get them out," said Ossi. They located him in one of the central compartments. He was sitting with his jacket off and his boots resting on the opposite bench. His comrade had taken his boots off and lay barefoot, sprawled on the bench. It was hard to imagine a less martial-looking man of war. The floor in the compartment looked like a garbage bin. Cigarette butts everywhere, mixed with orange peel and pips, grape stalks and spit: a veritable pigsty.

Dino nudged Henry with his elbow.

"Look, Mussolini's soldiers of the *Impero Romano*!"

He then knocked at the glass partition and opened the door.

"*Per favore*, would you unlock the other compartments? The men are suffocating in there."

Both militiamen stared at him in silence, stolidly, but did not move. It was Ossi's turn for quick thinking this time. He took his cigarette case out of his pocket, opened it and held it out invitingly. Each of them helped himself to a handful of Macedonias, but that was all. They were in no hurry to oblige. It was clear they wanted more. Ossi's eyes began to scintillate ominously and to prevent an outburst Henry intervened. One look at their mocking faces and the littered floor convinced him that it was futile to invoke the Geneva Conventions. He fished out a penknife from his pocket, beautifully ornate and inlaid with mother-of-pearl, a cherished birthday gift from long ago. Henry's eyes fixed tenderly on it for one last moment.

"You can have this penknife, but first open the doors. They need some fresh air, toilet..."

Both made a grab at the penknife.

"You can't keep that anyway where you're going," said the smallish man as he took it without a trace of shame. But soon after, he opened the compartment doors and lifted the shutters and glass panes all round. The narrow corridor, which had been deserted and dark, was flooded with daylight and jostling humanity. Joyful greetings, laments and curses blended into a confusion of sounds. Immediately a frantic queuing for the toilets began.

"Another minute and my bladder would have burst!" shouted a stocky little man with a big moustache under a straw hat. His name was Lubicz.

"Oh! What a relief!" cried another. "I thought I was going to suffocate in that bloody stink-hole in there!" He was a shortish bald man with a rich growth of bristles covering his face.

"Never mind, Mr Wolf," Scholz, an athletic youth, reassured him. "We have survived worse things."

One man in the queue compelled attention: an elderly man with a grey beard and side-locks, an orthodox Jew. He was very pale and haggard and seemed to be swaying while waiting for his turn at the toilet. No doubt the long journey in the stuffy compartment had taken its toll on the old man's endurance.

After the first joyful reaction, one question was uppermost in everyone's mind: "Where are we going? A village? A prison?"

"What do you expect, you *shmocks!* The Waldorf Astoria?" retorted Szafran sarcastically. *Well! They are still capable of cracking jokes and despite everything, seem in good spirits,* thought Henry. Good old Israel, full of resilience and recuperative resources, used to the blows and whims of Fortune. Their irony and ability to laugh at their plight was their strongest weapon.

A loud thundering voice suddenly cut through the racket.

"*Appello!*"

Out of the far end of the corridor a tall, pompous-looking official, flanked by two *carabinieri* in their traditional uniform, Napoleonic hats and the rest of the paraphernalia, appeared on the scene. The *carabinieri* looked so grotesque that Dino could not restrain a chuckle.

"Do you know John, why the *carabinieri* always come in pairs?"

Henry shook his head.

"Because one can read and the other can write," replied Dino.

"*Appello!*"

The voice shrieked again and then the roll call started up with again the comical distortion of their names.

"Altman."

"Here," called out a chubby, rosy-cheeked middle-aged man.

"Reimer."

"Here," called out a high-pitched voice of unmistakeable German inflexion, belonging to a young man with flaming red hair.

And so it went on, with the pompous official struggling to maintain a semblance of decorum, while his tongue was stumbling over the unfamiliar constellation of consonants and vowels. Had the occasion been less ominous it would certainly have provoked hilarity. As it was, everyone had to strain to catch and recognise his own name. The official's face grew redder until it became almost scarlet. When his tongue got entangled in the effort to pronounce the name 'Przebylewski' Henry turned to look at the bearer of that tongue-twisting name, an insignificant man with a sallow complexion and a blank, faraway expression in his eyes. At long last the roll call was over.

"*Preparate le vostre valigie*! Get ready!" the voice barked again.

Everybody busied themselves with their suitcases and bundles. The train began to slow down and came to a halt with a jerk.

They had arrived.

Chapter 3

Camerata 3

There was a fine red dust drifting everywhere as they stood by the big pile of luggage, perspiring profusely. Some carried umbrellas and raincoats and one or two optimists had a camera slung from their neck, but there seemed to be no official reception. Not a uniform in sight save for the crumpled ones, worn by the watchdogs who had escorted them. Considering the circumstances the morale of the prisoners-to-be was fairly high. It had been a morale booster anyway just to get out of those stuffy sealed carriages into the bright morning sun. Except for one or two black-clad peasant matrons and a slim man in riding gear, complete with hunting crop, there wasn't a soul about the station (if you could call that God-forsaken halt with a cracked iron bench by that name).

Suddenly a loud, angry bark made them jump.

"*Attenzione!*"

This unexpected yell came from that lean character in breeches, who now planted himself firmly before them, legs astride, chest and chin out, clutching his whip with both hands.

"*Attenzione!*" he repeated *fortissimo* in a distinctively peeved and angry voice because no one had taken the slightest notice of him before. Out to repair this loss of face he shouted again, "*Disciplina!*" though there was no need to reprimand anybody. Next, up went his arm like a railway signal, with a studied gesture of majesty, worthy of a Roman Emperor. This was too much for Dino who, struggling hard to suppress his laughter, ducked his head murmuring, "Julius Caesar reviewing his cohorts." Ossi shot him a warning glance.

Hitching that arm a notch higher and doing his best to transfix them all with a piercing stare, he launched into a speech.

"Internees! *Internati di guerra!* Now listen carefully and get this firmly into your heads! I am the camp comandante, and I can be nice, or, if need be, not so nice. It's up to you. What I require is *Disciplina! Disciplina assoluta!*"

To everyone's relief his budding speech was cut short.

"*Signor Comandante*," reported a dusty little soldier, "the transport's come, sir."

Looking rather vexed the comandante abandoned his statuesque pose and his speech. Turning on his heels he snapped, "Follow me."

As everybody dived to retrieve their luggage from the pile, a temporary confusion ensued which quickly subsided at the renewed hysterical shriek of "*Disciplina!*"

Despite his theatrical performance, the internees had been somewhat frightened by him. They had not far to go to reach the two ramshackle lorries. It was getting hot and the reddish dust, swirled up by so many trampling feet, was settling on their faces and hair, covering them with a sweat-soaked cake of crimson grime.

Dino smiled at Henry.

"You look like a Red Indian, John!"

Henry did not reply. He felt weary and tired. Ossi took in the spectacle with silent dignity, standing erect and cool, as he waited for his turn. Most of them were packed into one lorry, the rest with the luggage, into the other. They sat huddled up together, each hanging on to his own thoughts, fears and hopes. Their morale, which had been almost euphoric on emerging from the train, had sunk considerably since.

The vehicles had tarpaulin covers allowing glimpses of the landscape through the loose back-flaps. Most of it was hilly, stony and barren, but where there was some vegetation it seemed luxuriant, despite the film of dust which covered the plants. Wildflowers were plentiful, especially cornflowers and poppies, but grew only in patches in isolated marshy clearings. The hills and mountains, often reaching considerable heights, were denuded, because of poor planning and ruthless deforestation. They saw no cattle during that journey, only donkeys, mules and goats. Henry was pretty sure they were somewhere far south of Naples, but didn't know where exactly. Small, primitive tumbledown stone shacks, with gravity-defying roofs, leaned against the sloping hills. They had over-taken several carts drawn by smallish short-legged donkeys, wearing straw hats with ear-perforations, as well as some barefoot women balancing huge earthen jars or amphorae on their heads. Though dust-covered and in shabby attire, they looked very dignified with their upright, gliding walk, almost regal in their classical posture. *The daughters of Mycenae,* thought Henry.

The vehicles slowed down as the screeching noise of gates turning on their hinges rang out. The lorries came to a halt. They had arrived at their destination and for all they knew at their destiny too. Dismounting, they saw two sentry boxes flanking the gates with guards presenting arms. The heavy gates closed and looking around they soon realised that their destination was a desolate plain, surrounded by a triple row of barbed wire: a concentration camp.

They were ordered to queue in single file in front of an improvised checkpoint where their luggage was to be searched. All their cases and parcels were opened by two regular soldiers who played safe by confiscating all reading matter, books, journals and even dictionaries. This was not really surprising for neither of them looked like a literary expert, so they wouldn't be risking any subversive material slipping through. Cameras and films were confiscated, as were pocket knives. Wallets, packets, trouser turn-ups and in some cases even shoulder pads, were minutely examined. Except for two incidents it all went smoothly enough and the queue snaked quickly through the checkpoint.

The first commotion occurred over the confiscation of some phylacteries, which a baffled soldier extracted from their velvet pouch with its gold embroidered Star of David. He clearly couldn't make head or tail of these two black cubes joined together by leather straps. He eyed them with mistrust and then, to be on the safe side, started to put them away, when the bearded Orthodox owner broke into an impassioned torrent of protest in Yiddish, German and Hebrew. He clutched desperately at the velvet pouch, but the soldier snatched it from him with a curse.

"*Porca miseria!* This bloody bag has to be left here."

At this point poor Mr Meiersohn, tears in his eyes, began to gesticulate wildly, folding his hands in supplication. The soldier's face softened at his distress and in this unguarded moment Mr Meiersohn grabbed his phylacteries and began to demonstrate their use. First he placed one cube on the forehead, then he secured the second cube with leather straps to his forearm, pressing it against his heart. Both soldiers looked on in amazement, exchanging puzzled glances.

"What is it? A radio?"

Henry left the queue and approached the soldiers, smiling. "This is no radio. There are sacred writings in the cubes. It's for praying, like a rosary. Quite harmless."

Half-baffled, half-amused, the soldiers exchanged looks, shrugged and let the old man keep his most precious earthly possession. His pale, haggard face lit up and turning to Henry, he thanked him from the bottom of his heart.

"May the Lord give you many years of happiness and a long life."

Strangely enough, the second incident concerned Ossi Gerber, not one usually prone to petty arguments. From his student days in Montpellier, he had several French novels, which he'd brought along, hoping to re-read them at leisure. Although he was annoyed when the soldiers confiscated them he suppressed his anger, realising the soldiers didn't understand French and might well suspect anti-Fascist propaganda. But when they prepared to confiscate his medical books he really exploded. His habitual pallor was enhanced by the ominous blaze of his dark eyes.

"These are medical books! *Libri di medicina!*" They would not listen. To prove his point Ossi opened one of the books to show them some medical illustrations. Unfortunately the text book fell open at a page showing the vaginal exploration of a pregnant woman!

"What obscenity! *Che porcheria!*" exclaimed the soldiers, laughing. Then they said stolidly,

"All books have to be confiscated. Even dirty ones!"

At that Dino and Henry gave up their books without protest.

When the inspection was over, the internees were left standing for a while to take stock of their surroundings. They were in a square close to the main gate containing the administrative section. In each of the four corners stood a majestic tree

and so—by a stretch of the imagination—this could be regarded as the "*piazza.*" A white house, the only solid building,
was near the front corner on the left. Next to it, a low green
wooden shack, open-fronted like a market stall, was presumably the provision stores. On the right side the piazza was
framed by a long wooden barrack, inscribed in bold letters,
'*Polizia del Campo*'. The front of the square consisted of barbed
wire coils and the heavy gates flanked by sentry boxes. A Nis-
sen-hut type of structure, painted white with a red cross on it,
stood at the back of the square: the medical centre. After a
fleeting glance, Dino instantly dubbed that square the "*Piazza
de Ferrari*" - the 'Piccadilly Circus' of Genoa—and the name
stuck.

A tallish young man with greasy black hair and a wispy
moustache approached them. He wore civilian clothes, a holster strapped to his hip and a disgruntled expression on his
face.

"Follow me!" he called out. The procession of internees,
loaded with their belongings, walked past the medical hut into
a vast expanse of scorched desolation strewn with heaps of
building materials and debris. Cement bags, gravel, sand,
wooden planks, ladders, shovels, hammers and nails, were
scattered all over. Only a few tufts of grass and thistles grew in
this sun-baked stony soil although, inexplicably, the occasional
trees grew to astonishing heights.

The site, about twenty acres in all, was situated in the low-
est plain of a valley surrounded by barren hills. The first impression was one of dreariness, desolation and oppressive
heat. There was nothing at all to gladden the eye.

There were only two wooden barracks, with a third under
construction. The young agent entered the second barrack and
ushered them in. They were confronted with two long rows of
camp beds with a narrow corridor between them. The beds,
wooden X-shaped frames of poor quality, supported a rectangular length of coarse canvas held fast with rough nails. The
ceiling was formed by rows of triangular rafters, rising from
horizontal beams. Rough cast cement covered the floor and the
inner walls were just hardboard, distempered white. On each
bed lay a pillow case, an empty mattress and a blanket of

shoddy grey ticking. The new arrivals were then directed to a shed full of bales of straw and mouldy hay with which to fill their mattresses and pillow cases.

"Is this all we'll have to sleep on?" asked Wolf, a pocket-sized Polish Jew with a shining bald head, rubbing his bristly chin.

Lubicz, the dapper stocky man with the straw hat, looked at him mockingly. Pulling at his big black moustache he said, "What did you expect, a four-poster bed?"

It was interesting to watch the way each of them stuffed his *palliasse*. Some went very meticulously about the business, taking a great pride in it. Others took a slovenly approach. Reimer, a German Jew, a *'yekke'*, gave a demonstration of methodical, truly Teutonic thoroughness. He also advised filling the pillows with hay, "because it is softer."

"It also stinks! Can't you smell mould, you *yekke?*" retorted Wolf as he continued to stuff his bag, muttering curses under his breath. "Oh how I wish it was Hitler sleeping on this bloody mess and getting his arse pricked!" he grumbled.

Dino seemed to be in good spirits, as if the whole thing was still one big joke. Ossi seemed annoyed and despondent as he looked down his nose. As for Henry, well he had never been much use with his hands and impatiently stuffed his mattress in a half-hearted, careless manner. Carrying the palliasses and pillows on their heads, they returned to their barrack, or "*camerata*" as the agent referred to it. The doctors were allowed to occupy three adjoining beds in *camerata* 3.

Dino unpacked his food parcel again and began to munch a sandwich. No one had had a bite since their arrival, but Tommasini, the agent, said there was no time for eating as the *comandante* wanted them back in the *piazza*. Back there, they were kept hanging about until such time as the same comandante thought fit to make his appearance. Then he started off again.

"*Internati di guerra*! This is the concentration camp of Ferramonti, in Calabria. We Italians with our glorious past and heritage are no barbarians! But we shall expect of you obedience, order and discipline. *Disciplina*! The State will be paying each of you five lire a day. This is not much, but I am sure you must have money of your own!"

There was a muffled murmur of protest, which the camp comandante soon quelled by raising his arm. "Now, this war is not going to last long. Our glorious troops under the enlightened leadership of *Il Duce*, and in brotherhood with the *Führer's* armies, have already brought about the collapse of France. Our bombers together with the *Luftwaffe* are hammering London day and night. So *Perfida Albione* must surrender soon! Therefore your stay here will not be very long, but while you are here under my command you will behave yourselves!"

He rubbed his hands together, clearly very pleased with himself. Obviously one who liked to hear his own voice, he continued, "We will provide your cooking utensils, but the cost of these will be deducted from your daily allowance, one lira a day from each of you. So it will take about a month before your debt will be paid."

He paused, probably because he anticipated some objections, but since no one protested he went on again. "You will appoint a cook from your men and a spokesman, a *Capo Camerata*, who will be responsible for your conduct. There will be three roll calls each day, at 8 a.m., 12 noon and 8 p.m. at which you must all be present in your *camerata*. This area is malaria-infested and you will be provided with Quinine and Atebrin. You will not try to leave the camp, or else be prepared to take the consequences. You may write letters once a week. Twelve lines, no more! The letters will be handed over unsealed for censoring. No weapons, radio or cameras are permitted. Except for special reasons you are not to come over here to the administrative area. But you may visit the provision stores when necessary. Any transgression of rules will be severely punished. *Viva Il Duce!*"

As the speech ended, the internees looked at each other in dismay. How on earth were they going to exist on five lire a day? In those days when the official exchange rate for the British pound was 80 lire, five lire amounted barely to a 16th of a pound. True, most internees did have some money, but how long would it last? Besides, several of the refugees from Austria, Germany and Poland had arrived in Italy penniless, thankful to have got out in one piece.

One lonely man was racking his brain about problems of a different kind: how would he get kosher food? It was useless to discuss it with the others. Mr Meiersohn knew they would not understand and would mock him as well. There was only one thing he could do: pray and leave the rest to God. The God of Abraham, Isaac and Jacob, who had led his children out of Egyptian slavery, and who had delivered him from Hitler's clutches, would never abandon his faithful servant in his hour of need. This belief comforted him while others turned their thoughts to more earthly matters.

Most internees had gone back to their *camerata* but Henry stayed behind.

"Signor Tommasini, may I see the *comandante*?"

"What for?"

"I'd like to ask him a favour."

"A favour? Cavaliere Rizzi isn't keen on favours."

"It's a simple matter. Will you help me please?"

Tommasini did not particularly like these internee Jews and had no wish to put himself out for them; but Henry spoke good Italian and seemed *una persona per bene*, a gentleman. So he went into the white house and emerged soon after, nodding approval. Cavaliere Rizzi received him on the doorstep.

"What do you want?"

"It's about the books, *Cavaliere*."

"What books?"

"Our books that were confiscated."

Rizzi seemed puzzled; most likely the soldiers had just acted on their own initiative.

"*Entrate*! Come in!" The tone was not unfriendly. Henry followed him into his study. He was still wearing his breeches and an open-necked shirt, which Henry considered a not unfavourable augury of the man's character. At least he had not sought to impress with a uniform. True he had acted the paper tiger, but his vanity had been ruffled at the station.

Comandante Rizzi sat down at his desk, crossed his legs and leaned back in his swivel chair.

"What sort of books are they?"

"Novels and medical books."

"Novels and medical books?" he repeated. "What sort of novels?"

"Only novels of literary value. Nothing political, I assure you."

Signor Rizzi seemed to be turning something over in his mind.

"And why so keen to have them?"

"To keep our minds occupied. Books will help pass the time and keep us in good spirits."

The comandante smiled ironically. "I'm not so sure we want you in good spirits exactly. Besides who said you won't have to work? Surely you've heard of forced labour."

Henry retorted without hesitation, "The Italians would never do such a thing. I have lived long enough here to know the Italian people."

Signor Rizzi laughed. "I would not be so sure. After all we are at war."

Most likely he had perceived that Henry's last remark was genuine, for he pointed to a chair inviting Henry, who had been standing awkwardly, to sit down. In fact Henry did like the Italians, especially the working classes and peasants, whom he had always found kind-hearted and compassionate. The camp comandante stared at Henry.

"What do you do? I mean your work or profession."

"I am a doctor, *un dottore in medicina*."

"Then why have you not left Italy in time?"

"I could not. My passport was taken from me."

At this point the comandante's eyes narrowed as he examined Henry closely. "Taken from you? What had you done?"

"Nothing at all," replied Henry. "The Polish authorities did the same to many thousands of Jews living in Austria to prevent their return to their native land, after the annexation of Austria. They deprived them of both nationality and passport. My parents and I lived in Vienna."

Signor Rizzi remained silent for a while, weighing Henry's words.

"And how did you come to be in Italy in the first place?" he asked eventually.

"Mussolini invited foreign students. There was no anti-Semitism in Italy then!"

"But you say your parents lived in Vienna. Surely Vienna has a famous medical faculty?"

Henry smiled. "The medical standard was high enough, but anti-Semitism at Vienna University was even higher, even before Hitler's *Anschluss*. Besides, part of my family lived in Italy, until recently."

The comandante took his time weighing up Henry's story. Then he suddenly arose. "All right then, *va bene*. I will sort out these books."

The audience was over. Henry thanked him and was about to leave when he was recalled.

"Your name?"

Henry gave it and wrote it down for him.

"Well *dottore*, you'd better be the spokesman, the *capo camerata*."

Leaving, Henry felt pleased. The interview had gone better than he'd expected. Apparently Signor Rizzi's bark was much worse than his bite. He hurried back with the good news about the books; but when he mentioned, somewhat apprehensively, his appointment as *capo camerata*, he noticed a flicker across Dino's face. But it was gone directly.

"So he's made you the boss has he?" said Dino, slapping him on the shoulder. "Good luck John."

It was very hot, so most of them had changed into shorts and sandals. Henry followed suit and felt more comfortable in that oppressive heat. Mr Altman, the middle-aged man with the friendly chubby face and respectable paunch, was unable to get into his shorts; they were too tight.

"Hey, Mr Altman! Don't worry about your damned shorts. Wait till next week. I bet you'll have lost your paunch by then!"

Henry had a fleeting sensation of unease, for despite Dino's display of good sportsmanship, he felt that he had begrudged him an appointment he had never sought. But he dismissed the intuition, hoping that he was mistaken.

"Shall we have a stroll round the camp, *capo*?" Dino asked.

Henry nodded and Ossi was also willing to explore the place.

"Have you seen the latrines yet?" exclaimed somebody. "You must!"

As the three doctors went out of the back door of the *camerata*, they were pleasantly surprised to find a huge tree nearby. It was a beautiful specimen; a mighty oak, spreading its branches over a wooden bench.

"This is great!" said Dino, "Fine for bridge or chess!" At once he hoisted himself up by one of the lower branches, doing a Tarzan act, swinging from branch to branch, and performing acrobatics with great skill. Impersonating a gorilla, he bared his teeth, grunting and chest-beating until tired of these antics. He was about to lower himself, when something caught his eye.

"I can see them from here!"

"See what?" asked Ossi.

"The latrines! Right over there."

They went straight across to inspect them. There were two pits about six feet deep, crossed by a wooden plank from which to defecate. The bottoms of both pits were covered with human excrement, topped by a moving slime of maggots. Swarms of bluebottles hovered above this repulsive *cloaca* left by the men building the camp. Henry felt his stomach heaving with the sudden urge to vomit. By some strange association of ideas he recalled Vesuvius, its skies a Symphony in Red. Turning away from these nauseating heaps of shit he murmured to himself: *Cacophony in Brown.*

On Ossi's face there was an expression of horror and disgust. "This is dreadful...inviting an epidemic of dysentery or typhoid!"

Dino's healthy, life-asserting attitude soon prevailed even over this dismal spectacle.

"Let's go and get some *vino*!"

With his parents in Genoa, free to pursue their business, for him money was no problem. This was not so for Ossi and Henry. However, on this first day in the concentration camp, they were inclined to throw caution to the wind.

"The question is," said Ossi, "where do we get it?"

The camp stores were the most likely place, but they had been told not to visit the piazza, unless there were special reasons.

"But we have special reasons: *vino!*" objected Dino.

There was no one to be seen in the stores at that hour so Dino began to bang his fist against the door. "Anyone here?" he called out.

From the shadows amongst the vats and sacks emerged a skinny man, completely bald: that was how they first met Giuseppe.

Even though the light was fading they were struck by the dreadful state of Giuseppe's teeth. Some were eroded or decayed, some purulent and the rest just missing.

"A mouth like a sewer," whispered Dino, "he'd do to kill all those flies in the latrines." Aloud he said, "We want some *vino!*"

"No bottled wine here, *niente bottiglie!* Only big casks."

But while saying this, he must have had second thoughts. "Wait a moment," he called out and then, scanning the horizon nervously for any observers, he took an empty bottle, tipped a big vat over a funnel and filled it with wine. "Ten lire," he demanded.

It was an exorbitant price. The money would go into his own pocket clearly, but they were glad to pay it. It was also good to learn that things could be had for a price here. They felt pleased with themselves and even though the *piazza* was out of bounds, they sat down in a corner under a tree and passed the bottle round. The wine, of humble local origin, had a nice bouquet and was pleasant to the palate. On their empty stomachs it went straight to their heads. Their mood was elevated, most likely the result of strained nerves. The sun was setting and the bluish twilight made their surroundings appear less harsh. Their heads swam lightly as they stretched themselves out under the tree. Alcohol had certainly helped to soften the rough edges of their world. Now that the sun had set, the heat was less oppressive, so they could even feel reconciled to the idea of spending some time in this place. They must have fallen asleep, exhausted as they were, for suddenly they came to, awakened by loud voices and torches shining into their eyes.

"You must be mad! All three of you! Do you want to miss the roll call on the very first night?"

"Stop shouting," hissed Dino, who was first down to earth. "Let's run for it."

Apart from the twinkling above it was pitch dark. But on arriving at their *camerata*, it was even darker, for there were no stars to brighten the blackness.

"We will have to do something about this!" protested red-haired Reimer in his high-pitched voice.

"Certainly! We'll send a delegation to Mussolini, you *yekkisher shmock*," retorted Wolf mockingly.

Luckily this exchange of niceties could not degenerate into a quarrel because a loud yell of *"Appello"* brought them to their senses.

"Ai vostri posti! To your posts!" A torchlight shone into their faces. There followed the usual distortion of their names, raising a chuckle from the internees, emboldened as they were by the protective darkness.

After the agent had gone, they went to bed in spite of the early hour. All felt exhausted; besides what else was there to do in the dark?

"I'm going to water that tree," said Schindler, a pleasant middle-aged Jew from Silesia.

"Then I am going for a shit," said Szafran.

"Be careful you don't land in the shit-pit yourself!"

This set off a chorus of silly giggling in the darkness. The merriment became contagious. Almost everyone in the *camerata* laughed or chuckled gaily. From this frivolous refrain, they might have been mistaken for a group of day trippers, not inmates of a concentration camp.

A strange people, the Jews, reflected Henry. *Where do they get this resilience from, this contempt for the hardships of life?*

Though most of them were sleepy when they flopped onto their beds, it now appeared that the chattering few would keep the majority awake for some time.

"If you appoint me as your cook," called out Lubicz across the darkened room, "you'll have an expert chef."

Immediately burly little Wolf interrupted. "Why you? You don't even know what a decent meal tastes like. You *shnorrer!*"

Lubicz retorted indignantly, "I used to be a cook in the army, you *shmock!*"

"In what army?" called out Reimer derisorily in his strident voice, "The Polish army?"

"Shut up, *yekke*! *Kraut!*" yelled Lubicz furiously. "What do you understand about cooking?"

"More than you! I trained for hotel management in Frankfurt."

"Gentlemen! Gentlemen!" broke in Mr Altman's soothing baritone. "Please let us get to sleep. You can continue your arguments tomorrow."

Others joined in protesting: "Quiet! Shut your gobs!" but they were ignored. Lubicz renewed his attack.

"Never mind that *Kraut*! Just let me take over. I'll prepare such pasta Bolognese, such cutlets *alla Milanese* ..."

"What is this rubbish about Bolognese and Milanese?" interrupted Henry angrily, losing all patience. "All on five lire a day?"

This remark had the sobering effect of a cold shower and all was still for a time. In his naïvety, Henry could not see why anyone should fight over the doubtful privilege of extra work. Obviously he had forgotten the adage that cooks never go hungry, a consideration not to be despised in a concentration camp.

All was quiet in the *camerata*, when suddenly someone exclaimed, "Oh! This bloody mattress! It's driving me mad."

There was a penetrating yell — more of a roar — and it came from Ossi.

"For God's sake will you all shut up?"

Henry smiled in the dark. Ossi, it seemed, could be incisively authoritative if he wanted to. As was his habit, Henry had saved a last cigarette for the night. This ritual had got him into endless trouble with his mother and landladies, who all feared he'd drop off and set the place on fire. Cupping his hand over the lighted match, so as not to disturb the others, he saw Ossi to his right, all curled up, his blanket drawn halfway over his face.

Henry folded his arms under his head, to avoid the unpleasant contact with his pillow. His mattress, only half-filled, was uncomfortable. He inhaled deeply and felt a slight dizziness in his head. His stomach was rumbling. Strange, no one had offered them any food from the time of their arrival. Snores and sighs around. Some people had already fallen asleep. *What is it like in Genoa just now*, he wondered? The snoring increased and there was an occasional breaking of wind. *Oh what I'd give to be in a room of my own*, he thought. Mona had no idea what had befallen him. He had not written to her, nor to anyone else. Staring into the blackness, suddenly the obscenely repulsive image of the pit crawling with insects and maggots pushed its way in front of his inner eye. He could see it clearly. *A cacophony in brown*, he murmured. Soon after, he fell asleep.

Chapter 4

Day 2: Food!

Henry awoke with a parched throat, a sore back and aching limbs. Ossi was still asleep, blanket drawn over his face, revealing only a pallid forehead and a tuft of raven-black hair. To Henry's left Dino, his hairy bare chest exposed, snored away as if he hadn't a care in the world. Some internees were already up, shaving, yawning or just sitting there brooding.

"What a night!" complained tiny Wolf, rasping away with a razor at his stubbly chin. "Who could sleep with all that snoring and farting?"

"People get used to worse," retorted Lubicz.

"Maybe you can, growing up with that pong, you *Polak*!"

Though himself of Polish origin, Wolf had lived many years abroad and looked down on Poles. Lubicz found it beneath his dignity to reply. All he did was flap his hand as if shooing away a troublesome insect.

Wolf, his bald pate covered in perspiration, got on with his shaving. The thin layer of lather, coupled with a blunt razor, made the business of shaving an arduous task, considering the thickness and luxuriant growth of his bristles. He was an odd little man, whose face perpetually wore a grumpy expression, as if the weight of the whole universe rested on his shoulders. The dapper Lubicz, his straw hat at a crazy angle, sat on the edge of the bed dangling his legs and pulling at his handlebar moustache.

"None of you lot seem to care, but I'd like to know when we are getting something to eat."

Reimer the redhead looked at him mockingly. "Why, breakfast is served in the lounge, Sir!"

"Be quiet, you carroty-head *yekke*! My guts are turning over and this *shlemiel* just makes stupid jokes!"

"Quiet!" snapped Dino, awaking. "What's all this bickering about?"

"We are all hungry, *Herr Doktor*," explained Scholz, the youngest of the internees, emboldened by his empty stomach. "With all due respect, *Herr Doktor*, it isn't everybody who has a loving mother in Italy to pack provisions for a month. Some of us are penniless refugees, remember. We are hungry. So we look to you doctors for some action."

Dino ignored the jibe, passing the buck to Henry.

"Hear that John? What are you going to do, *Capo*?"

The loud yell of *Appello* reverberated through the *camerata*.

"Get up! *Alzatevi!*" No one had noticed Tommasini's presence.

Again the mutilation of names, which by now grated on Henry's nerves; some people were absent, which sent Tommasini frantic. "*Porca miseria!*" he screamed. "Fetch them immediately! Everyone must be here for *appello!*" After this was done and he had calmed down, he added, "The cooking utensils have arrived. You must collect them from the *piazza*."

Stomachs knotted with hunger accelerated their march towards the *piazza*. Here they found a strange assortment of kettles, pots and other cooking implements, including bellows. An enormous copper cauldron, far too big for their needs, stood out. Copper, scarce anyway in Italy, was doubly valuable in times of war. Therefore, Henry thought, such lavishness from on high could only imply an exuberant confidence in a quick victory. And who could blame them for their optimism, with France on her knees and London in flames?

Dino, eager to show off his physical prowess, lifted the huge cauldron unaided. He was in his element, enjoying the physical challenge as well as a spot of clowning.

"Make way for Atlas with all the world on his shoulders!"

The rest, carrying smaller loads, followed in Indian file. It was the oddest Jewish caravan. A meeting was called to elect a cook. Just like the night before, there was much angling for the job. Lubicz again started to extol his culinary skills, when Dino suddenly produced his candidate, a man sitting quietly and apparently not interested at all.

"Why not Mario? He's worked for years as a cook in Genoa."

Mario, a smallish man with rosy cheeks and greying hair, was perpetually humming away to himself. He liked to keep to himself, though one could have hardly called him shy. No one knew much about him, except that he had been co-habiting with an Italian woman of dubious reputation.

"Yes! Let's have Mario!" repeated Dino. "He didn't exactly work at the Ritz, more likely in a sailor's *bordello*, but that's good enough for me."

Mario himself said nothing at all. In fact he did not seem enamoured of the idea. And it was precisely his lack of enthusiasm which landed him with the job.

"But what about me?" protested the indignant Lubicz.

Henry decided on appeasement. "And we will have Lubicz as an assistant. It will be better to have two shifts, as well as a reserve cook in case of illness."

It now only remained to appoint a provision buyer, someone of integrity, business acumen and practical know-how. The choice fell almost unanimously on Mr Altman, the jovial businessman who had found his shorts too tight for his paunch. He came from Wroclaw, was renowned for his shrewd knowledge of human frailties and an exquisite sense of humour as well as good-heartedness. His rotund bulk, fresh complexion and twinkling blue eyes, radiated benevolence. There was something else unique about Mr Altman: he was the only internee who possessed an entry visa to a country overseas, to Argentina. Why he was ever interned was a mystery since he had only been in Italy *in transit*. Most likely he would be allowed to leave the camp, when his ship sailed.

"Let's not waste time," said Henry. "Everybody wants Mr Altman so let's get on with the job."

Altman stood there with a big smile on his face.

"I am very touched and flattered by your confidence and particularly happy about the high salary you offer not to mention the elegant cooking facilities. But, jokes apart, let's make a start. Just now we have no cash at all. As you know the daily allowance of five lire per man is credited to us with the stores. That's no good. We must do bulk buying. It's the only way we can exist. Besides we must build up a stock and not live from hand to mouth." He paused for a moment, endeavouring to assess the assembly's mood. "I suggest each of you gives 10% of what cash he owns to the common cause. This will give us some capital to manipulate."

Several of the internees looked at each other in dismay.

"But what about those who have nothing in their pocket?" asked Scholz timidly.

"They'll simply give 10% of that nothing, but will not be any worse off for it," replied Altman, kindly.

In the end the sum of 1758 lire and 80 centesimi was collected from among the twenty-three internees. This corresponded to roughly twenty-two British pre-war pounds. Altman did not make any comment, so no one knew whether he was pleased or disappointed.

First of all firewood and food had to be bought and everybody was anxious to accompany Altman on his first shopping spree.

"What do you want?" asked Giuseppe, the lanky store man, in his thin little whine.

Altman, to establish his authority from the start, went straight up. "Now, we need some milk and ..."

"No fresh milk," Giuseppe interrupted him. "*Non c'e'*. It would go sour. Too hot here."

Obviously the store had no refrigerator. Altman frowned. "*Avete del caffè?*" His Italian was passable for he had studied Spanish in preparation for his emigration and this, as well as bits of Italian picked up in Genoa, now stood him in good stead.

"*Non teniamo caffè. Non c'e'*," replied Giuseppe, grinning to reveal his putrid teeth. "No coffee, but we have chicory."

There seemed little prospect of any breakfast in the conventional sense. All that was on show was a pile of potatoes, tomatoes, large vats of olive oil and wine.

"Any sugar?" enquired Altman.

"You must be joking! That's rationed, and so is bread."

It dawned on Altman he would have to purchase whatever was available. So he started buying almost indiscriminately. Luckily olive oil, tomatoes and potatoes were plentiful and cheap. To his surprise he was also able to lay his hands on a sack of flour, though it was a bit mouldy and full of lumps. Better still, hidden in a corner was a whole sphere of *mortadella*, which was comparatively inexpensive. Finally when Altman asked for firewood, the answer was, "*Non c'e'*," which all too familiar form of denial soon established itself as a stock-phrase among the internees. However, Giuseppe promised to order some firewood. For the highlight of their meal Altman bought a basket of overripe cherries.

In order to light a fire the internees had to gather twigs, pieces of sawn-off planks, wooden boxes, anything that would burn. But the fire would not start. Only a stream of smoke and curses came out of the kitchen.

Lubicz was beside himself. "Damn! It will not burn!" he cried in exasperation.

Reimer had the bad taste to pull his leg. "What, our great chef from the Polish army can't even light a fire?"

"Shut up, you redheaded *yekke* fool ..."

"Gentlemen! Gentlemen! Now please!" interjected Altman. "I hope we can find some way of lighting the fire yet. Greater problems have been solved by modern technology."

"Have you opened the damper in the kitchen range?" asked Mario casually.

Lubicz looked perplexed and struck himself on the forehead. "Would you believe it? I forgot to pull the damned thing out!"

"I thought so," said Mario quietly and unsurprised.

This produced an outburst of hilarity, which escalated at the sight of Mario in a white chef's hat; he had brought it with him, in anticipation of his lot.

"What's he wearing that for? Afraid of ruining the *mayonnaise*?" asked Szafran in his usual ironical manner.

Breakfast time was long past and the way things were going there was no way of knowing when they'd get something warm in their bellies. To distract attention from gnawing hunger, the internees clogged up the kitchen and made a nuisance of themselves, though meaning to be helpful.

"Thanks for your help," said Mario. "Now then, all out of this kitchen. You only make a *bordello*!"

While all this joking and bickering was going on, two men sat quietly in the *camerata*, immersed in thoughts of their own. One was Przebylewski, whose name had tripped up the tongue of that pompous official. He wore the same vacant expression as on the train. *A strange fellow*, Henry thought. Then his eyes went to the second man, Mr Meiersohn, the orthodox Jew. He was apparently lost in contemplation, stroking his beard as his lips moved.

"What are you doing Granddad," asked Wolf. "Saying your prayers?"

Mr Meiersohn did not reply, but his lips continued to move soundlessly. He looked worn and sad.

"Worrying about something?" Wolf enquired.

The old man nodded.

"What about?"

The old man did not reply. Wolf had a hunch. "Is it the food you're worrying about?"

The old man's nodding confirmed Wolf's intuition. "Look, Granddad, it's only vegetables, it's kosher."

"You don't understand," Mr Meiersohn said gently. "It's not only the food. The pots will be unclean, '*treyfe*' as well."

Reimer, who had been listening with one ear only, suddenly got interested.

"What's all this about *treyfe*? What does it mean?"

"Quiet, you carroty *yekke*," snapped Wolf. "Don't show your ignorance! Weren't you brought up in a Jewish home?"

Altman intervened. "It's no good blaming Mr Reimer, if he comes from a home of German Jewish assimilants. Some of them were more Teutonic than the Germans themselves." He then proceeded to explain to Reimer the basic laws of *Kashrut*, the dietary principles of orthodox Jewry.

"Most of these laws arose out of hygienic and medical considerations in a country with a sub-tropical climate. Other laws have ethical implications. Some are of mystical origin and obscure."

"But we no longer live in a sub-tropical climate," retorted Reimer. "One has to move with the times."

"This must be left to each individual. Only he can decide how far he wants to move," said Altman.

At this moment Lubicz, shirtsleeves rolled up to the elbows and sweat pouring from his brow, appeared in the doorway. "Lunch is ready!" he yelled. "Come and get it!"

Sudden animation seized the internees; they were both ravenous and curious to taste this first meal. Bowls in hand, they queued in front of the kitchen. This bowl was to be their universal receptacle — dish, plate and saucer all in one. Spoons and forks were provided, but not knives (that might endanger the Fascist regime, as Dino put it). Lubicz at the kitchen door, dipping his ladle rhythmically into the steaming kettle, felt very important. "Next!" he kept on shouting at the top of his voice.

Henry inspected his food, inhaling the steam. It smelt quite good or maybe it was hunger that supplied that extra spice. The concoction was basically a thick mixture of macaroni, potatoes, tomatoes and onions. This was the first warm food he had tasted in forty-eight hours. He enjoyed the sensation of warmth in his mouth more than the food itself which despite needing salt was otherwise quite palatable. There was also a faint meaty flavour which, Henry discovered, came from a lonely slice of mortadella. Immediately he looked for Meiersohn, but the orthodox Jew was nowhere to be seen. The crowning feature of the meal consisted of the overripe cherries, which would not have lasted another day. Young Scholz, who still had plenty of room in his stomach, was delighted with them. The poor German refugee was really half-starved.

Though their meal had only been frugal, a sudden torpor overcame them in the oppressive heat. The sky was deep azure with not a cloud in sight, the blazing sun flailing down on the camp. The best thing to do was to take cover in the barrack and lie down.

"Let's all do a boa constrictor," suggested Dino.

"What does a boa constrictor do, *Herr Doktor*?" asked Scholtz innocently.

"First it swallows a deer or something. Then it winds itself round a branch and goes to sleep for days."

Despite his drowsiness, Henry could not get off to sleep. The flies were a persistent nuisance that seemed to multiply.

Wolf sighed as he turned on his side. "The fucking flies!" he mumbled. "They get up your nose as well as your arsehole!"

It was the more astonishing that Dino managed to fall asleep so promptly as his bare chest was covered in flies, but already his snoring filled the *camerata*. From time to time his hand came up to scrape his chest automatically, like a dog

scratching in his sleep, but this never woke him. A few feet
away, Ossi got under his blanket and drew it over his face.
*How can he put up with a blanket in this goddamn heat? But then
maybe it's better than being molested by the bloody flies,* Henry
thought. Unable to sleep, he stared at the ceiling, his mind
ticking over. The war would soon be over, unfortunately, for
there was no hope now of an Allied victory. Great sufferings
lay ahead for the Jews therefore the future looked grimmer
than the present. Here at least one was not directly involved in
the brutality and madness of the world. The loss of freedom in
a wretched world like this was no great deprivation. Thus trying to console himself, he eventually dozed off, despite the
swarm of flies.

"How long are you going to laze about, John?"

Henry deep in slumber woke with a start, regarding Dino
with glassy eyes. His head felt woolly and muddled.

"Let's take a stroll through the camp, *Capo*! We've hardly
seen anything of it."

"What's there to see?" asked Szafran. "The stones? The
flies? The shit-pits?" He was right of course. There was hardly
anything worth looking at in this dusty desolation.

"I went this morning to the lower end of the camp," said
Scholz, "and further down, just outside the barbed wire it
looks quite nice. All green."

The camp was on a distinct slope which continued to descend until it reached the distant foothills. There the vegetation
became progressively richer and even luxuriant. As they went
down they caught distant glimpses of red and blue, poppies
and forget-me-nots, but their exploratory enterprise was suddenly halted by sighting a sentry box and more barbed wire.
From afar the sentry box seemed empty, but as they neared it
something began to stir, and gradually an elongated figure detached itself from it. This sentry was unbelievably skinny and
when he presented arms it seemed as if the rifle was sustaining soldier and not the other way round. Height and extreme
emaciation made his uniform hang loosely on his body; in fact
he looked like a cross between a beanpole and a scarecrow.
However, his yellowish, wrinkled face was friendly and kind.

It was all nose and eyes, which latter darted swiftly from one to the other of the group.

"What are you looking for?" he asked, smiling, baring his toothless gums.

"Is that a river, further down below?" asked Dino in his best Italian, pointing in the distance.

"Ah! *Siete Italiano*? You're Italian!" exclaimed the sentry. "Yes, it is the river Crati. And my name is Pasquale," he added, unusually matey for a sentry.

The internees stood there for a while, not knowing what to say, but Pasquale soon broke the silence. "Wish I hadn't to stand here in the heat. Mind you, it's not too bad in the box. But I'm fed up with it all."

"So you don't like it here either, eh?" asked Dino ironically, scrutinising this quixotic character—a caricature of all martial pretensions.

"I'm ill, you know. That's why they put me here. No good for fighting. Should have been left to tend my vineyard. My wife needs a man about the house."

Dino grinned. One could easily guess at his thoughts: *what a man to have about the house*! But he bit his lip and asked instead, "Is the Crati deep enough to swim in?"

"*Perbacco!*" said Pasquale. "It's deep enough, but you are not allowed to go there."

Ossi pointed to a nearby line of concrete channels. "And what is all this?"

"These?" replied Pasquale, "These are the irrigation canals. There is not much water in them."

Henry had a sudden inspiration. "Signor Pasquale, this heat is dreadful. You're used to it. Would you allow us to take a stroll over to the canal and have a wash?"

Pasquale looked at him, taken aback. "*Non e' permesso*. It's not permitted."

"But look," insisted Henry, "It's only a few yards. I'm the *capo camerata* and I'll vouch for these men."

Pasquale put his rifle down and took his cap off to scratch his head. "*Ma come posso?* How can I? It's not allowed." He seemed visibly disturbed and uneasy.

Henry, sensing Pasquale's defences weakening, pressed on. "I give you my word, we shall be ten minutes only."

Ossi joined in to reinforce Pasquale's surge of humanity. "Come on, be a good fellow and let us."

Pasquale was a kind soul, so he gave way to their pleading. Joined soon by others seeing their success, they got through the narrow gate and a strange sensation pervaded them all: the bitter-sweet feeling of freedom. Everything looked and felt different; even the air had an unusually balmy aroma. The air's sweetness was not just an imaginary effect of their temporary freedom, for the canal's bank was lined with mint which grew in profusion. They plucked some, rubbing it against their foreheads, and inhaled the refreshing scent. Some took off their sandals and waded in the canal, which was only ankle-deep. Most of them threw their shirts off and wetted their chests and arms.

Henry and Ossi scrutinised the terrain leading to the Crati. There were stagnant pools and bogs, ideal breeding grounds for the Anopheles larvae. They exchanged significant glances but said nothing. Why spoil the enjoyment of the *camerades*, who seemed to have forgotten where they were?

There was a sudden yell. "Porca Madonna!" followed by an avalanche of curses and imprecations. "You stupid fool!" shrieked Tommasini at the top of his voice. "*Cretino*! Don't you understand? You can be court-martialled for letting prisoners out."

Pasquale did not seem unduly perturbed. "Listen, you sniffing police dog! These men were simply doing their ablutions a few yards from me. I have a rifle. They are unarmed. What harm is there in that?"

Henry came to Pasquale's defence. "The fault is ours. We only asked him to let us cool off in this dreadful heat."

Tommasini threw him an angry, contemptuous look and ignored him, addressing Pasquale instead. "I'm going to report this," he bellowed.

Ossi's dark eyes flashed with fury. "Now you listen to me, Tommasini! We are not criminals or prisoners. We are civilian internees. This place is no paradise! All Signor Pasquale did was to exercise his common sense and kindness!"

This harangue left Ossi out of breath and trembling with fury. Tommasini made no reply and stamped off. Henry went up to the sentry to apologise for the trouble he had caused him. But Pasquale did not seem to be taking the whole matter too much to heart, for he grinned at him amicably. "Not to worry. Damned petty bloodhounds, these *pollzhiotti!*"

Pity their little adventure had to end on an unpleasant note, but they were glad to have found an unexpected ally in the camp.

"To hell with them! Let's get back and have some food," Dino said, shaking off the gloom.

The evening meal was identical to the one before, except for a few extra slices of *mortadella*. The queuing was a nuisance. It was also uncomfortable to eat, sitting on the edge of the bed with a bowl in one's lap. *Perhaps we'll be able to make some tables and stools from all the wood lying around,* Henry thought to himself. He looked about him as he ate. Again Mr Meiersohn was nowhere to be seen. Dino got his extra helpings from the little suitcase. He gobbled his titbits in great haste, occasionally emitting sighs of delight. Ossi ate in silence. His face wore a pensive and grave expression. He chewed very slowly, almost absent-mindedly, showing no real interest in his food.

"*Appello!*"

Oh hell here we go again, thought Henry. The roll call went without a hitch until Mr Meiersohn's name was called.

"Meiersohn!" repeated Tommasini, but there was no response.

"The old man is in the latrine," lied Altman. "He only went there a minute ago."

Everyone knew this was untrue, including Tommasini, but he let it pass probably because he'd had enough for one day. He turned to Henry. "*Capo camerata!* Cavaliere Rizzi wants you. Right away!"

"Here it comes," thought Henry. "The pay off."

He was admitted by an elderly woman servant, who took Henry straight into the comandante's office. He was sitting at his desk in his usual riding attire.

"Your books. You can take them now."

"Grazie, Signor Comandante," said Henry and began to put the books into a box. He did not betray his relief over not being reprimanded. As he hesitated, not knowing whether to go or wait to be dismissed, Cavaliere Rizzi suddenly asked, "Any problems?"

"Yes, Signor Comandante. These open latrines are dangerous for hygienic reasons."

"Anything else?"

Henry's mind worked overtime. The best defence, he thought, is attack. "There are no showers or baths."

"And so?" interrupted Signor Rizzi.

"I wonder, could we ... would it be permissible to use the canal?"

Signor Rizzi shot up. "Who told you about the canal?" He fixed Henry with a penetrating stare. The answer required quick thinking.

"We saw it from the camp," lied Henry.

"You did? You must have eyes like a hawk."

Henry thought it best not to reply, especially as there was an enigmatic smile on the comandante's lips. So perhaps he knew, preferring not to discuss the guard's inefficiency with an internee. Anyway, he did not prolong the conversation; he made a gesture of dismissal and Henry was glad to go. It was getting dark but the sky was illuminated as he had never seen it before. The stars seemed to hang low from the firmament and looked bigger, brighter and closer than in northern latitudes. He was in no hurry to go back, enjoying this rare opportunity of being on his own. With the ebbing of the day, the air was cooler and it seemed to him that the evening breeze bore that sweet scent of mint up from the Crati. So he sat down and drew in lungfuls of cool air.

When he got back to the *camerata* there was an animated discussion despite the complete darkness. The strategy of war was the topic of debate.

"And I tell you, the war is far from lost yet," Dino's deep baritone resounded, drowning out the rest.

"With all respect, *Herr Doktor*, if you are as good a physician as you are a strategist, God help your patients." That was

Szafran's voice with its Yiddish-German drawl, and it went on, "Hitler, may he rot, is certainly going to invade Britain."

"Not so fast my friend!" retorted Dino. "What about the British Navy? That's no pushover! Greater War Lords than the painter and decorator have barked their shins on it." (Dino was a born optimist and a great admirer of British naval forces.)

"Well I think the war will be over in a month." This was unmistakeably Reimer's high-pitched nasal voice.

"And who asked your opinion, you red-headed fool?" exclaimed Wolf, on whom Reimer exerted the same effect as a red rag to a bull.

"I should not be surprised if Hitler attacked Russia," said Altman. "He needs both *Lebensraum* and grain."

Henry was sick to the back teeth of this political and strategic chatter. He had heard all this *ad nauseam* many times before, so, to put an end to their idle talk, he made his presence known, for they had not noticed his return in the dark. Immediately the noisy polemic stopped.

"How did it go?" they wanted to know. "Did you get a ticking off?"

Henry briefly outlined the salient points of the interview and was gratified to get their thanks, for bringing their books back. Henry lay down. What else could one do in the dark? The chatter went on however.

"Let's get some candles tomorrow," said Dino, who did not take kindly to the enforced inactivity.

"God, I have dreadful belly-ache," exclaimed young Scholz, suddenly shooting out of bed to run for the latrines.

"Try to bring the food up," said a small voice.

Henry, recognising the voice, sat bolt upright. "Mr Meiersohn! Where have you been all day?"

"I have been in the camp, *Herr Doktor*."

"Have you had anything to eat?" There was no reply.

"You know, Mr Meiersohn," said Reimer, "Manna does not fall from heaven here."

"I am aware of that."

"So what are you going to do?"

"The same God, who looks after the birds, will look after me."

"Don't give me that rot," yelled Reimer.

"You shut up, *yekkisher shmock*!" intervened Wolf.

Lubicz, whose bed was next to Meiersohn's, tried to reassure the old man. "Look Granddad! I like kosher food too, when I can get it. There was nothing *treyfe* in the meal today. Only vegetables and pasta."

"There was meat," said Meiersohn calmly.

"Meat?" protested Lubicz. "What meat? A slice or two of *mortadella*."

"One or two, it makes no difference: evil is evil even in small doses."

At this point Altman thought fit to intervene. "Mr Meiersohn, you are a learned man and know the law, your *Mishnah* and *Gemarrah*. You know the rule can be broken if there is danger to life."

"What danger? I am used to fasting. Many Jews fast several times each year, and every Jew, who calls himself a Jew, fasts during Yom Kippur. A day's fast is no danger to me. I didn't have a bite for three days, when I was crossing the Austrian border on foot."

"And what do you expect will happen tomorrow? We shall still be here," said Reimer.

"Tomorrow is another day. God will put the right ideas into my head."

It was no use arguing with him.

Another man started to writhe in pain. "Oh damn it! It feels like stilettos in my bowels. These damned cooks are poisoning us!" This was Dvorak moaning. His pains must have been excruciating, as he, a sturdy athlete, was not one for whining.

"This has nothing to do with the cooks!" said Henry, to dispel unjust resentment against them. "It's those blasted open latrines, the heat and the flies. Maybe the rotten cherries were also at fault."

And then the avalanche began; more people writhing in pain or vomiting. And so the second day in Ferramonti ended for most with a bellyache.

Chapter 5

Day 3: A trip for the Triumvirate

It had been a hectic night with continual coming and going to and from the latrines. Some people had vomited all over their blankets, having been overcome before they could get out of bed. Everyone felt exhausted after a sleepless night and the stench of vomit was worsened by the heat and poor sanitation that abounded.

"Well John, what do you make of it?"

"It looks to me like summer diarrhoea, gastro-enteritis, probably caused by the abrupt change of environment and diet. Although come to think of it, those cherries looked a bit suspect."

Ossi did not seem quite satisfied. "It could be dysentery you know; I think this diarrhoea ought to be investigated!" Apart from his special interest in public health, Ossi showed the usual zeal of the newly qualified, having completed his studies only the year before.

"*Appello!*" Bloody hell! That was all they needed.

"Get up!" shouted Tommasini, but several internees were too exhausted to take any notice.

"They are sick," explained Henry.

Tommasini was not convinced. "What kind of sickness?"

"Diarrhoea and vomiting. I had better see the camp doctor. This could be contagious."

Tommasini's inquisitive attitude suddenly switched to one of alarm. Clearly he was now concerned for his own safety. "Come with me," he said, anxious to get away as quickly as he could.

So Henry asked for two colleagues to come with him and Tommasini did not object. On reaching the Red Cross hut they were led by a 'crocerossina', a young nurse, into the doctor's room where they were confronted by the huge flabby mass, the camp *medico. Falstaff*, thought Henry. The rotund figure, with its enormous paunch, was literally drowning in fat. His bald head was a small globe, resting on a big spherical trunk. His face had only a sparse growth of beard, his skin was waxen and his small eyes seemed almost lost in all that grease.

He undoubtedly suffered from a glandular disorder. With a forced smile on his countenance he put out his hand and introduced himself.

"Dottore Sabatini. What can I do for you?"

"Dottore Sabatini," said Henry, "we have come to inform you of an outbreak of diarrhoea and vomiting among our companions."

"Ah, that! It's nothing," retorted Dr Sabatini, "it's the usual summer diarrhoea, diarrhoea Calabrese. Half Calabria has it."

Ossi was getting impatient. "Some of them have blood in their stools," he muttered, letting his annoyance show.

Henry gave him a warning look. "You are quite right of course Dr Sabatini, but as a precaution, to avoid the possibility of dysentery ..."

"Dysentery?" Dr Sabatini interrupted Henry, "Dysentery takes time to incubate. You only got here two days ago!"

And he was right of course. But the newly qualified Ossi had his bacteriology still fresh in his mind. "There exist fulmination forms of dysentery, which can strike in less than twenty-four hours especially in debilitating conditions."

Henry thought this a bit far-fetched, but theoretically it was possible. Dr Sabatini began to vacillate. "Well, what do you want me to do?"

The three doctors felt uneasy. It was not their place to tell the camp doctor what to do but since he expected some kind of advice, Henry ventured, "I wonder whether as a matter of precaution, a microscopical and serological examination is not indicated?"

Dr Sabatini looked at them aghast. Most likely he had not practiced medicine for some time, possibly because of his physical condition. In times of war, doctors are valuable so only the most expendable would be sent to a place like this. However, he soon regained his outer equilibrium, taking refuge in officialdom and the authority of his position.

"Leave it to me," he said coldly, "I will arrange everything."

He put his little pudgy hands where his flanks should have been and to show that the matter was closed, he changed the subject. "This zone is malaria-infested. Have you received your rations of quinine yet?"

"So far we have not," replied Henry, concealing his anger, for it was unforgivable to expose people unnecessarily to the risk of malaria for almost three days if prophylactic measures were available. Dr Sabatini handed over a carton of one thousand quinine tablets with instructions for the internees to take one tablet three times a day.

As they were leaving Dr Sabatini had a sudden inspiration. "I would like all three of you to come with me to inspect the marshes. Anopheles breed there. Maybe we can devise something to control them. I'll see you tomorrow morning at ten."

As soon as they left the doctors looked at each other, smiling.

"What an *ignoramus*," hissed Dino, contemptuously.

Although Henry was worried to see a man like Dr Sabatini at the helm of the camp's medical services he came to his defence. "The man is ill no doubt and must have been out of touch with medicine for years. We must be tolerant."

Back in the *camerata*, Ossi took it upon himself to instruct the internees in the basic principles of hygiene. The two cooks in particular, who luckily were not affected, were made aware of their great responsibility. "One cook's dirty hands can spread infection to us all."

News of the outbreak of diarrhoea must have reached the camp comandante by bush telegraph for he turned up in person. Though he did not seem alarmed, his tension was betrayed by the way he twisted his whip and slapped his thigh with it.

"How many are ill?" He addressed the *capo camerata*.

"So far only seven have severe diarrhoea, but some of the others have stomach pains and have been vomiting profusely."

"Have you contacted Dr Sabatini?"

"We have. Though it is very unlikely, dysentery must not be excluded."

For a split second a hint of anxiety flickered in Signor Rizzi's eyes.

"Dysentery," he repeated, shaking his head, "not likely."

Ossi was impatient. "If something is not done about the hygienic conditions here we shall have an epidemic sooner or later."

"And who are you?" asked the comandante, turning his head towards Ossi.

"My name is Dr Gerber, specialising in public health."

"And where have you studied?"

"In Montpellier, Florence and Genoa."

"Bit of a gypsy, eh?"

Clearly Ossi did not like this remark for his dark eyes glared ominously, but he ignored the comandante's sarcasm and retorted instead, "Open latrines are a danger to public health!"

Dino seized the opportunity for further psychological pressure.

"Excuse me, *Comandante*. I took my medical degree in Genoa. No one suggests this is an epidemic, but if an epidemic should ever arise it would spread outside the confines of this camp."

Signor Rizzi seemed impressed by Dino's impeccable Italian and the logic of his argument. After a moment's reflection he turned to Henry. "Make a list of basic requirements and bring it to me."

With these words he left them. He obviously could not think much of Dr Sabatini if he wished to deal with these matters himself.

None of those who remained well felt inclined to eat because of the food's potential hazards. But food was a luxury not to be made light of and in the end, the Jewish sense of humour prevailed. "Better to die on a full stomach than an empty one."

"What are you grinning at, Granddad?" asked Wolf.

All eyes were suddenly directed on Mr Meiersohn, who had been sitting quietly in a corner, smiling. "Maybe my fasting was not such a bad idea after all."

Though there was no glee or malice in his remark, Reimer was needled by it. "Enjoying God's special protection?"

"Shut up! You ginger-haired *yekkisher shmock!*" interrupted Wolf. "He has more brains in his arse than you have in that thick skull of yours."

After their afternoon nap the doctors got down to compiling a list of the most elementary requirements, paying special attention to the open latrines. All kinds of disinfectants were suggested. Ossi preferred quick lime, both for its cheapness and rapid effect. In order not to offend Dr Sabatini, Henry suggested that Dino went over to him to establish rapport. Secretly Henry was also motivated by his desire to delegate some responsibility to Dino. As he had hoped, Dino was delighted to assume the role of the second-in-command, a vice-capo, and went off immediately. Meantime Ossi continued to enrich his list with numerous requests.

"I am afraid, Ossi, if you overload the list we shan't get anything at all."

Ossi seemed to sulk at this remark. "Whatever you do, don't give in on the question of covered latrines! This is a *sine qua non!*"

Soon after Henry made his way to the white house. Inwardly he was convinced that the outbreak of diarrhoea was a false alarm but it was wise to exploit the situation to prevent serious trouble in the future. He was admitted unceremoniously.

"Give me the list."

As soon as Signor Rizzi glanced at it, he frowned. Grabbing a red pen he crossed most items out, then he gave Henry a penetrating look. "*Perbacco!* What kind of list is this? You must have mistaken this place for a holiday camp!"

Having foreseen such a reaction and being convinced that the comandante would have reacted exactly the same way, whatever the length of the list, Henry remained silent.

"We are at war!" he bellowed, "and this is a concentration camp. Do you understand?"

Henry nodded his head, but did not reply.

"Covered latrines!" resumed Signor Rizzi, "What nonsense. What about the soldiers at the battlefront? Do they get covered latrines?"

"Signor Comandante, we are civilian internees. We have not chosen to be here. Nor have we committed any crime."

"You are Jews!"

Henry felt anger flaring up. He clenched his fists, then controlled himself. "If being Jewish is a crime, then we are criminals," Henry said icily, "but in all the years that I have lived in Italy I have never been made aware of any criminality involved in being a Jew."

Signor Rizzi looked away. He seemed rather ill at ease.

"These recent anti-Semitic feelings," continued Henry, "cannot stem from Italian hearts. They are artificially implanted German propaganda."

"*Basta*! Enough!" exclaimed the comandante. "Watch what you say! You could get yourself shot as an *agent provocateur*! Germany is our ally. Do not forget that."

All this time Henry had been standing in front of the comandante. He began to feel utterly drained and weary. "I have no interest in politics. I am a doctor and as such responsible for the physical welfare of all my comrades. This list contains only essentials; it is for you to decide what to do with it."

The interview was over and Henry stalked out with his head erect. By the time he got back to his *camerata*, Dino had already returned from his visit to Dr Sabatini, loaded like a Calabrese donkey with first aid medical supplies as well as a wealth of information. Dr Sabatini had qualified in Naples some twenty years ago and had been in the colonial service in Tripoli and Somalia for several years. The nearest laboratory was in Cosenza and the *crocerossina* was the comandante's sister. By the way, Dr Sabatini was married.

"Has he any children?" asked Henry.

"You must be joking. With that big paunch, how could there be?"

Ossi was more interested in the outcome of Henry's interview.

"He was offensive and bombastic but in spite of the usual fireworks he did not give a definitive 'no' to our requests."

It was getting cooler and most internees took a stroll. Already a strong bond was developing between them. Though they came from such different walks of life, they gradually began to blend, drawn together by their shared experience. As Jews they were the most downtrodden, humiliated and persecuted people in Europe. Not surprisingly they developed a strong sense of belonging, mutual trust and coherence.

"John, I forgot to tell you, a further convoy of internees is expected any day now."

"The more the merrier," remarked Altman. "We shall have more diarrhoea, more flies and fewer provisions."

A thin string of smoke rising from the lower end of the camp caught their attention. They decided to visit Pasquale to see if he'd got into trouble on their account. Nearing the sentry box they saw a man squatting on the ground. There was a little fire flickering beside him.

"Who the devil can that be?" asked Schindler. As they came nearer they could make out a skull cap on the squatter's head.

"Why, it's Mr Meiersohn!" exclaimed Scholz. "What is he doing here?"

Bursting with curiosity, the group approached. There was Mr Meiersohn crouching unceremoniously on a patch of grass. Beside him spread on the stony ground was a handkerchief, and resting on it a slice of melon and tomato. Over a fire of burning twigs rested a tiny casserole in which a solitary egg bobbed in boiling water.

"So that is what you are up to, Granddad," said Wolf, full of tender admiration.

Pasquale stood in the sentry box, grinning all over his stubbly toothless face.

"I brought him the eggs." He took a lighter out of his pocket, flicking it on and off. "Six eggs for this."

They were all astounded, especially Ossi, who could not get over his amazement. "How did they communicate without any language in common?"

"They had one," replied Altman with gravity. "Simplicity and goodness of heart."

People began to feel famished, their hunger being stronger than their fear of diarrhoea. Besides, those so affected were beginning to feel better.

Approaching the *camerata* they saw the smoking chimney and felt sorry for the cooks toiling in the kitchen while the 'diners' took a pre-prandial stroll.

"It's no good us just feeling guilty," said Altman. "We ought to give them something for their sacrifice."

"Why?" protested Szafran, still sore at having been rejected as a cook. "After all they volunteered." But he was out-voted.

After food, when the *appello* was over and the day drew towards its end, Altman had a pleasant surprise for them. He had bought candles. Three candles were lit at strategic points and the *camerata* came to life again. Dino began to rummage among Mamma's delicatessen, Ossi took up a book and Wolf began to shave, of all things.

"Look at this, meshuggener!" said Szafran. "Why shave at this hour?"

Wolf could not reply, for his tongue was pushed against his cheeks to stretch it better. The rasping noise of the razor against his bristles was audible throughout the *camerata*.

"Whatever is he doing, the fool," asked Reimer, "sawing his beard off?"

"Be quiet, you *yekkisher shmock!*" hissed Wolf between his teeth. He looked most comical. His bald pate, on top of the lather covering his face, was shining bright. He had placed a little mirror by a candle and the light reflected from it, lent his bald pate a halo.

"*Der Schlag soll es treffen!* The devil take it!" he cursed. "This bloody razor is blunt. If I leave it until tomorrow, I shan't be able to shave at all." Wolf's beard growth was really extraordinary.

"When he shaves it's like chopping wood," said someone.

Finally the laborious shaving act was over, but Wolf could not relax yet. "This *camerata* stinks," he said. "Look at all the rubbish on the floor. We'll have to get a broom."

Henry, closed his eyes, lazing away despite the prickling palliasse, wondering what the morrow would bring. Some of the older internees began to grumble about the lights; they wanted to sleep.

"What's the rush?" asked Wolf. "At least when you're awake you aren't farting!"

Irritated, Reimer shot up from his bunk. "You speak for yourself!"

"Keep quiet, *yekke* with the short skin!"

"Short skin?" asked Reimer, nonplussed. "What do you mean?"

"Everybody knows you have a short skin," replied Wolf. "As soon as you close your eyes you open your arsehole!"

At this explanation the whole *camerata* burst into laughter. So it was on a hilarious note that the candles were blown out at the end of their third day in Ferramonti.

Chapter 6

East meets west

Dino was usually the first to rise to start his physical exercises. He was a little in love with his body and proud of his muscular torso and arms.

"Get up you lazy bastards!" he shouted.

Ossi hated to be disturbed in his sleep and resented his morning slumbers being punctuated by Dino's shrill alarm. He shot up from the palliasse to transfix Dino with a piercing look.

"If you don't shut up ..."

Ossi in anger with his flared nostrils and flaming eyes had a fearsome look about him but he soon regained his composure.

"One of these days Dino, you'll get it. Who the hell wants to get up at six o'clock in the morning?"

"Like the chickens," chirped little Wolf.

In truth the early morning was indeed the best part of the day. The air was still cool and moist; the flies had yet to begin their daily torment. Soon the *muezzin's* cry, "Come and get it!" resounded. Everybody ran out to get the 'coffee,' that darkish beverage of uncertain origin, because it was hot. Everybody, except Meiersohn, who waited until they were out of sight before commencing the elaborate ritual of his morning prayer. First he wrapped himself in his prayer shawl and after removing the phylacteries from the gold-embroidered velvet pouch, he strapped one cube to his forehead, pressing the other against his heart. Western, and especially German, Jews who had absorbed the *Deutsche Kultur* were prone to look down on orthodoxy as a misshapen relic of the Dark Ages. Orthodox Jews, on the other hand, who were continually exposed to moral and physical persecution, despised the westernised Jews, to whom they referred as 'Assimilants' and 'Goyim'. They regarded them as traitors who had forsaken the 'Law' in exchange for moral cosiness and material prosperity.

Tommassini, emboldened by the news that the 'epidemic' was abating, plucked up sufficient courage to enter the *cam-*

erata. No longer was anyone amused by his familiar distortion of names.

It was almost 10 o'clock so the three doctors went off to meet Sabatini. The camp doctor, his flabby paunch swaying to and fro, appeared in the doorway.

The three of them were delighted to step out of the camp confines, particularly as no guards were summoned to go with them. The soldiers at the gate presented arms, saluting Black-shirted Sabatini, and let them pass. For a while they walked along the dusty road outside the camp, but soon they branched off into a narrow path in the direction of the river Crati. Gradually, with the increasing moisture in the soil, the landscape underwent a transformation. At first there were only a few patches of grass, scattered with red and blue. But these became denser until the expanse was filled with a fragrance of its own, which they inhaled deeply. It was a thrilling experience. Here was nature going its own way, undisturbed by war, revealing its beauty. It was unbelievable that all this verdure lay so close to the barren soil of the camp.

As they moved on, the soil became soggy, their feet sinking into waterlogged ground. Trickles of water filled their shoe imprints, creating tiny puddles behind them. An ever-increasing number of rivulets and canals intersected the area. Here and there stagnant water had accumulated, its oily surface coalescing in phosphorescent patches; clearly this was an ideal breeding ground for Anopheles. In spite of their balancing acts over narrow ridges of firm land it became obvious that they could not proceed much further; besides they could already hear the Crati River.

"*Porca miseria!* Bloody hell!" cursed Dr Sabatini. Having trodden on a swampy patch, he was stuck in the mud up to his shins. "*Porca miseria!*" he cursed again, trying to free himself. With his enormous weight it was surprising he had not been swallowed up already by the bog. Despairingly he spread out his arms in a helpless gesture.

"Look at this mess! What can one do? It would take years!"

In fact the Fascist government had proclaimed for many years its intention to reclaim the bogs and marshes of Calabria, promising to eradicate malaria and to improve general living standards. Instead, the Fascists embarked on the Abyssinian venture and there was no money left for drainage and reclamation.

"I only arrived here last week," said Dr Sabatini apologetically. "The camp is so dry, who could imagine all this mess so close by?"

He wiped his forehead with the back of his podgy hand. His eyebrows were dripping with sweat and it seemed as if this enormous mass of fat was melting in the sun.

"No good wasting our time!" he said. "It's hot. Let's get back."

"'Back to prison," thought Henry with a heavy heart.

All of them felt the effect of the blazing midday sun, but Ossi always managed to keep cool. For some reason heat did not seem to affect him and there was hardly any perspiration on his brow. Although there was no need for stimulation, the morning walk had increased their appetite.

"Rice and peppers! Come and get it!" called Mario.

"*Risotto con pepperoni!*" exclaimed Dino with delight. To his credit he never complained about the quality of the food, in spite of his gourmet tastes. Once their frugal meal was over most of them stretched themselves out for a siesta, which was the best one could do in that infernal heat. The *camerata* was filled with the sour smell of perspiration. Dino got off to sleep right away; it would have taken an earthquake to prevent him doing so and soon his mighty snore out-snored the rest. Henry had great difficulty in dozing off in all that noise, but when he finally succeeded he was sharply awakened by a fracas of hammering. The *camerata* was almost empty, but an uproar of human voices mingled with the racket of banging came from the courtyard. Henry looked out. There stood Ossi, a hammer in his hand, knocking nails into what was to become a table.

"Not like that, *Herr Doktor,*" begged Scholz. "That nail is too long. It will only split the wood."

Ossi took no notice. His black hair falling over one eye, he continued to wield his hammer unperturbed.

"We have no proper tools," protested Scholz, who had been apprenticed as a joiner. Born and bred in Germany, he had absorbed Teutonic thoroughness with his mother's milk.

"Who needs proper tools!" exclaimed Ossi. "We don't want Louis XIV cabinets!"

"If we do it your way the table won't last long!" objected Scholz.

"I should hope not!" retorted Ossi. "Who wants to stay here for long anyway?"

"*Doktor* Gerber," remarked Szafran, "You have missed your vocation."

Ossi gave him one of his looks and Szafran piped down. There, finally, stood Ossi's masterpiece. It was wobbly, but it would do.

There was only one hammer available, so the internees had to take turns to prove their craftsmanship. In this way the whole afternoon passed, each man trying to better his predecessor by learning from his mistakes. Someone managed to borrow a hacksaw from the labourers and the standard of joinery became more refined and almost showy. No one enjoyed his work more than Dino.

"Robinson Crusoe!" he proclaimed, waving the hammer wildly. Any kind of pioneer work stimulated his adolescent thirst for adventure. While he worked on the wood, his bare chest and arms displayed the smooth interplay of his muscles. Vulcan himself could not have looked more majestic.

"When this stool is finished, even Sabatini's hefty arse won't break it," he boasted.

Gradually they assembled an array of stools, tables and shelves, which they hoped would make their existence a little more bearable. Secretly and unknown to Henry, who as *capo camerata* was responsible for his comrades' conduct, Dino and Wolf had spirited away several full-length planks, although it had been agreed to use rejects only. But now Dino had set his heart on a large table under the oak, for a game of bridge or chess. The collective creative fever had raised morale and they felt in tune with the world again.

The sun was sinking rapidly. Strange how quickly it moved in the south, once it approached the horizon.

Appello rang out, making everyone jump.

"This bloody *appello* will drive me round the bend," protested Wolf. The roll call went smoothly enough until Mr Meiersohn's name was called. There was no reply.

"Meiersohn! Meiersohn!" Tommasini called for a second and third time, growing impatient. "That man is never here!"

Henry thought he'd better intervene.

"He is an old man and can't walk very fast."

"I don't care if he is Methuselah himself! He has to be here at *appello!*" and turning to Henry, "*Capo camerata!* I shall hold you personally responsible for him in the future. *Capito?*"

As soon as Tommasini had gone, the internees looked at each other, smiling, for this was not the first time the old man was absent at *appello.*

"I wonder where he's got to," said Henry. "He did not look too well this morning."

"Nonsense!" replied Reimer. "He is probably over with Pasquale, eating his eggs on the sly."

It was time to light the candles as the darkness had gradually crept into the *camerata.* Ossi was examining the little table he had placed between his and Henry's bed. The legs were shorter on one side, but that didn't matter much.

The door opened and in walked Mr Meiersohn, immersed in thought.

"So here you are!" called out Reimer. "High time too! You'll get us all into trouble."

"Into trouble? God forbid! Why should I do that?"

Henry thought it opportune to put in a word. "Look, Mr Meiersohn, you are a very nice old gentleman, and if you do not want to eat with us that is your business. But you must be here at roll call."

Meiersohn looked at him, surprised. "Why must I be here? Are they afraid that an old man like me will run away?"

Henry grew impatient. "Mr Meiersohn, it does not matter what you or I think. What matters is what Tommasini says. He wants us all here at *appello* and that includes you!"

Meiersohn shrugged his shoulders. "If that is what he wants, then I shall be here."

Henry intended to let the matter rest there, but Reimer had different ideas. "What makes you think you are extra special, unlike the rest of us?"

"I never said I was."

"But you behave is if you thought you were."

"That was never my intention. I only want to do what I think is right."

"To stay away from *appello* and get us all into trouble, is that right?"

"I never realised it would cause you trouble and I am sorry and apologise."

But Reimer would not leave it yet. He wanted his pound of flesh. "You *Ostjuden*, you eastern Jews, have been the cause of all our troubles! Your manners, the way you dress, your side-locks and beards! You continuously draw attention to yourself and just create anti-Semitism!"

"Is it so dreadful to follow one's tradition and the dictates of God?"

"If you live amongst other people you have to adapt yourself, but you *Ostjuden* have always stayed foreigners, relics from the dark ages!"

Wolf could not contain himself any longer. "Now listen to me, you *Kraut!* If you don't leave Mr Meiersohn alone ..."

"No need to upset yourself, Mr Wolf," Meiersohn interrupted him, "I do not need any advocates. I can speak for myself." And turning to Reimer he continued, "Young man, you blame us, eastern Jews, for having kept the old traditions of our fore-fathers and not having become assimilants like yourself?"

"Yes I do! You cannot live in a country, feed on it like para-sites and yet reject its customs and ways of life."

Mr Meiersohn paused, stroking his beard and looking in-tently at Reimer. "Tell me, Mr Reimer, who has an easier life, we *Ostjuden* who are conspicuous or you assimilants who have adopted western ways?"

Reimer did not quite understand what the old man was leading up to. So he was on his guard. "What has that got to do with it? But anyway, since you ask, there is no doubt that we westernised Jews lead a fuller and more worthwhile exist-ence."

"Then tell me, Mr Reimer, why have we chosen to be despised by the Goyim, humiliated because of the clothes we wear, oppressed because of the Yiddish and Hebrew we speak, tormented because of the beard and *pejos* and spat on because of our rituals and traditions? Are we *meshugge*? Mad? Are we trying to chew up our own flesh? Do we enjoy pogroms and persecutions? Would it not be much easier for us to become assimilated like yourself, unless we were raving mad? So why do we do it, Mr Reimer?"

"I suppose it's because of ignorance, superstition and fanaticism," snorted Reimer, who was beginning to feel uneasy.

"Ignorance and superstition, Mr Reimer, are not enough to sustain people, to keep people going through two thousand years of persecution and slaughter in exile. The real answer, Mr Reimer, is Faith."

"Don't give me all that mumbo jumbo! Faith, my foot!" spat Reimer. "Do you really believe all that tripe? The creation of the world in seven days? The Jews crossing the Red Sea? Manna falling from Heaven and such nonsense?"

Meiersohn drew a deep breath and looked Reimer straight in the eye. "Mr Reimer, it is much easier not to believe. Any fool can do that. To believe is very hard. When Abraham was an old man and Sarah an old woman past childbearing, he was told by the Lord our God, blessed be His name, that his seed would multiply like the grains of sand in the sea. He believed it."

Reimer could not contain his laughter. "Don't be ridiculous, Mr Meiersohn! This is the twentieth century you know!" Reimer pressed his attack. "Let's leave religion out of it for the moment but tell me, Mr Meiersohn, why have these eastern Jews to look so shabby, so unkempt in their appearance to invite ridicule and distaste?"

Mr Meiersohn paused for breath. The old man was getting tired. "The Goyim usually associate Jews with riches. But most of the eastern Jews in the little villages of Poland and Russia live in hovels and are poorer than a church mouse. What do you know about scraping a living in the midst of continuous persecution? When you lead such a miserable existence, hungry and humiliated, what do you care for your external appearance?"

The whole *camerata* listened intently to the argument without taking sides. The problem in discussion was not new to them and involved deep human and social matters, as well as a question of principles and a philosophy of life. There were faults and merits in each of the views, there always are, and although the arguments for and against had by no means been exhausted most felt the discussion had gone on long enough.

"Let's change the subject," suggested Ossi. "This is getting us nowhere."

"What about a game of bridge?" suggested Dino. "We can give Ossi's table its baptism with a game of cards."

Altman was a keen bridge player too, and so the four of them settled down at Ossi's wobbly table. At first their hearts were not in the game. The old debate between the eastern and western Jews had left them pensive, for it was very pertinent to each of them. However, as the game went on they became more absorbed, playing for hours, until the protests of their comrades forced them to put the candles out and go to bed.

Chapter 7

The Kosher Ham

Henry's sleep that night was erratic and restless. Eventually he fell into a troubled nightmare-filled slumber. At one point he dreamt of brown-shirted Nazi thugs surrounding him, spitting in his face and pulling him by his beard, and strangely enough, even in his dream, he thought *that's impossible, I don't have a beard!*

"You look as though you've been through the mangle. What's the matter with you?" asked Dino. There was no denying Dino had a keen clinical eye and a kindly interest in his friend.

"I did not sleep well. That's all."

"You ought to give your mattress a face-lift! No wonder you can't sleep with all those lumps and bumps in the straw."

There was a sudden commotion in the *camerata*. Someone had managed to get a newspaper from a labourer in the camp. This was their first glimpse of what was going on in the world outside.

"Our glorious pilots, *nostri gloriosi piloti*," read Altman aloud, "have the honour of joining the *Luftwaffe* in their raids on London."

"London is in flames," read another. "The British lion is having its tail twisted."

It was disheartening and sad. A gloomy atmosphere of sinister foreboding pervaded the *camerata*.

"And I tell you, they are counting their chickens before they are hatched!" Dino's powerful voice suddenly boomed out. "The war is far from over. England always loses all her battles but the last. Anglo-Saxons are slow to warm up."

"From your mouth into God's ears, Amen!" said Szafran. "But you are an optimist, *Herr Doktor*."

There followed the usual debate of would-be strategists, amateur psychologists, socio-economists who knew everything better. Ossi did not partake in that sterile discussion. Balancing himself on his newly-made stool, he was playing with the chain of his key-ring. He had the habit of winding and unwinding the little chain round his index finger by circular flicks of his wrists.

"Henry!" he said all of a sudden, "when you next see the *comandante*, ask for newspapers. After all, we are civilian internees and have a right to know what is going on in the world."

"We also need stamps, *Herr Doktor*," said young Scholz. "I would like to write to my parents and tell them where we are."

Henry nodded. He had not quite recovered from his nightmare and was in no mood for conversation. Instead his attention was drawn to Przebylewski who was sitting on his bed with a faraway expression on his face. There was something odd about him. He was the most inconspicuous among the internees and Henry could not recall having ever exchanged a single word with him. True, he trailed after the rest wherever they went, but he was always silent, made no demands and never got involved in arguments or discussions.

"*Capo!*" said Dino, "It's still cool, how about a game of football?"

In Henry's present frame of mind, this was a most welcome diversion. Dvorak was the proud owner of a football. He was meticulous in matters of sport as he was fully trained in physical education. So he insisted that they first stretched their muscles by a number of exercises. Then they began dribbling, shooting and passing the ball. But their enjoyment was spoiled by the stench of the open latrines.

"We ought to plant some violets there," joked Dino.

Ossi could not see the funny side and wore a constant expression of disgust. Young Scholz was an accomplished goalie and the small crowd of spectators clapped his most spectacular saves. In the heat, the players soon got out of breath, especially Ossi, who was puffing and had to sit down.

"What's the matter with him?" asked Dvorak.

"Supposed to have had rheumatic fever as a child," replied Dino. "It could have left him with a leaky valve."

"You needn't have heart trouble to get exhausted on our diet and this heat," remarked Henry.

Altman, who was passing by, called out, "What do I see? A football? Who brought that?"

"It's mine," said Dvorak with pride. "I brought it all the way from Poland."

Altman's face broke into a grin and he began to chuckle.

"Some people brought their Bible to the concentration camp. Some brought the Iliad or Goethe's Faust. Others brought a lock of their mistress's hair or a picture of their wife — but Dvorak, he brought his football!" And he burst into his usual good-humoured laughter, which shook his whole body.

That morning, while bulk-buying and bargaining with Giuseppe, humouring him to get his own way, Altman suddenly stopped dead in his tracks. He had discovered an entire smoked ham hanging from a beam in the provision store.

"To find a ham in that God-forsaken store," he told his comrades, "was like finding a pearl in a dustbin." But he hadn't asked whether it was for sale in order not to betray his interest to Giuseppe. Apart from tactics, how many internees — apart from Meiersohn — would object to eating pork? Secondly how much would they be prepared to pay?

"I know, on our five lire a day, ham is a great luxury. But quite soon commodities like ham will completely disappear from shops, even in towns. To have found a ham in a concentration camp store is a major miracle. I say let's grab it at all costs."

A long discussion followed wherein it transpired that no one (Meiersohn excepted) objected to ham on religious grounds, so the question was whether they could afford it. Tied as they were to such a stringent budget, this matter required the fullest consideration.

Mario, as the senior cook, was consulted with regard to the usefulness of ham in his provisions; considering they would be unable to buy any meat because of high cost, ham would be an ideal means to give their food some flavour and nutritional value. "I could use small bits to give the soup some taste, mince it for a sauce for macaroni, or serve a slice with potatoes for special occasions."

Asked how much a smoked ham would normally cost, he reckoned that in time of peace, it might fetch between 130 and 150 lire. On no account, he opined, should they pay more than 180 lire. Henry felt weary. One hundred and eighty lire was a full day's allowance for 36 men. As *capo camerata* he could hardly avoid his share of responsibility.

"How much reserve do we have in the kitty?" he asked Altman.

"We have precisely 875 lire plus roughly 500 lire in stocks, like flour, olive oil, pasta, etc."

After a long discussion it was decided to purchase the ham, providing the cost was not too outrageous.

"Leave it to me!" said Altman. "Watch me bargain with Giuseppe until the sparks fly!"

The heat that afternoon was almost stupefying. Swarms of flies of all descriptions and sizes were buzzing in the air or crawling over their helpless victims, who tried hard to doze off. Wolf kept cursing and hitting out at them with his pyjama top. Henry was uncomfortable on his mattress. A few stalks of straw had come through the cover and kept pricking his back and behind. However, exhausted from the nightmarish visions and lack of sleep, he eventually fell into a deep slumber. He did not know how long he had lain there, but somehow the words *hundred and twenty* kept on drumming in his ears. There it was again.

"A hundred and twenty, a real bargain, a *meziye!*"

"What's all this noise about?" he asked, coming round from his *siesta.*

"What a *meziye!*" replied Szafran. "Mr Altman got the ham for 120 lire."

The whole *camerata* was in turmoil and in the middle of it all, there was Altman, the paunchy big teddy-bear, chuckling and laughing, his blue eyes watering from laughter.

Everybody wanted to see the 'kosher ham', as it was jokingly called.

"It must be hung up in the kitchen out of reach of greedy hands," said Lubicz. And in fact it was hung on a hook from the kitchen ceiling, beside a garland of onions and garlic.

"Isn't it funny," remarked Szafran, "there it hangs: a '*treyfe*' ham in a Jewish kitchen with everybody looking up at it as if it were the seventh wonder of the world."

When the excitement had died down, Dino invited Henry to have a look at his 'masterpieces': two benches, well planed and solid, as well as a large table resting on four firm legs. Placed under the oak, all this looked very inviting.

"What about a game of chess?" Dino asked. "I've heard you're quite a champion."

Dino too was renowned for both bridge and chess, so it would be a good chance to pit their wits against each other. They sat down and set up their game. Soon, unfortunately, the rest of the benches were taken up by other internees who had nothing else to do and for whom the opportunity to watch chess players of repute was a major diversion. Chess can be all-absorbing, as it demands a high degree of concentration and makes a welcome escape from reality, but not if the two players are surrounded by *kibitzes*, uninvited observers, who continually talk, advise and criticise every move of the game. Then a game of chess can become an ordeal, a plague and a nightmare.

"*Kibitz halt's Maul – Kibitz* belt up!" is the usual imprecation, which rarely has any restraining effect, in spite of warnings and curses. Under such conditions chess players have no chance at all. One *kibitz* is bad enough, but when there is a whole bunch of them the game becomes a farce.

"Let's pack it in," said Henry. "I can't concentrate. We'll play at night when these blessed *kibitzes* are snoring their heads off."

Leaving their aborted game, the *kibitzes* and players went for a walk instead. A *camerata* next to theirs was almost completed and further down there were more heaps of gravel, cement bags and shallow excavations, ready to erect more barracks.

"They keep on building, those *Katzelmachers*," little Wolf called out. "They're not so sure of a quick victory."

Dino rubbed his hands. "I told you so. This war is by no means over."

As they continued their walk they caught a glimpse of a solitary figure, standing motionless and staring into space.

"It's Mr Przebylewski," said Scholz. "He seems to always be alone."

"He prefers his own company," remarked Reimer, "and looking at you lot I don't blame him."

When the meal was served Scholz was first in the queue. Peeping through the kitchen window he announced excitedly, "They're carving the ham!"

In fact Mario and Lubicz were concentrating on carving the thinnest of slices. The evening meal consisted of boiled potatoes on which a wafer of ham looked more like a decoration.

"I could find him a job in a medical laboratory," remarked Dino, chewing his food.

"Who?" asked Ossi.

"Mario, of course."

"But why a medical laboratory?"

"Well," resumed Dino, picking his teeth, "because he cuts the slices so paper-thin they could dispense with a microtome and save a lot of money."

Scholz, eager to expand his knowledge, asked what a microtome was so Dino explained it was a delicate machine for cutting the finest sections of tissues for microscopic examination.

"They help to make a correct diagnosis. Understand?"

Young Scholz was not quite clear, so Wolf came to his aid with a simple illustration. "Now listen, puppy. Suppose we took a slice of your brain and put it under a microscope to find what is wrong with it. Do you know what we'd find?"

"Well, what would you find?" asked Scholz innocently.

"We'd find it was made of straw!" They all burst into laughter, including Scholz, who could take a joke without offence.

For some reason the roll call was late and when Tommasini eventually made his appearance he was fuming with anger. Kicking the door open with one swing of his boot he made straight for Henry, his eyes ablaze.

"You are going to have to control your men better! Next time we'll shoot!"

He seemed all out of breath and his forehead was covered in perspiration. Henry looked at him aghast and the rest of the *camerata* stood silently, wondering.

"I don't understand, Signor Tommasini. What's happened?"

"One of your men was caught trying to run away. *Scappare!* We had to chase him all the way down to the Crati!"

Henry's eyes darted swiftly from man to man. Meiersohn was there.

"It must be Przebylewski," whispered Altman. "I can't see him."

"And where is the man now, Signor Tommasini?" asked Henry.

"In the Police office. He'll be sent to prison."

"I am sorry, but I'm sure the man meant no harm. There must be an explanation."

"*Cazzo!* Explanation my foot! He was trying to run away. If it happens again we'll put a bullet in him!"

After a rudimentary roll call, he slammed the door behind him and departed, muttering. "*Maledetti Ebrei,* cursed Jews!"

There was a deadly silence of dismay.

"It's unbelievable." Altman broke the silence. "Of all people, Przebylewski was the last I'd have thought to give them the slip."

Henry was bewildered. "It just doesn't make any sense. He wouldn't say boo to a goose!"

"Still waters!" remarked Reimer, shaking his head.

Whatever the explanation, it could mean a lot of trouble for them all.

"He's just the type. Quiet and sly," said one.

"He is not the type at all," was another's opinion.

"The bastard should have thought what he is doing to us," said Szafran.

Henry, losing his patience, put a stop to these sterile speculations. "Quiet! Let's not be the judge and jury before we know the facts!"

Hardly had their turbulent exchange of opinions died down when the door was pushed open again.

"The Chief of Police wants you," said Tommasini with a nasty grin. Henry followed him in silence. Sitting at the desk was a thick-set man with short cropped hair and horn-rimmed glasses. He turned to Henry with an impatient and angry gesture.

"I cannot get any sense out of this man. He speaks such poor Italian. I want you to interpret for me."

There stood Przebylewski, pale, dejected and miserable, staring at his feet.

Henry took up his role of interpreter.

"Why did you run away?"

"I did not."

"What were you doing outside the camp?"

"Just walking."

"How did you get through the barbed wire?"

"I crawled underneath."

"Did you know it was forbidden to get out of camp?"

"I was not thinking."

"Why weren't you back for your evening meal?"

"I have no appetite."

"What business had you by the river Crati?"

Przebylewski hesitated with his answer. "Because … I don't know. I was thinking."

"What were you thinking?"

"Just thinking."

The Chief of Police grew impatient and banged his fist on the desk. "What sort of answers are these?"

Przebylewski jumped as the policeman's fist thumped the desk. He looked very drawn and thoroughly scared.

"Why did you run when the agents went after you?"

"They frightened me. They were shouting. I did not mean to run away."

He said this almost in a whisper. The Chief of Police got up, disgust mingled with bewilderment in his face.

"This man is either mad or a fool, or else he's trying to make fools of us," and turning to Tommasini, he added, "Take him away and lock him up. He'll have to be taught a lesson."

There was something infinitely pathetic about Przebylewski. He certainly did not strike one as bold enough to make a dash for freedom. Henry felt extremely sorry for him and even the Chief of Police seemed uneasy.

"He will just have to learn the hard way," he muttered as if to convince himself.

Back in the *camerata* Henry was bombarded with questions and went over the interview almost word for word. There was an uneasy atmosphere and as so often occurs in troubled times, most men took refuge in their oldest and best of friends: their beds.

"John," ventured Dino, "now the *kibitzes* are out of the way, how about a quiet game of chess?"

Henry was not really in the mood. Przebylewski, tired and frightened, preyed on his mind but he agreed to play. Ossi was already in bed, blanket over his face. They had to keep quiet and move in silence. Most of the candles had been put out, and little of their own candle-stump remained. It stood beside the chess board on Ossi's wobbly table and they hoped it would last out the game. Gradually they got absorbed. Dino's clever moves demanded a mind at full stretch. Deeper and deeper grew their concentration, shorter and shorter their candle-stump. Apart from the snoring, occasional sighing and farting, the *camerata* was quiet. The rest of the room was wrapped in darkness and their minute island of light shrank steadily as the candle guttered to its end. The two contenders, bent over the table, recalling the *Matmids*, those learned Hebrew scholars of old, who spent most nights at the Yeshivah, studying the Talmud or Kabalah by candlelight, until they fell asleep from sheer exhaustion. In an unwary moment, Henry made a slip and the game was over.

"Goodnight Dino. And thank you for a fine game."

"Goodnight *Capo*," replied Dino, snuffing the last flickerings of the candle.

Chapter 8

Rain and reunions

Most of them woke late next morning. Sleep afforded a welcome escape from reality which none of them was keen to face. Dino was the first to shake off the gloom.

"*Alzatevi, condannati!* Get up you bastards!" he yelled at the top of his voice. "The world isn't coming to an end!"

Unexpectedly Mr Meiersohn, who seldom took part in conversations unless obliged to, backed him up.

"No need to worry about Przebylewski. We Jews have faced greater tribulations than this."

Calmly he donned his prayer shawl and proceeded with his morning prayers.

It was pouring with rain and the air was crisp and cool. This was a most welcome change and no one minded getting wet while queuing for 'coffee'. As soon as their mugs were filled, each one stood beside his bed in readiness for the roll call since no one felt like putting Tommasini's back up that particular morning.

Soon the door was flung open and in stumbled Przebylewski, shoved unceremoniously into the *camerata* by a vicious thrust from Tommasini. Regaining his balance, Przebylewski walked slowly towards his own corner, eyes glued to the floor.

"You'd better watch him, *porca miseria*! Next time it won't be as easy as that for any of you!"

After he left there was an uneasy silence as most eyes turned on Przebylewski.

"Well, you old reprobate, what do you think you were up to?"

Henry gave Dino a prod in the ribs. Then he went over to Przebylewski and put a hand on his shoulder.

"We don't know why you did it, but please don't do it again, because you only make it difficult for all of us." With this and an eloquent gesture of his hand, Henry indicated that the matter was at an end.

So they left him in peace and walked out of the *camerata* into the pouring rain. Some of the older ones wore raincoats, but the young—imitating Dino—walked barefoot and barechested in swimming trunks. It was exhilarating to feel the cool raindrops on the skin. In the hothouse of Calabria a heavenly shower that cleared the air was a blessing. Despite the downpour the ground remained almost dry, as the sun-baked soil had an endless thirst for moisture.

A man wrapped in a black oilskin made them a sign to stop. He had a leather satchel flung over his shoulder and began to unzip it.

"Which is the *capo camerata*?" and when Henry came forward he handed over a small parcel. "There is your mail. You can distribute it."

"Letters!" the cry went up. "Letters! But how did they know where we were?"

Back they rushed to the *camerata* to undo the parcel. There were fifteen letters including one for Henry. Those who had no post were visibly disappointed and dejected. Ossi was one with a long face. His eyes looked sad and pensive. Sitting on his locker he indulged mechanically in his familiar practice of winding and unwinding the little key chain round his finger. Dino, stretched out on his back, beaming all over his face, was reading some passages from his letter aloud.

"... and Ulla, the Pekinese had three little pups—how about that, John!"

Henry lit himself the stump of a cigarette before opening his letter. It bore a label 'Censura' and the Genoa postmark. The sender was Enrico Linzer, the friend who had accompanied him to the questura the day before his arrest.

"Dear Henry,

The day of your departure I learned of your whereabouts from the Chairman of the Jewish community in Genoa. He told me ... (there followed two lines which the censor had crossed out in red ink). All your friends send their best wishes and miss you (again a censored line). I went to see your landlady, who promised to look after your belongings and your saxophone.

Write in Italian. Foreign languages take much longer because (again a line crossed out). I have written to Mona and given her your address. Keep up your spirits. Coraggio! Best wishes, Enrico."

Henry regarded the letter tenderly, for it came like a gentle breeze from the world of freedom. It was good of Enrico to have sent his address to Mona, especially as he had been unable to do it himself.

Henry's eyes casually fell on Altman, whose face was brimming over with pleasure and excitement. He held an elongated white envelope in his hand, a letter with official overprints, which had been redirected to the concentration camp.

"My entry visa to Argentina has been confirmed," he called out, unable to contain his joy. "Now it will be only a matter of waiting for a ship." His blue eyes were shining through a mist of tears; but as soon as he looked at the others his chubby rosy face darkened and lost its lustre. "Oh, I'm sorry. I almost feel like a heel, but I am sure no one will begrudge me my good fortune," and then, almost apologetically, he added, "Anyway, I am not going yet. Many things can happen."

Dino, still wrapped in a world of his own, re-reading his letter for the umpteenth time, called out, "My mother is sending me a parcel. She says not to sit too long in the sun! How do you like that?"

All letters were similar in that they were short and contained several erasures by the censors. In spite of the fifteen letters, there was little real news in them because the senders had been instructed to keep to the barest of personal detail only.

Przebylewski went up to Henry. "Was there no post for me?"

Henry shook his head, gravely.

Przebylewski seemed to hesitate. "But everyone else got a letter."

"Not everybody, only those from Genoa. Where do you live?"

"In Milan."

"Well, then that's why. They won't have your address yet."

The rain had stopped and gradually the sun burnt through the clouds. When it rained here, it rained like hell, but it was soon over. The air smelled good with a distinct tang of ozone. The table and benches under the oak were almost dry now.

Dino sat down under the cool shade of the mighty tree.

"Aah!" he exclaimed, "It's like being on holiday!"

To him the whole thing was still a kind of adventure, a lark. With parcels from home and his parents in freedom, he was an internee in name only. "I'll ask my mother to send my accordion," he said suddenly.

Szafran could not bear this apparent loss of all sense of reality.

"In case you have overlooked it, we are in a concentration camp. Remember?"

Their midday meal was lousy. Altman had to plug the huge hole which the ham had made in their budget. Ossi had been quiet all the morning and now he chewed this tasteless concoction in silence. As soon as he had finished eating he took refuge behind a book.

Henry, who sensed Ossi's preoccupation, tried to get him into conversation. "What are you reading?"

"Gustave Flaubert. Salambo." Then after a moment's hesitation he volunteered, "I was expecting news of some importance, which might have also been of interest to you."

"To me? How?"

"Well, I shan't talk about it until I have something more concrete to offer."

With these words he took up his book again. Henry stretched out on his palliasse. The usual sultriness was lifted after the heavy rainfall. He did not feel like sleeping. Should he take advantage of the lull in the heat-wave to sort out his mattress? He dismissed the thought. Strange how little he had thought of Mona since his internment. There were so many new impressions, so many bizarre situations, he could scarcely have found a minute to reflect on Mona. And yet, this thought somehow frightened him. It was alarming. *Tout passe, tout lasse, tout casse*, he remembered wistfully. It might be a good idea to write to her. So he got up and started rummaging in his case until he found some crumpled writing paper and envelopes. He began by numbering the lines from one to twelve. In this way he would be forced to ration the outpourings of thoughts to bare essentials.

1. *"Dear Mona! A week has passed since my arrival at Ferramonti.*

2. *There was so much to do I have not felt like writing. No time.*

3. *The heat here has a stupefying effect too and saps one's*

4. *energy. Today it has rained so I feel better. So far I have no*

5. *stamps but hope to get some soon. Things here are not too bad.*

6. *One can get used to anything as I have learned recently. Man*

7. *can live without most things he once thought indispensable. I*

8. *miss you but am too confused and busy to think much of you.*

9. *Sorry but you like me to be truthful. Please write soon. I am*

10. *looking forward very much to your letter. How are you? All*

11. *happened so suddenly I've had no time to digest it. I miss you,*

12. *the beach at Viareggio and the Pineta. Please write soon. Love Henry."*

Well, there it was. He was glad to have made the effort. No one knew when the stamps would be available but they were bound to arrive some time. He folded his letter, put it in an envelope and stuck it in a book.

Little Wolf had taken it upon himself lately to sweep out the *camerata*. He had acquired a broom of some sort, although no one knew from where. Obsessed as he was with the nuisance of flies, he tried his utmost to keep the *camerata* clean and while sweeping the floor would curse the fleas and flies. He had also a knack for improvising songs, which usually ran like this:

"Oh! I wish old Hitler would break his neck and Mussolini too.

The pair of them would make a show in any respectable zoo."

Somehow he managed to constantly vary his rhymes, though confining his songs to the one topic. Ossi called these lyric effusions 'variations on a theme'. Today Wolf was particularly active, raising clouds of dust as he swept, to everyone's annoyance.

"You should be glad, you stinkers, that someone tries to keep this pigsty clean for you!" he yelled back when they protested.

Ossi lifted his eyes from the book. "We are all most grateful Mr Wolf, but there is no need to raise so much dust. You make us inhale millions of germs, including tubercle bacilli. Why not sprinkle the floor first?"

These words placated Wolf. He liked Ossi, and sometimes he would also listen to reason.

The door was flung open suddenly and young Scholz burst in. "They have arrived!" he screamed, half out of breath.

"Who has arrived?"

"The new transport. The new internees!"

They shot up from their beds like one man. No one wanted to miss the spectacle in the *piazza*; but they were not allowed to come too close. The new arrivals, about 20 in number, were huddled together, bedraggled, bewildered and frightened. To look at them was like looking at themselves in retrospect, a kind of autoscopy. The same bundles, rucksacks and cases covered in dust. The same faces coated with the reddish cake of sweat and powdered loam. And again, as if a film were rewound, there stood the *comandante* in all his pomposity, talking down to them. It was pathetic to see their faces drop at the mention of their paltry daily allowance. Henry felt sorry for them and wished he could tell them that it was not as bad as it sounded. Now they too went through the 'customs' to be searched for 'weapons' and subversive material.

"They have been weighed and measured and found worthy of admission into the paradise of Ferramonti," remarked Szafran sarcastically.

People tried to shake hands, exchange news, but the new *'chapper'* who accompanied the column shooed them off.

"Later! You will have plenty of time," he said ironically. He was a burly middle-aged man of ruddy complexion, blond with cold blue eyes, not a southern type at all. This convoy came from Turin.

"He'll probably be staying too," remarked Wolf. "Seems a nasty piece of shit."

Once their palliasses were filled and their beds allotted, the newcomers began to settle down; after a while the infiltration from the neighbouring *camerata* began. It started first as a trickle, but soon became an invasion, until the hut was choked with people. There was such an exchange of greetings, shaking of hands, patting of backs! What news? The war is lost. And what of the Jews in occupied France and Poland? Better not talk of them.

In all this excitement they were oblivious of the passing of time until suddenly jolted into it by the piercing shriek of *"Appello!"*

At the sight of the milling mob, Tommasini got really furious, because no one paid any heed to his presence. With the new agent accompanying him on this round for his initiation, he could hardly stomach such an affront.

"Ai vostri posti!" he roared. "And you bloody lot, get back to your own *camerata!"*

The new *chapper's* face bore an expression of amusement mingled with irony; he was visibly enjoying Tommasini's embarrassment. The newcomers scuttled away in confusion and Tommasini threw up his arms in a gesture of disgust, apostrophising the ceiling.

"Maledetti Ebrei!" He then snapped through the roll call, slammed the door behind him and together with the new recruit, went next door.

The evening meal was late owing to the cooks' additional load. Poor as they were, they could not let the new arrivals starve. But this could only be done by downgrading both the quality and the quantity of food. The 'natives' had also to lend them their eating bowls and so 'feeding time at the zoo' – as Wolf called it—dragged on and on. This prompted Szafran to remark that they had used more energy getting their food than they'd ever derive from consuming it.

Though no one was supposed to leave his *camerata* at night, with only a few yards between huts, people did not take this order literally. A mutual exchange of visitors took place which in itself was a novelty. Mario discovered a namesake and friend, a lanky fellow who owned a ramshackle restaurant of dubious reputation in the port of Genoa. Even Meiersohn found an old acquaintance from Poland, an orthodox Jew like himself.

At first, in all the confusion, no one noticed the slender timid youth who came shyly into the *camerata*. He stood undecided at the door, shifting his weight from one foot to the other, then eventually went up to Altman.

"Excuse me. Could I borrow a candle? I can't see to unpack in the dark."

A sudden shriek made everyone jump. "Heinz! Heinz! Is that you?"

Every head turned towards young Scholz.

"Rudi!" exclaimed the other youth. They ran towards each other arms outstretched and fell on each other's necks.

"I can't believe it!" Young Scholz, tears streaming from his eyes, turned to the rest of them. "It's my brother!"

It transpired that Heinz had stayed with his parents, reluctant to leave them unprotected. But when his father was arrested and sent to Dachau, it was mother who insisted he tried to escape and cross the border. So the Scholz brothers had plenty to say to each other and they were allowed to do so undisturbed.

It had been an eventful day but gradually the excitement began to wane. It was getting late and people realised how tired they were. There remained only two miserable candle stumps, whose dying flames threw strange shadows as they flickered out.

"See you tomorrow, Rudi." The brothers clasped hands before Heinz went back next door.

Soon the usual coughing and snoring indicated that they were all at rest.

Chapter 9

A matter of interpretation

Next morning Tommasini was out to impress the new agent and regain that prestige mislaid at the previous night's *appello*. "*Porca miseria!* By your beds!" he yelled out at least one octave higher than usual, and *fortissimo*. But the new agent still seemed unimpressed. He gave a derisory smile at Tommasini's distortion of the internees' names. As a north-Italian, he'd been better educated and was more familiar with foreign pronunciation. You could tell at a glance that he looked down on Tommasini as a mere southerner, though perhaps he did try half-heartedly to conceal this.

Henry went out into the *piazza* in search of stamps from the stores. There were none yet. It was again one of those sultry days without a whiff of air, oppressive and heavy, a real furnace which drove the sweat out in streams, sapping every vestige of energy. For a moment Henry felt dizzy and heavy as a sack of coal. He let himself sink into the shade of one of the corner trees. Perhaps his body had run out of salts from this unaccustomed perspiration? Or was this insufficient nourishment giving its first warning signals? He dismissed the thought. Not after so short a period, he reassured himself. When he began to feel better he made his way back to the *camerata* as the midday roll call was due any time. This was taken by the new agent. Unlike Tommasini, who liked to make his presence known by a great deal of noise, Signor Alberti planted himself squarely in the doorway, inspecting the internees coldly and in silence. His approach proved the more effective, causing everybody to hurry to their bedsides without any prompting. Once the roll call was over Alberti turned on his heel and went, as if glad to escape an unpleasant sight.

"He gives me the creeps, that bastard," said Wolf, with a scowl.

The meal that was served soon after was insipid, watery and tasteless, but Henry had no appetite anyway. Who could eat in that infernal temperature? All he felt was a desperate urge to escape from the stultifying heaviness of the midday heat. The swarm of flies seemed to prosper in the heavy airless fug and did its best to torment its unfortunate victims. Suddenly Henry's attention was roused by a cacophony of voices.

"They've come to fetch us for a ducking in the canal," cried Scholz excitedly. In fact both Tommasini and Alberti stood in the doorway, urging the internees to hurry up.

"Get ready! *Andiamo!*"

So the comandante had granted Henry's request in spite of Przebylewski's escapade? Was it because of this tropical heat? Anyway, what did it matter? Another of the comandante's imponderables.

In great agitation most of them put on their bathing trunks.

"Just look at them!" said Szafran. "You'd think they were off to the beach in Biarritz instead of that stinking canal."

Wolf decided to take his shaving gear with him and others followed suit. On reaching the sentry box they found Pasquale squatting in its shadow, smoking a cigarette. The two agents exchanged a meaningful glance.

"*Che soldato!* What a soldier," muttered Alberti, *sotto voce.*

"Get up, you!" snapped Tommasini, but Pasquale merely gave him a dirty look, stretched his legs out and went on smoking unperturbed. He grinned at the internees with his toothless gums.

As they passed through the gate, that same intense mint perfume hit their nostrils again.

"You'd never find this kind of scent in Biarritz," remarked Altman, nudging Szafran gently in the ribs.

The Scholz brothers, in high spirits, had to be restrained from making a run for the canal.

"Wait!" yelled Tommasini, "You'll be in your stinking puddle soon enough!"

When they got to the canal the internees almost flung themselves into the water.

"Look at them," remarked Tommasini with contempt, "those dirty Jews cannot wait to rid themselves of their filth."

Ossi transfixed him with one of his penetrating looks, biting his lip to control his anger.

Whereas the younger ones lay flat in the water, their stomachs sticking up, the older men preferred to splash themselves and each other, emitting guttural cries of delight.

"America!" exclaimed Wolf, to whom the lifestyle of the USA epitomised the *ne plus ultra* of luxury and refined pleasure.

Only two of the internees were still in the process of undressing: Mr Meiersohn and Mr Librowicz, his newly found orthodox friend. Both wore heavy, black trousers with old-fashioned underpants beneath, reaching to their ankles. The sight of their unusual attire provoked a malicious outburst of hilarity in both *chappers*.

"Look at those two old scarecrows!" exclaimed Tommasini. "Ever seen anything like it?"

Meiersohn and his friend felt embarrassed. As they had no swimming trunks they had to paddle, rolling their long underpants up to their knees. Both agents roared with laughter, almost splitting their sides.

Grumpy little Wolf got on with his shaving, placing a little mirror on the canal bank. It required some acrobatics to wet the brush in the water at his ankles and then to reach over to the mirror on the bank. However, he was used to putting a lot of effort into his shaving, and soon the familiar rasping noise of the razor resounded.

Mario's namesake, Mario Number 2, seemed unduly proud of the size of his genitals. He showed them off at every possible opportunity, leaving his penis casually dangling outside his bathing trunks.

"You ought to have it cut off Mario, and preserved in formalin!" joked Dino.

"He could put it in a museum," remarked Szafran, "it's useless anyway, despite its size."

Everybody seemed to be enjoying himself, the *chappers* included. Only one person was isolated from the merriment. Przebylewski, still fully dressed, sat apart on the canal bank in self-absorbed detachment.

"Hey you! Houdini!" Lubicz called to him. "Are you water-shy or something?" Getting no answer, he left him alone.

Dino was in his element, doing his Tarzan act, shadow-boxing and other silly tricks.

"*Avanti*! Get ready! It's five o'clock," called Tommasini. Most of them stayed in their swimming trunks, slipped into

their sandals and were ready to go; but not so Meiersohn and
Librowicz. They could not walk in their underpants and besides had to lace up their heavy shoes, and Meiersohn being
short-sighted had difficulty in tying them up. Tommasini,
growing impatient, finally exploded, "*Maledette Ebrei!*" He
seemed to enjoy cursing Jews at the slightest provocation.

This time Ossi almost lost control of himself. With flashing
eyes and fists at the ready he was going for Tommasini, when
Henry trod on his toe to calm him down.

"I will knock his smug block off one of these days," Ossi
muttered through clenched teeth.

On their way back Dino suggested a game of bridge. At this
hour when the heat began to abate it was pleasant to while
away the time under the majestic oak; besides, they had to pay
tribute to Dino's masterpiece, the big solid table, for it is ques-
tionable whether Michelangelo experienced any greater joy
and sense of achievement on completing his David. Dino and
Ossi took their game very seriously, using the Culbertson con-
vention. Henry, less experienced, had to be on his guard not to
upset them. Altman played quite well, but to him the game
was 'not a matter of life or death'. But to Ossi and Dino apparently was. Once, when Henry threw the wrong card on the
table, Ossi swooped on him.

"If I've told you once, I've told you a hundred times! The
third man as high as he can!"

It was getting dark and after the roll-call three candles were
lit in the *camerata*. The exchange of visits began. Mr Librowicz
popped in for a chat with Meiersohn. Reimer, who had nothing better to do, welcomed this opportunity to bait and heckle
the old man.

"Well Mr Librowicz, how do you like Ferramonti?"

"I've been in worse places."

"And how do you manage with the food?" asked Reimer as
innocently as a lamb.

"I manage."

Reimer looked at him askance, pretending to be surprised.
"I thought you were supposed to eat only kosher food?"

"It is permitted to break the law, when one's life is in
danger."

This time Reimer was genuinely intrigued. "How it is your friend Mr Meiersohn does not share your opinion?"

"I do share his opinion," interjected Meiersohn, "but 'danger to life' has different meanings to us."

Reimer broke into noisy laughter. "Is this one of your Talmudic, hair-splitting acrobatics?"

Bald-headed Wolf began to lose patience. "Will you stop this idiotic baiting, *yekkisher shmock*?"

Meiersohn pacified him with a calm, reassuring gesture. "Don't upset yourself Mr Wolf, I like discussions; Mr Reimer is entitled to ask or criticise."

Encouraged by Mr Meiersohn's attitude, Reimer continued his interrogation. "Well, Mr Meiersohn, is there or is there not a threat to life here?"

"Let me ask you something first, Mr Reimer. I am an orthodox Jew and you are an assimilant. Why is that?"

Reimer laughed, for this was an easy one. "Obviously we have different outlooks on life."

Meiersohn's eyes shone with an inner light. "There you are Mr Reimer, you have given yourself the answer. We both interpret life differently, have different opinions on the same subject: 'Life', but neither of us denies its existence. Why then should Mr Librowicz and I not have a difference of opinion in interpreting the Law, or the meaning of 'threat to life'?" Meiersohn was exhausted after this unusually long speech and he was breathing heavily. He did really look very tired and seemed to have lost a good deal of weight. He went on, "I have always been a poor man. The study of the Law does not bring great riches. So I am used to fasting and hunger, and if I eat only vegetables and an occasional egg, it is enough for me. But for Mr Librowicz, an '*Oysher*', a rich man, used to better things, such a diet would be a threat to life."

This was the second skirmish Reimer had attempted with the old man and on neither occasion had he emerged with flying colours. He resented this. Librowicz felt bound to make some further comments.

"It is not only a difference of interpretation. Mr Meiersohn is too generous and modest to mention it, but the truth is he is a *Gaon*, a learned man and a *Zaddik*, what you would call a holy man. I am not. That is the real difference."

The discussion ended there and then. Much to his annoyance Reimer began to realise dimly that in spite of his *Deutsche Kultur*, he was no match for these 'uneducated *Ostjuden*'. Henry was pleased with the way Meiersohn had handled the dispute. He liked the old man and his simple, dignified manner. Although he spoke mostly Yiddish, he had sufficient command of German to make himself understood, even by such a *yekke* as Reimer. Still, Henry thought, the old man was looking frail.

Henry stretched himself out on his palliasse. One by one the candles went out. These last moments of the dying day were the most precious for they afforded a measure of privacy. Only when wrapped up in darkness and isolated from the others did he experience himself again as an individual. Despite having been in Ferramonti only a short while, *it feels like a lifetime*, he murmured to himself as he sank into sleep.

Chapter 10

Time for a change

I t had seemed a very long week indeed. Thomas Mann in *The Magic Mountain* examines at length the subjective experience of Time. Contrary to popular belief, he holds that Time appears to move faster in monotony. In his opinion, if one day resembles another with little to stir the emotions or stimulate thought, then Time seems to accelerate its pace. On the other hand, when there is a plethora of events with ever-changing novel experiences, then Time seems to drag its feet. To a child each year seems an eternity for everything is new. It is only in old age, when life holds few novelties that the days and weeks seem to fly past, like chaff in the wind.

After that very long and eventful first week the internees stopped counting the days and prepared themselves for a long stay in Ferramonti. Although there were officially no newspapers available, news nevertheless filtered into the camp by different routes. Pasquale at the sentry box was perfectly willing to tell them what went on in the world and more than once he smuggled a newspaper into the camp. Discarded newspapers left by the labourers provided another welcome source of information. Apart from this, new convoys of internees arrived periodically to fill the gaps in their awareness of the general situation. Foremost in everybody's mind was the dreaded fear of the invasion of Britain.

One of the interesting new arrivals was Dr Bernheim, a psychoanalyst. He was a German Jew, tall and bespectacled, and with his bald pate and pointed skull he truly looked an egghead. Dr Bernheim had a dignified bearing, but his most outstanding feature was a gentle smile with a heart-warming quality about it. Henry took to him from the start.

Then there was a man named Funk, notorious not because of his homosexuality but the fact that he made a virtue of it. He proclaimed his appetites openly to all and sundry, inviting various men to 'have a go'. He was a loud-mouth; thick set, usually unshaven. He was unpopular, not because of his sexual traits but for the way he advertised himself.

Another original was Berenboim, originating from the Warsaw ghetto, but far remote from the image of a ghetto Jew. Berenboim was a *'balagula'*, a coachman, a *'Grober Ying'* and an ignorant clod. His frame was sturdy, his ice-blue eyes arrogant, a provocative leer on his pock-marked face, but in spite of all this, there was still — God knows what — something likeable about him.

Sokolow was yet another strange individual, a young man with a huge chip on his shoulder. He belonged to the pseudo-intelligentsia of Polish-Jewish youth with its strong left-wing beliefs. Sokolow was paranoid about anybody who did not share his views. He saw himself as forever exploited and persecuted by the Capitalists; he was short-tempered, impulsive and prone to insulting behaviour and brawls.

Just as the cook's voluntary efforts were eventually rewarded with a small salary, so it was inevitable that grumpy Wolf's pre-occupation with the cleanliness of the *camerata* should be ultimately acknowledged in some way. The inmates of the *camerata* appointed him *'piantone'* or barracks caretaker at the salary of 2 lire a week. This made no difference to his routine. He continued to struggle against the flies, to raise clouds of dust when sweeping, and curse Musso and Hitler while doing so.

The population in each *camerata* was constantly in flux with frequent exchanges. Thus Heinz Scholz came to join his brother in *camerata* 3 and so did Librowicz to be with his old friend. Two vacancies in the *camerata* were filled when two young Austrian Jews arrived. Both had previously been in Dachau concentration camp. At first they were unapproachable, suspicious and hostile. They seemed terrified, especially during roll calls, but gradually — realising that no atrocities had so far occurred in Ferramonti — they came out of their shells, and told of the brutalities to which they had been subjected in Dachau. They were typical Viennese Jewish assimilants. Trebitsch, handsome, well-built and sunburnt, was a sports enthusiast, a typical outdoor man. Laufman, an intellectual, craggy and bespectacled, was a journalist interested in politics. Apart from being Jewish, their only crime had been membership of the Austrian Social-Democratic party. Although most internees were aware of the Jew-baiting in post-*Anschluss* Austria, they did not know the full extent of moral degradation and physical brutality practiced in concentration camps like Dachau. Luckily Trebitsch and Laufman were kicked out of Dachau after three months and managed to cross the border to Italy.

A social class structure gradually emerged in Ferramonti. There were no rigid dividing lines but those from similar backgrounds and education somehow found each other, as with the Triumvirate of doctors. Sokolow, Berenboim and a few others gradually formed a group of the 'Proletariat'. Some individuals remained unattached to any group. Little Wolf was one such. He seldom went out of the *camerata* and people referred to him jokingly as being 'married to his broom'. Dvorak, Scholz, Trebitsch—the 'sporting trio' – soon formed a subgroup of sports enthusiasts to which Dino also belonged. These various sub-groups arose from common interests and hobbies, rather than educational or social background. Sokolow, for example, basically a member of the 'Proletariat', joined the 'Chess Set'. He was not particularly good at the game, but in spite of his professed proletarian leanings he was an elitist and a snob at heart, who regarded chess as a sign of intellectual distinction. Even Meiersohn and Librowicz gathered a small circle around them, not that Meiersohn went out of his way to attract followers. On the contrary, people gravitated to him for their spiritual needs and because they liked and respected the man.

Altman was one of those lucky individuals at ease with any group. His was a rounded personality, with a broad spectrum of interests and an enviable facility for communicating instantly with anyone. He had grown rather pensive of late despite his visa for Argentina; he was still waiting for a ship.

One day after the distribution of the mail, Ossi came up to Henry a letter in his hand.

"Remember I told you about an important letter which might interest you?"

"Well, what of it?"

"This letter is from a friend who works for an American shipping company. There is a chance of us getting out of Ferra-

monti — and Italy. All we need is to get ourselves hired as sail-
ors on a ship of some non-belligerent country."

Henry looked at Ossi askance. "What do we know about
sailing?"

Ossi grew impatient. "Don't be so stupid! You don't need to
be a professional sailor. A deckhand, a waiter or a dish-washer
will do. Don't you understand? It's the only way to get out of
this country without a visa."

"And how could we land without a visa?"

"We could remain on board ship. Anyway, if we did land,
we would only be arrested as illegal immigrants for a time.
Better than rotting here."

Once the idea had begun to sink in, it seemed much less
far-fetched.

"But would they let us out of here?"

"Altman will be going, so why not us? What do you say?"

Henry hardly knew what to say. For three years he had
been registered with the American Consulate in Naples for im-
migration to the United States, but he reckoned his chances of
getting a visa were nil. Perhaps Ossi's proposal was a stroke of
genius after all. It sounded fantastic, but not impossible.
Henry's mouth curled into a grin.

"Well, what is there to lose? If you want me to, I'll come
with you." They shook hands on this but Henry suddenly remembered to ask, "Have you told Dino about this?"

Ossi shook his head. "No, and I am not sure I should."

"Why not?" asked Henry, surprised.

"Because Dino isn't really an internee. His parents run their
business in Genoa and can send him all he needs. To Dino all
this is just an adventure. I do not want to ruin our chances by
getting a third person involved, either."

Henry did not like this one bit. Was it possible that the
struggle for existence had already begun to corrupt Ossi? He
did not like Ossi at this moment at all and his feelings must
have shown on his face. Eventually Ossi broke the ominous silence which had crept into their conversation.

"Be sensible Henry. Dino is still an overgrown adolescent,
despite his good brain. Everyone loves Dino, why wouldn't
they? But I would not rely on him in times of need."

There was a long uneasy pause; Henry still couldn't stomach it. Eventually Ossi threw up both arms and reluctantly gave in.

They could have saved themselves the effort of searching their consciences, for when they told him of their plan, Dino looked at them oddly and then brushed the whole thing off with one sentence.

"It would break my mother's heart! She'd have a stroke!"

Well, that was that. At least they had tried and now they both felt better.

Przebylewski unexpectedly approached Henry. "Is there no post for me?"

"Apparently not. Maybe they do not have your address."

Przebylewski was crestfallen and miserable. Rumour had it that all was not well between him and his wife. Henry felt sorry for him, but just now he was too much taken up with Ossi's extraordinary proposition to bother his head over Przebylewski's matrimonial problems.

Chapter 11

Love, war and madness

Time passed and gradually the demands of their new existence became routine. *Appello* followed *appello* and so did the 'feeding time at the zoo' as well as the afternoon *siesta*. The blazing July was followed by an even more blazing August. The flies multiplied. The latrines stank worse. The meals grew smaller and their appetites bigger. It was fortunate they were in a hot climate where fewer calories were needed to keep body and soul together. Besides they still had reserves, in their bodies as well as in their pockets. Those who'd started with a spare tyre round their waists still had some resources of energy from which to draw their calories. Those less fortunate, who had arrived already in a scraggy state of malnutrition, began to show danger signs, such as giddiness, lassitude and general *malaise*. Henry too had shed some weight, but so far that was all to his advantage. As time went on, a gradual deterioration of habits and comportment manifested itself. Many could not be bothered to shave, to comb their hair, or even to wash. The everyday vocabulary had become atrocious, with four letter words spicing even the most innocent conversation. It was amazing what a few weeks' segregation in an all-male prison environment had done to their standards of behaviour; how a lifetime's pattern of civilised conduct could be dislocated in so brief a space of time.

The labourers were putting up new barracks with astonishing speed as more internees arrived. There were by now over 150 internees in the camp. Among the latest intake was a group of baptised Jews, seven to be precise, all recently converted to Christianity. Clearly their little manoeuvre had not prevented them being packed off to a concentration camp. That group was understandably not popular with the internees, who looked on them with contempt. They were housed in a smaller building of their own and it soon transpired that they had been promised visas to one of the Latin-American countries. A Roman Catholic priest arrived in the camp soon after. He kept himself very busy and on most of his errands was accompanied by the converts, known to the internees as the 'Seven Apostles'. The leader of the converts was a Pole of mixed Jewish and Christian parentage, by the name of Kanopek, who gave himself such airs his conduct was described as 'Popelier than the Pope'. He and the priest were in constant conference and both of them could be seen plying busily between the comandante's office, the labourers' foreman and a new hut which was nearing completion. The reason for these fervent activities soon became apparent when a crucifix was attached to the gable of the hut. They had constructed and organised a place of worship, a little church. From that centre of Christendom discreet invisible feelers were sent out among the internees. The vesper bell tolled each evening and to those without a watch it was a welcome measure of the passing of time. As far as was known, the proselytising efforts of that Catholic centre were not very rewarding. Just two internees joined the group when the promise of a visa was dangled in front of them.

Early in September a huge parcel was handed to Dino during the distribution of post. He began to lick his lips in anticipation of more of Mamma's delicatessen, but to his surprise and delight, the cocoon of wrappings revealed a magnificent accordion. Dino went almost mad with joy and straightaway tuned up with a song popular at that time: "*Come e' delizioso andar sulla carrozzella.*" ("How lovely to ride in a horse and carriage.") An accordion in a concentration camp! A most unlikely combination! This could happen only in Italy, basically humane and tolerant, despite the megalomanic sabre-rattling of the Duce and his fascist cronies.

The Jewish High Holidays *Rosh Hashanah* (New Year) and *Yom Kippur* (Day of Atonement) were approaching. The question arose whether or not to celebrate them, considering the expense, which could only be borne by their reserve fund. Altman was of the opinion that they should not allow their spirit to be broken, pointing out that they had a few weeks to start saving. As usual, opinions were divided and everybody tried to speak at the same time.

Altman chuckled to himself.

"A typical Jewish assembly. As many Jews, as many opinions. We are a stiff-necked nation of individualists!"

Reimer was dead against any celebrations.

"If the camp authorities see we have money to spare for festivities, they may even try to cut our miserable allowance."

This was certainly a point which could not be dismissed lightly. Sokolow, though he did not belong to their *camerata*, had to have his say.

"I don't think we should waste our money on religious hokus pokus!" and to impress the others with his originality he produced the well-worn cliché, "Religion is the opium of the masses."

Little Wolf interrupted him curtly. "You get back to your own *camerata*! This is not a party political meeting."

Meiersohn, who had been listening quietly, made his contribution.

"I am delighted that you even consider celebrating the High Holy Days. I judged you wrongly."

He paused because of shortage of breath and then resumed, "Mr Reimer remarked they may cut our meagre subsistence if we celebrate, and that is quite true, but our ancestors in Spain may have feared the Spanish Inquisitors would cut off their heads if they didn't convert, and yet they didn't convert. To be a Jew still means to live dangerously, as it always did."

Altman tried to clarify the situation. What he had in mind was a modest symbolic gesture, not a culinary feast. All *cameratas* would be bulk-buying together which again would reduce cost.

"Besides, during the fast of *Yom Kippur*, we could recoup our losses."

"I do not want to fast," objected Reimer, "and no one is going to make me!"

Altman looked at him calmly but intently.

"No one is going to force anyone. I only thought that the minority, out of a sense of solidarity, would join the majority." Reimer piped down. In the end it was decided to hold a celebration of modest proportions. The dispute might have dragged on, but for the arrival of the post.

Henry recognised Mona's elongated bluish envelope before it was handed over to him. He experienced the strangest ambivalent feelings at the sight of it. Why had it taken Mona so long to write to him? He looked at the postmark. The letter had been posted three weeks ago.

"My dearest Heini,

What can I say? I am so dazed and unhappy, I hardly know what I am doing. For weeks on end I did not know what had happened to you. Only just now your letter arrived, covered in many official stamps from all over. That is probably why it took so long to arrive. I read those twelve lines of yours over and over again and I could not stop my tears. The world seems empty without you. I cannot find any rest. Mother continues to press and harass me. If it were not for the piano and organ which relieve my pain a little, I'd go mad. How long will all this last? xxxxxxxxxx (censored). Please write as often as you can. I study every word of your letter and turn it over constantly in my mind. You say we must keep our letters short, so I will finish now. All my love and thoughts for you, my darling. Mona."

Henry was deeply moved. He folded the letter and put it away, intending to read it again later in the evening, to savour every word of it in peace and quiet. There was a sting in Mona's letter: 'Mother continues to press and harass me'. Henry could well imagine what that was for. He couldn't blame her mother. Who wanted a foreign Jew, imprisoned in a concentration camp, as a future son-in-law at that time? Mona's letter had provoked a chain reaction, not only emotional but also perceptual in nature. For a moment he could almost smell the salty air of Viareggio's beaches, the resinous scent of the Pineta and see faces, not only Mona's, but many others, especially the merry, mischievous faces of their friends, the Weismanns, with whom they had spent so many happy and carefree hours.

There had finally been a letter for Przebylewski, but after reading it he seemed gloomier than ever.

An animated discussion was going on in the *camerata*. Pasquale had again brought a newspaper and now the 'experts' were dissecting the bulletins. The internees had gradually developed an uncanny proficiency — a sixth sense — in interpreting the headlines. From small hints, seemingly casual remarks and veiled threats, they had learned to put two and two together, as if they'd succeeded in breaking a cryptic code.

Laufman, the Austrian journalist, usually quiet and reserved, seemed to be churned up.

"They're up to something. These continuous references to 'arrogance and provocation' by the Greeks do not bode anything good."

He spoke seldom, but when he did his words usually made sense.

"You see, Musso is green with envy. Hitler's spectacular successes stick in his throat. There is Hitler, carving up Europe and taking the fattest morsel for himself. Musso has to prove he is no push-over. They'll swoop on Greece like vultures. Any old pretext will do."

In fact the Duce had shown signs of restlessness of late, urging his generals in Tripoli to get on with the job: the Suez Canal. And not long after Mussolini's rantings, big headlines announced the Italian offensive. Their forces had crossed the border into Egypt, as far as Sidi Barani.

The initial success of the Italian campaign in Africa was another blow to British prestige and was reflected in the cockiness of the agents, who strutted around the camp like peacocks in the mating season. There were six *chappers* now in the camp, whose arrogance and boisterous behaviour seemed to flaunt the success of Italian arms. But they never resorted to physical violence. Compared with their Axis partners they behaved almost humanely in this respect.

And yet, despite the African setback, the internees' morale had been lifted from sub-zero to above freezing by the stubborn endurance of the British. Regardless of the heavy bombing, Britain was holding out, and despite Hitler's repeated boasts of imminent invasion, it still had not happened.

Dino was on top of the world. "Didn't I tell you not to bury the lion before he is dead?"

Gradually others began to share his glimmer of hope, especially as very few attached much importance to the Italian feats of arms in Africa, least of all Wolf. "Them *Katzelmachers* will only get stuck in the sand up to their arses out there."

In fact, after Sidi Barani, there was no news of any further advance. If England could hold out a little longer, the USA would eventually come to her aid. This was Dino's considered opinion and slowly the number of converts to his point of view increased. The *Blitzkrieg* seemed to have run out of momentum. Perhaps the cliffs of Dover were 'too steep for the Panzers' after all.

This reassessment of their situation gave the internees new hope and they retired to bed looking forward to a brighter future and peaceful slumbers.

And then, when all was quiet in the *camerata*, there was suddenly a heart-rending cry in the darkness.

"No!" somebody howled. "Oh! No! I am innocent! Don't kill me!"

Ossi was first to shoot out of bed in search of the man who had dared to shatter their peace. He lit a candle to reveal Przebylewski standing by his bed and gesticulating wildly. Again he emitted a distressing yell, like some hunted animal in mortal fear.

"What is it Mr Przebylewski? Have you had a nightmare?"

"They are coming for me!" cried Przebylewski, cowering in terror.

"Who is coming?" enquired Ossi.

"Them! They are coming to kill me!"

Ossi was losing his patience. "What nonsense! You've only had a bad dream. Now go back to sleep."

But at this point Przebylewski gave another spine-chilling shriek, like the neighing of a horse in deadly terror. "Here they are! They are going to cut off my head!"

Ossi turned to Henry. "What are we going to do with him?"

Przebylewski went on raving. "Oh, why didn't they let me die? I went to the river ... I can't swim ... but no! They had to bring me back." He started sobbing, his whole frame shaking convulsively as he covered his head.

Henry drew Ossi aside. "This is no nightmare. The man is psychotic. This is textbook melancholia: guilt, depression, delusions of persecution."

No matter what the diagnosis, something had to be done immediately to calm him down. To get Dr Sabatini at this hour of night was out of the question. Hyoscine or Paraldehyde might have effectively controlled his agitation, but they had none. Dino had some Veronal and to everybody's relief Przebylewski accepted and swallowed the tablets. Gradually his raving and wailing diminished as he fell asleep. In fact, he was the only one in the *camerata* who slept through that night. The others were too frightened to do so.

"How can you sleep with a *meshuggener* in the same room?" Wolf voiced their fears. "For all we know, he could get up and chop off your cock while you sleep."

It was certainly no laughing matter.

Next morning, exhausted and worn out after a sleepless night, everybody walked on tiptoe so as not to wake the 'beast'. Dr Sabatini was surprised to see the doctors at such an early hour.

Henry explained briefly why they'd come.

"*Un matto?* A madman you say?"

Henry nodded. "A case of acute depression and extreme agitation."

"What are we going to do with him?" pleaded Sabatini wringing his hands and looking at each doctor in turn.

This voluntary admission of helplessness from the camp doctor was embarrassing. What little medicine he knew was mainly tropical.

"Do we have any drugs to sedate him?" asked Dino discreetly.

"There is Valeriana …" Sabatini paused to search his memory.

Valeriana? That won't even tranquillise Przebylewski's little toe! thought Henry, but instead he asked as tactfully as he could, "Perhaps there is Paraldehyde?"

"Of course there is that," said Sabatini, puffing himself up to resume his official air, anxious not to betray his ignorance in front of the *crocerossina*.

"It would be advisable to send him to an asylum," ventured Henry.

"An asylum? *Un manicomio?* There are none in the vicinity and I cannot authorise a long journey. You'll have to see Signor Rizzi."

Apparently the comandante was not in the best of moods for he received Henry coldly, scrutinising him from his head to the dust-covered toes which protruded from his sandals.

Henry outlined the problem briefly. "It is the same man who was found wandering by the Crati weeks ago."

"I gathered as much. But why come to me? This is a medical matter."

"We have already seen Dr Sabatini. He referred us to you …"

"So he is washing his hands and passing the buck to me?" Signor Rizzi interrupted him angrily.

"No Signor Comandante. Dr Sabatini felt he had no authority to arrange for a long journey."

This flattery satisfied him. "Why ought this man be sent to an asylum?"

"Because he is very agitated, even suicidal."

Noticing the comandante's expression of disbelief, Henry added, "He was trying to drown himself that night he was found by the river. We found that out last night."

"And what could an asylum do for him?"

"There is a new treatment, invented by Professors Cerletti and Bini of Rome, called Electro-Convulsive Therapy. It is very effective in cases of depression such as this."

Henry was slightly amused by the turn their conversation had taken, for the last thing he'd expected was to be lecturing Signor Rizzi on psychiatric treatments.

"Will they have this treatment in the south? Taranto or Bari?"

"I doubt it. Most certainly in Rome and probably Milan and Turin."

"Then he'll have to stay here. We are at war and transport is needed badly. I cannot send him all the way up north."

"But he needs supervision and …"

"You'll have to do it!" broke in the *comandante*. "You and your colleagues. You have nothing to do here anyway. That's all."

And with a wave of the hand, they were dismissed.

Chapter 12

Pièce Touchée: the Game of Life

Mussolini's motto '*Roma doma*' sustained a shattering blow. Not only did the Greeks beat off the Italian offensive, they even managed to chase them back into Albania, which the rapacious Duce had invaded in April 1939. However hard the Italian press tried to disguise the débacle, it was obvious they were taking a beating of the most sensational kind. This farcical and catastrophic campaign, coupled with Britain's stubborn resistance, lent new heart to the internees for more than food, they needed hope in the drabness of their existence.

At the start of September 1940, the camp authorities had begun to busy themselves in the construction of covered latrines. This was very strange considering the seasonal decline of both the swarms of flies and the stench from the open ones. These new latrines consisted of a row of primitive cubicles exposed to full view from the courtyard. No toilet seats were provided. People had to crouch on top of the holes and instead of the usual flushing system, there was a shower in each cubicle, which was far too weak to effectively flush the excrement away. Owing to one's full exposure at short distance it took some time and courage to get used to this utter lack of privacy. However, as Henry had already discovered on more than one occasion, man can get used to almost anything.

Hand-in-hand with this degradation of human dignity went a hardening of the soul and a degeneration of manners. The colloquial abuse of language became progressively cruder and filthier and hardly a sentence was spoken without a 'fucking', not to speak of 'bastard' and 'shit', which was one of the more refined expressions.

Nevertheless the internees had not lost their zest for disputation and speculation. The rapid construction of covered latrines intrigued them.

"It's obvious," said Dino, "the bastards have realised this war is no flash-in-the-pan."

"But why this sudden hurry?" asked Szafran. "They can't be bothered with hygiene or they wouldn't have placed the latrines so close to the kitchens."

Various theories were expounded, none of which fitted the facts completely. True, the war was dragging on and Hitler, inferior in naval power, was unlikely to confront the Royal Navy during the late autumn storms and fog to attempt an invasion of England.

"So Hitler, the great General, has missed the bus," said little Wolf. "He ought to fit the SS with propellers in their arses so they can fly over the channel."

As he went on sweeping the floor, he enriched the annals of lyric poetry with yet another variation on the old theme:

"Hitler and Musso beware

Who do you think you can scare?

If you don't pull up your little cotton socks

You'll both get hung up by your little rotten cocks."

It really was quite amazing what the Muses bestowed on bald-headed, pint-sized little Wolf.

Once the latrines were completed the builders switched their efforts to the speedy construction of new barracks. These were placed some distance from, and opposite to, the row of existing barracks.

"Where will they find enough Jews to fill all these barracks?" young Scholz wondered.

"Don't worry your head," replied Szafran. "These sniffing dogs are well trained to find their prey."

Another intriguing aspect was the construction of small units at the lower end of the camp, quite close to Pasquale's sentry box. It was difficult to figure them out and in the end the internees gave up their sterile guesswork, and transferred their attention elsewhere.

The *comandante*'s refusal to have Przebylewski committed to an asylum thrust the responsibility of restraining and watching him on *camerata* 3. This was no mean task at a time when the modern major tranquillisers were still unknown. At first, when he was still very agitated, the three doctors applied 'continuous narcosis' using the barest medication in their possession. None of them had any direct experience of this treatment, although they did understand the principle. The aim was to keep the patient sedated in a twilight state for several days and then gradually reduce the medication. To everyone's relief this method worked and eventually Przebylewski was allowed to get up. He was far from well, still odd and self-absorbed, but at least he did not disturb the peace. He would sit on his bed, gazing at the ceiling, as if listening to voices or else wander off, haggard and unkempt.

Henry had been developing a closer relationship with Dr Bernheim, the psychoanalyst, who was also a *capo camerata*. Their first contact occurred at the periodic meetings of all the *capi*, when matters concerning the overall welfare of the internees were discussed. Henry was impressed by Dr Bernheim's objective judgement, his quick appraisal of essentials and of any new problems that arose. Though he spoke quietly, he usually put his point of view forcefully and convincingly. At first they exchanged niceties on a superficial level, but when Henry spoke of his intention to take up psychiatry after the war, if he survived, Dr Bernheim showed more interest. In his younger days, Bernheim had worked with Professor Carl Jung and up to his confinement had practised psychotherapy in Florence. He was an ardent student of early civilisations for he felt modern man could be understood only if his remote archaic past was excavated.

At first they met only occasionally, but soon their meetings became regular. Henry was fascinated by Dr Bernheim's description of the Sumerian people, of whose existence he had never heard. Their origin, like that of the Etruscans, was shrouded in the mists of antiquity. Sumeria had never achieved the might of the Assyro-Babylonian empires. It was a small nation and yet it had exerted an enormous influence on Mesopotamia, the whole of the Middle and near East and through them, on western civilisation. The Sumerians were an elite and seemingly, the first to conceive the idea of the written word.

"If you want to understand your disturbed patient," said
Dr Bernheim, "you have to explore not only his childhood, but
also the childhood of mankind as a whole."

Henry had sensed of late a change in Dino's attitude, a sort
of indifference. He seemed to avoid him and gave monosyllabic responses. This change was inexplicable at first, but after
some derisory remarks about Dr Bernheim, the 'Teutonic egghead', Henry realised what was biting him: Dino resented the
intrusion of a stranger into their intimate trio. He came up
with a plan.

"Dino, how would you like a chess championship? Ten
games to decide?"

This suggestion struck a spark for Dino was fond of chess
and highly competitive; he even wanted to start straightaway.
It was decided to play one game on each of ten consecutive
evenings and strictly '*pièce touchée*', when a man touched a
piece, he must move. Despite the cool of approaching autumn,
Dino suggested they played their games under the oak, thinking it might keep *kibitzes* away, or perhaps it was his love for
that masterpiece, the table of which he was so proud. Henry
was happy to humour him either way. Dino was a popular figure, impossible to refuse with his winning smile and appealing
manner.

At first they were allowed to play in peace, but soon the
news of the wager spread over the camp. Sensation-starved as
they were, *kibitzes* soon began to flock around the table. They
were warned to 'keep quiet or else', but it was like trying to
hold back the tide. As the days went by, the chess tournament
progressed with alternating success for each player. Onlookers
became more excited and some even placed their bets out loud
as the game progressed. In the monotony of their existence, the
tournament was a major event, but the *kibitzes* who fancied
themselves to be experts, had a field-day.

"Not that bishop, *Herr Doktor*!" cried Szafran, unable to
help himself.

"Shut up!" thundered an incisive voice. There was no mistaking Ossi's sharp, commanding inflection.

But it was not only the continuous interference of the *kibitzes* which wore Henry down; their uninterrupted flow of obscenities grated on his nerves too.

At five games to four in Dino's favour, the *kibitzes'* excitement had reached its peak. Dino needed one win only to be champion, whereas Henry at best could only achieve a draw by close of play.

Next morning when breakfast had been particularly sparse and some other pastimes were needed to appease their grumbling bellies, Dino decided to resume the game.

The news spread; there was the usual scramble for seats.

"Fuck off you fool! This is a game for brains."

"You've no room? Sit on your head. It understands as much chess as your arse and takes up less space."

Sokolov, the pseudo-intellectual, sat there unshaven, his hair in disarray, with a superior grin on his face. He obviously knew it all!

Henry had to go all out for a win. A draw was no good, as it would have given Dino a narrow victory. He therefore went over to the offensive right from the start, but Dino neutralised his attack and wouldn't give an inch. After two hours' tense play the game was still undecided. Much would depend on Henry's next move and there was a good deal of subdued whispering among the *kibitzes*, which even Ossi's glare was unable to control. Henry was about to move, his hand hovering over his castle, when there was a sudden piercing yell.

"Women!" shrieked someone, "Women and children! Here!"

END OF PART ONE

Part Two

Chapter 13

Women

Women?

What was that supposed to mean? Everyone looked stunned. Was this a joke?

"Women I tell you! The place is alive with them!"

Suddenly they all shot up and in the ensuing rush and confusion the chessboard and pieces were knocked over. Nobody cared. Frantically they made for the *piazza*, elbowing each other out of the way. They still could not believe it; but it was true! Truckload after truckload discharged their packed freight: men, women and children. More trucks arrived until the entire *piazza* was jammed with them. It was pandemonium with the noise of foreign tongues, hollers and calls from one truck to another, between drivers and passengers, mothers and their children as the Ferramonti agents strutted about shouting orders at the new arrivals. In every truck there were children, some crying, others clinging to their mothers fearfully; a few older ones jumped down to take a look around. Several women were clutching their precious infants in their arms. Husbands looked grim as they surveyed this desolate patch of stony barren ground; was this where their families would exist for God knows how long? At last the convoy came to an end and the camp gates were closed. Bursting suitcases, trunks, bundles and pushchairs were dumped in a huge, unruly heap before them. Most of the newcomers appeared young or middle-aged, though there was also a smattering of haggard and bedraggled elderly people. It was a dismal, chaotic spectacle. Rumours were flying around that these were Jews from Africa but their appearance suggested otherwise.

To clear the *piazza*, the children were allowed through first; the rest had to wait for the usual search, except for one woman, who seemed to be in charge of the children. She was sturdy, middle-aged, with short cropped hair and forbidding steely blue eyes. Most of the children were too tired to move, but some more vivacious specimens attempted to explore. However one loud command from the woman stopped them in their tracks and they came back without any fuss.

Two checkpoints had been set up: one for men and one for women. Elvira, the *crocerossina* and Rosa the comandante's maidservant were entrusted with searching the women, a humane gesture to spare them being manhandled by the guards. To search several hundred newcomers and belongings seemed to take an eternity.

By evening the *piazza* was cleared except for a pile of heavy trunks. A young man with a bewildered expression came close; Henry approached him. "Don't be scared. It's not half as bad as it looks."

The young man, dishevelled and dusty, shrugged his shoulders but made no reply.

"Where do you all come from?" asked Henry.

The young man spread his arms in a shrug of hopelessness.

"We are Jews—what can I tell you! We are from every-where! Poland, Germany, Austria, Hungary, but now many are stateless! Citizens of nowhere! We were just now in prison...in Naples!"

"In Naples? For how long?"

"It's too long a story! Another time..." He moved on.

But Henry, hungry for news of his family, pressed the young man for more. "Please! What news of the war—what is happening? We know only what the Italian press wants us to hear."

"Look I can't tell you anything! We have been prisoners! We began in Trieste months ago! We had a ship to take us to Erez Israel and ended in Africa! Tripoli! We have been prisoners in Benghazi...I can't tell you anything of the war!"

The young man's voice trailed off as he left in search of his family leaving Henry to ponder his unanswered questions.

Next morning, Henry awoke early after a restless night. As well as the thought-provoking issues of the previous day, his bad night was also attributable to that damned mattress which still had not evened out. Something really would have to be done about it. The arrival of the new internees had suddenly transformed the camp. The presence of women in the provisions queue, the sound of their soft voices, the wails and shrieks of small children, reminded the men of what they had left behind. Though most folk had neglected their appearance of late, walking about with bristle-covered faces and crumpled shirts, they were now keen to tidy up their exteriors as well as their language.

The *camerata* already smelled of soap, with everybody shaving. Suitcases were unpacked in the search for clean shirts, cologne and ties. Henry retrieved his own shaving gear and joined the ranks of beautifying males.

Soon afterwards the door opened to admit a girl, who stopped on the threshold and examined the *camerata* with great interest. She was a beauty with long blonde hair, blue eyes and sunburnt complexion. The girl smiled and greeted Henry with a 'Shalom'.

Henry stared at her incredulously, as if she were a ghost. Recovering his composure, he smiled back. "Are you looking for anybody in particular?"

The girl's smile illuminated her face. "No, there is no one I know here. I was simply curious to see how the other half lives."

There was something in her appearance which struck a deeper chord and suddenly Henry realised she reminded him of Golda, his first love of long ago. "What's your name?" he asked.

"My old name—back home—was Yadranka Mirkowicz. But when I joined the group, I took the name Yalda."

"Yalda? But that simply means 'girl' in Hebrew," laughed Henry.

"Correct! And that is all I want to be. Simply a girl and never grow old."

"Where are you from?"

"Zagreb. But when the war broke out I was a History student at Belgrade University."

"You look too young for a university student. How old are you?"

Yalda gave him a saucy look. "At my age it is no compliment to say I look younger. I am nineteen."

There was something spontaneous and unsophisticated about this girl, a directness and simplicity which were touching.

"Are your parents with you?"

"My mother is. Father is dead. We are lodged on the other side, just opposite here. That's why I wanted to know how the other half live."

With these words she turned nimbly and went. Henry gazed pensively after the girl, whom he had already secretly nicknamed 'the girl with the flaxen hair.' How good it was to feel the presence and beauty of a young woman after so many months of separation from the gentler sex.

He went outside and soon discovered Dino, carrying a huge trunk on his shoulders. An elderly woman, gesticulating and pointing towards a barrack, walked in front of him.

"There it is. Not far now," she said in broken Italian.

Henry winked at Dino. "Already your first conquest?"

Dino grinned all over his face. "I'd gladly exchange this sixty-year-old for three of twenty," and he went on, swaying under the load of the heavy trunk.

A number of agents had accompanied this large transport. Most of them would probably remain now that the camp's population had more than doubled at one stroke. Because of the chaos, there was still no sign of *appello*; the arrival of so large a convoy had thrown all regulations out of gear, but when a high-pitched whistle eventually announced the roll call, Henry hurried back to his *camerata*. There he found the place in turmoil. Everyone was giving his own version of the news and information he had collected. As usual there were plenty of contradictions and arguments, with each one insisting stubbornly on his own version.

A woman, petite but sturdy, entered the *camerata*. She had a bundle of shirts thrown over her arm.

"Good day, gentlemen. Does anyone want to have his shirt washed, socks darned?"

"Look, Missis," replied Wolf before she could finish, "we have no money for such luxuries!"

The woman, who might have been in her late thirties, smiled at him.

"I know, I fully understand, but all I ask is a few centesimi. And those who cannot pay can have their washing done for nothing."

As soon as she said 'for nothing' she was approached by a peculiar looking man, Dr Wunderstein, who had joined their *camerata* recently and was already renowned for his avarice and dirty exterior. Even by concentration camp standards his clothes and person were filthy in the extreme. Little Wolf remarked once, "You can grow mushrooms between his toes." He was about forty years old, had short greying hair, staring blue eyes and a stammer which made conversation with him almost impossible.

"H-h-ere M-m-issis, t-t-ake my b-b-bundle."

The poor woman looked at him, taken aback by the filth of his laundry but she quickly recovered and smiled. "What is your name? I'll have to mark it on your shirts."

He made a heroic effort. "Dr W-W-wunderstein," he finally blurted out.

The woman attached a tag with his name to his bundle, touching it very lightly as if afraid of contamination. "My name is Halpern, Mrs Frieda Halpern. I'm in *camerata* no 12."

Dr Wunderstein was very odd. He had been practising medicine in Lucca, Tuscany for several years and had considerable savings. On occasions, believing he was unobserved, he had been seen counting out bundles of notes, but no one had ever seen him spend a single centesimo, never mind a lira. How a professional man could neglect himself and behave in that manner was a mystery, unless his personality had changed. Rumour had it that he had been severely beaten up by fascist thugs and had developed a hysterical stammer ever since.

All the while, an animated discussion was taking place at the other end of the *camerata*.

"That's why they built those covered toilets and barracks in such a hurry."

"What do you mean?"

"It's obvious, isn't it? Because of the women. They knew about this huge transport and had to put them somewhere."

"And that's why they built these funny looking *sheisser* huts—for families," said Wolf. "They look more like dog-kennels."

Henry suddenly remembered that abandoned chess game, when the board had been knocked over.

"Hey Dino! We never finished our last game."

Dino grinned and said good-naturedly, "Never mind, *capo*. Better so. This way there's neither victor nor loser. Let's all take a walk instead."

The Triumvirate stepped out into the mellow autumn morning. The camp had been transformed overnight. It was not so much the women as the children that lent the place a different character. The barren stone and mortar heaps looked somehow friendlier with children playing over them. As they walked they came across the woman who seemed to be in charge of the children.

"Are you a teacher?" enquired Dino, introducing himself and Henry.

She smiled. "Why? Do I look like one?" They shook hands. "Mrs Feinberg, gentlemen."

Henry faced her steel-blue eyes as he intervened.

"Not at all, Mrs Feinberg. We saw the children with you and so…"

"No need to explain," she interrupted him. "I'm not a teacher by profession but I have taken it upon myself to look after the children. They have had a difficult time and need a firm hand."

"How many children are there?" asked Ossi.

"No more than 20 but at times it seems there are 100! The older ones are the worst!" she replied, brushing her fingers through her short-cropped hair.

"Do the little ones really need a teacher?" Ossi looked a little surprised.

"These children have to grow up quickly if they are to survive."

Henry scrutinised her unobtrusively; her Spartan appearance seemed to endorse her no-nonsense approach.

"There are qualified teachers among us," Mrs Feinberg continued. "I only supervise and try to protect them."

She laughed. Her eyes were shining. She gave the men a sardonic smile.

"Jewish children need protection from their over-indulgent parents, especially in these hard times."

"What about your own children?" asked Dino, lightly.

"I have no children," she replied, so abruptly that Ossi deemed it opportune to change the subject.

"Do you know this area is malaria-infested?" he asked, observing the children with a frown.

"So are many parts of Palestine!"

She folded her arms, as if accepting the challenge.

"We will have to tackle this problem. Perhaps you doctors would care to lecture us on preventative measures."

"Where can we find you? Is your husband with you?"

"My husband died." She paused. "Well we must get on. I am in *camerata* 14. Come on, children!"

Just before she set off, Dino ventured to ask, "Would you mind telling us what you did before the war?"

Mrs Feinberg looked him squarely in the eye.

"I was senior lecturer in Jurisprudence at Vienna University."

And with that, she left them.

The doctors looked at each other, half smiling, half in awe.

"What a character!" chuckled Dino.

On reaching the *piazza* they found the place in turmoil, teeming with humans and inanimate objects. The cooking implements were being unloaded. Not surprisingly, considering the size of the new group, the exhibition of kettles, cauldrons, pots, lids and suchlike, amounted to an ironmonger's bazaar. People were coming and going in all directions, like a procession of ants. Altman, who was among the crowd, had a real field-day advising the women what to buy in the food stores and what to avoid.

"Unless you enjoy maggots, avoid the lentils!" he warned.

And there was Yadranka, with flushed cheeks and struggling with an array of cooking utensils. "Can I help you?" asked Henry.

"Please," she replied, looking relieved and smiling. They walked slowly to her barrack and deposited the cooking utensils in the courtyard. Walking beside this fresh, lovely golden-haired girl was like balm to the soul after the deprivations of the previous months. Henry stood there, undecided what to do next.

A smaller, older and somewhat faded edition of Yadranka came over to take the pots. "Mother! This is Dr Raupner." Mrs Mirkovicz looked very much like her daughter. The same eyes, only sadder; the same hair, only speckled with grey; the same open forehead, but grooved by the plough of experience. She extended her hand.

"I am very pleased to meet you. Have you been here long?"

"Two months but it feels like eternity. Only it isn't nearly as bad as it looks."

Mrs Mirkovicz smiled.

"No need to reassure us. We are not squeamish. Many of our brethren under Nazi occupation would give anything to be here." She again proffered her hand. "You must excuse me, I have to help in the kitchen and you, Yadranka, had better come along too."

Yadranka put an arm round her mother's waist, nodded to Henry and they left.

When Henry returned to his *camerata* he found a letter in a blue envelope on his bed. He recognised Mona's writing and was about to open the letter when to his surprise he noticed a postcard which must have slipped onto the floor. Was it for him, he wondered? The postcard had a Russian stamp, a Soviet censor stamp and also bore the imprint 'Oberkommando der Wehrmacht'. Yes, it was addressed to him. His heart beat faster. Could it be? Yes! It was from his parents. This was the first sign of life from his family since his confinement. He had not been deeply worried about them. His parents had returned to their home town of Lvov, which after the partition of Poland became incorporated into Russian Ukraine. It was fortunate they had not fallen into German hands, although Russia with its history of pogroms and persecution was notorious for anti-Semitism. However, a communist country could not officially afford to persecute Jews. He read the postcard avidly.

"Dear Henry, we got your letter through the Red Cross. Thank God you are alive and well. We had no news from you for so

long and were terribly worried. Please write as often as you can.
We are all well here. Ask your brothers and sisters to write! All
our love and best wishes for a happy reunion one day. Mamma
and Papa."

Such a brief missive, but enough to brighten his heart.
When the apostolic Nuncio had visited the camp he'd promised to make sure their short notes would reach their destination. Henry was very sceptical at the time but just the same
had handed over a brief letter for his parents. It was a near
miracle that his letter had got through to them and even more
miraculous that their postcard had reached him here. He read
the few scribbled lines again and again, feeling the stab of nostalgia.

He'd forgotten all about Mona's letter and when he suddenly remembered it he felt guilty.

"My dearest! I wait but still no further news of you. Are you
well? Why don't you write more often? What prevents you?
(censored) I was puzzled and intrigued by your remark that you
have a chance of leaving the camp. You did not fully explain. I
am worried and torn apart twenty-four hours a day. Everything
seems empty and senseless without you. Mother continues to
pressurise me. She says I must face facts. What am I to do?
Please, please write! I am so confused. You don't know how
much a letter from you means to me. Love and tenderest
thoughts. Your Mona."

Henry read the letter twice, seeking some hidden meaning
between the lines. He recalled the effort it had cost him to hint
at the possibility of his leaving camp, torn as he was between
wariness of the censorship and the lack of space. Now he
would somehow have to explain the project about the ship,
and God only knew how he'd manage that.

There had been an exchange of letters between Ossi and his
Genoese friend. Some months previously there was a chance
of using Greek ships bound for Rio de Janeiro but Italy's invasion of Greece had shattered that hope. The USA and South

America were non-belligerent so far but they kept their traffic with Italy to a minimum. In spite of this Ossi was still hopeful; Henry was less so. The smuggled newspapers had become a regular supply so Henry was well informed about the general situation. From recent hints in the Italian press it seemed that the British offensive in North Africa was gathering momentum. The Mediterranean was getting hotter and hotter each week and it was most unlikely that passenger ships would take the risk of sailing there.

The Future lies on the knees of Jove, thought Henry, *and I am so small I can't even see his big toe.*

Chapter 14

Rosh Hashana

The Jewish High Holy Days were imminent; there was great excitement in the camp. The 400 new internees from all over Europe and the Balkan Peninsula, brought their own particular customs, cuisine and languages to add spice to the melting pot. Due to their sheer numbers, small communities were becoming established in which each took charge of their own cooking, amusements and day-to-day living. They were relieved to be in a place of safety, even if behind barbed wire; imprisonment firstly in a Benghazi army camp and then in Naples, left them eager to join in the New Year celebration planning. After long deliberation among all the provision buyers, at Altman's suggestion, the bulk purchase of turkeys, which were relatively cheap in Calabria, was agreed upon.

Once the truckload of slaughtered turkeys had arrived, the courtyards in front of the camp kitchens were crammed with would-be helpers. Despite the cooks' protests it proved impossible to curb their enthusiasm. The courtyards were teeming with volunteers and there was a continuous coming and going of visitors from neighbouring *cameratas*, to check and report on the relative progress of each. The pluckers sat holding the turkeys between their legs. The air was filled with noise and swirling plumage. Everyone was suddenly an expert in turkey husbandry.

"You are ripping off the skin with the feathers!" yelled Lubicz.

"Don't waste the feathers!" screamed Reimer, "They'll do for pillows."

Mario, who usually left menial tasks such as dishing out the food to Lubicz, now showed his real expertise. He taught them how to cut open the birds and remove the innards; how to cut the stomach in half and peel off the lining. Then he gave a skilful demonstration of how to detach the liver without rupturing the gall bladder. No surgeon performing a skilful operation could have gone more deliberately about his task. The production line of turkey trussing was truly a spectacle, quite apart from the accompanying cacophony but it was all good humoured as visions of their Rosh Hashana meal helped soothe the constant rumblings in their bellies.

The sense of excitement around the camp in all its cultural corners grew with the anticipated New Year celebrations and the gravity of what followed, namely the Day of Atonement. Memories of shared *yamim tovim* with families, were never far from the internees' quieter moments, while fears for loved-ones left behind to uncertain fates were assuaged to a degree by the solidarity that only those freed from persecution appreciate.

These festive preparations broke the monotony of their existence with a wholesome, civilising effect on all. The *camerata*s looked a little more inviting with a few extra candles to promote a festive atmosphere.

Reimer, who didn't give a damn for the whole thing, was bored and on the lookout for some free entertainment. "I do hope, Mr Meiersohn, that you will honour us by taking part in the festivities?"

"I certainly will!" replied the old gentleman.

But Reimer would not be content until he'd shot his poisonous dart. "And we all expect you to share the communal meal with us."

Meiersohn shook his head. "I will share with you, but cannot eat. One can share without eating. God knows, I would gladly eat the food, if it were kosher."

Reimer thought he had him where he wanted him. "So you're refusing to partake of our meal and commune with your fellow internees?"

"I'd rather commune with God, by observing his commandments."

Little Wolf, who had been listening to their conversation with growing anger, snapped at Reimer. "You stupid y*ekkisher shmock!* Each time you set out to provoke Mr Meiersohn you only end up looking the fool that you are. But you won't give up."

Altman thought it wise to intervene and divert the discussion into different channels.

"Mr Meiersohn, we are privileged in having so learned a man among us and I would like to seize this opportunity of hearing your views on some points. How does our New Year celebration differ from that of other people?"

After some reflection Mr Meiersohn replied, "I believe our New Year celebration is more sombre. It is not all joy, not all 'simcha', because the shadow of Yom Kippur, the Day of Atonement, falls over it. On Rosh Hashana we give thanks to God, because it has pleased him to keep us alive for the past year. On Yom Kippur, so the tradition goes, our fate for the coming year will be decided." He paused to catch his breath and clear his throat. "On Yom Kippur we are all 'weighed and measured'. We ask God for forgiveness and start our prayers by forgiving others. We confess our sins and repent."

"Do you mean," broke in Reimer, "because we fast, beat our breasts and repent, all our shabby deals are forgiven us so we can go on robbing for another year?"

Meiersohn looked calmly at Reimer. "Not quite that, young man. We can confess and repent, but it is for God to forgive. There is no automatic absolution after confession in the Jewish faith."

Meiersohn's words hang heavily in the air leaving Reimer momentarily silenced.

The New Year celebrations were to be held in the open air as there was nowhere under cover big enough for over 600 internees. The strange array of wobbly tables and stools was arranged in concentric circles with corridors for 'waiters' to serve up the food.

At first the agents objected to these extensive preparations but eventually they grudgingly acquiesced; the 'Meshimeds', the 'Seven Apostles', turned up their noses whenever they went by. They really had no reason to pass that way at all, unless they were driven by nostalgia for their roots.

Everybody turned up in 'Sunday best' with his head covered—apart from a few rebels, the Free Thinkers—or 'Free Stinkers' as Wolf promptly dubbed them. Reimer and Sokolow were amongst these.

When the first star appeared in the sky on that October evening they all sat down at tables adorned with wild flowers and mint. Meiersohn and Librowicz sat at the table of honour. Mr Meiersohn had his own little silver beaker in front of him. He had salvaged it and carried it with him into Exile, as it was his most precious possession with which to make *Kiddush*, the blessing. How he had wished to bring his candlesticks with him, for they too are the most priceless object for an orthodox Jew but he was not able to do so. Now he filled his little cup and gave the blessing, to which the congregation responded with a resounding, "Amen."

The aroma of the cooking turkey had already been getting the gastric juices going for many hours but when the turkey broth was served it sent the starved internees into raptures with a great many 'oohs!' and 'aahs!' Every mouthful was relished with such exclamations of delight while Altman declared the soup 'music to my nostrils.'

During the dishing out of the second course a comic incident occurred. One of the internees protested because he had been served a turkey leg. Pointing to his neighbour's plate he complained to the waiter: "I told you, I wanted a piece of breast, like that one."

His neighbour, a peaceful man, was willing to exchange their portions. But as soon as the piece of breast landed on the complainant's dish he found it too small and wanted his turkey leg back. So the two portions changed places again, leaving each of them with his original piece.

"That reminds me," said Altman chuckling, "of the two Jews who went for a walk by the river. One was an *Oysher*, a rich man, the other a *Kapzan*, a poor devil. As they walked along, enjoying the fresh air, they heard the croaking of frogs on the bank. The rich Jew on a sudden impulse of mischief turned to the Kapzan. 'Look Shmuel, if you catch that frog and eat it, I will give you twenty roubles.' The poor Jew was very upset and offended so he told the *Oysher* where to get off. However, as he walked on he had second thoughts. His poor wife and children could make good use of twenty roubles. So, overcoming both pride and physical revulsion, he suddenly snatched up the nearest frog and swallowed it. The *Oysher* was taken by surprise but had to keep his word and reluctantly paid out the twenty roubles. They continued their walk in silence, but the poor man's heart was churned with anger. *What a pig this rich man is! Why could he not just give me twenty roubles without humiliating me in such a disgusting way?* A host of violent emotions struggled in his breast. *I'll show this 'hazer', the pig that he is, that a poor man can also have his pride.* And so he turned to the *Oysher*.

'Listen Jankel, if you'll catch a frog and eat it, I'll pay you twenty roubles.' For an *Oysher*, twenty roubles was less than nothing, but like many rich people, he was a miser at heart. When proposing the wager he had not expected Shmuel to take it seriously and had been reluctant to part with the money. To cut it short, after some hesitation he fished out an unsuspecting frog and swallowed it in one gulp. Shmuel took out the twenty roubles and gave it back to Jankel with a gesture of triumph and contempt. As they walked on, Jankel suddenly stopped. Gripping his head with both hands he exclaimed, 'Shmuel! What the hell did we eat those frogs for?' Everybody burst out laughing, and Altman almost split his sides. More than ever he looked like a big, cuddly bear.

They had invested in a big vat of cheap Calabrian wine and being no longer accustomed to the effect of *vino*, the sombre air of *Erev Rosh Hashanah* gradually changed into one of hilarity. Some had brought their musical instruments to the meal, and while awaiting their food, entertained neighbouring tables with tunes from their homelands. Normally, the evening meal would have been followed by attendance in a synagogue but here there was nowhere to go and so the atmosphere degenerated into excessive mirth and frivolity.

Henry surveyed the scene with keen interest, reflecting how this earthly sense of humour had served the children of Israel as a potent weapon of survival. It was amazing to see how these men, oppressed and deprived of freedom, managed to keep themselves in such high spirits. As his eyes wandered over the assembly, Henry noticed that the table of honour was empty. Apparently Meiersohn and Librowicz, who had not partaken of the food, had gone back to the empty barrack to say their prayers.

After three months of near-starvation diet Henry was unaccustomed to the bulk of food consumed and experienced an unusual heaviness. His head was swimming from the Calabrian wine and he felt slightly dizzy. Ossi, who shared the table with him, sat wide-eyed and quiet, his fine face leaning on his palm. The lustre and sharpness had gone from those keen black eyes which were veiled by the mist of early inebriation. Dino, who sat at Henry's right, was full of mischief and exuberance, his accordion by his side, ready to strike up a tune.

"Hey John! What a celebration, eh?!"

Out of the blue Alberti, the agent, appeared. "Which of you is Altman?"

A little unsteady on his feet, Altman got up. Alberti beckoned him to follow. Most of the internees were too distracted, or too far gone, to pay much attention to this incident.

"Now Mario! Give us a song!" Dino called out as he picked up his accordion.

The quiet and usually retiring Mario had undergone a remarkable transformation and was up from the table, dancing the *tarantella*, with such foot stamping that the wobbly tables shook all the more.

"Come on Mario! A song! A saucy *barzeletta!*" insisted Dino.

Mario, his sparse hair on end, his eyes shining, stopped dancing and smiling foolishly, intoned a naughty tune about a little friar – '*un fraticello*' – who nursed a sick maiden back to health in his own miraculous way. People applauded, though most of them could only guess what the miracle cure was from the saucy raised eyebrows of the singers.

Altman re-joined the congregation. He seemed unusually agitated and his habitually rosy cheeks showed an unaccustomed pallor.

"Friends! I've heard it from Signor Rizzi," he called out. "My great day has come! A telegram has arrived. I leave Ferramonti tomorrow! My ship sails from Genoa the day after." His voice choked so that he had to stop for an instant. "Don't think me a hypocrite, but the truth is I am happy to go and unhappy to leave you behind. As we say, one eye smiles while the other cries. We'll meet again one day, when this bloody war is over."

A cloud of silence blanketed the congregation. Altman was much loved and respected by everyone, so that the prospect of losing him saddened their hearts. Bristly Wolf, annoyed by this long silence, burst out, "You miserable lot! Aren't you going to wish him luck?"

They responded as one. No-one begrudged him his good fortune. They had only been stunned by the suddenness of the news.

"*Eviva!*"

"*Mazel and Broche!*"

"May he prosper in Argentina!"

Altman acknowledged their congratulations, smiling.

"The irony of it all is that I shall have the doubtful pleasure of travelling with the 'Seven Apostles' on the same boat." His voice trembled and he had tears in his eyes. "My brothers! How I wish we could all travel on the same boat instead!"

As Henry got up from his stool, he went giddy and sick. His stomach must have shrunk until it was incapable of accommodating a meal of this size. He felt the nausea rising inexorably as he hurried back to his *camerata* to lie down, but that did not help either. On the contrary, it made it worse for it felt as if his bed and the whole *camerata* were spinning round and round. Cold sweat covered his forehead as the nausea became more intense. He had to get up. He staggered towards the door and on reaching the courtyard could no longer contain his urge to puke. He almost brought his heart up as his urge to spew persisted. *All that precious food, gone to the devil. What a way to end New Year's Eve!*

Chapter 15

Bank of Ferramonti

As Laufman had forecast some weeks before, the vituperations and slanderous attacks on the Greeks increased in the Italian press, until the Italians finally invaded Greece, or at least they tried to. Soon after Altman's departure, Enrico Linzer, Henry's Genoese friend who had sent him his first letter, arrived in Ferramonti. He had tried hard to remain at large and continue to run his menswear shop, but eventually his luck ran out. It was not long before Linzer was appointed joint provision buyer for Henry's, as well as their adjoining, *camerata*.

Linzer did not possess the charm and direct approach of his predecessor, but he had qualities of a different kind. His approach in business was evasive and oblique. People said he would always scratch his right ear with his left hand. So, if he saw something worthwhile in the store, he would hardly give it a glance. Eventually he would casually ask for its price and then dropping the subject he would start talking about something different altogether. Such tactics had a disconcerting effect on the seller.

Away from the business, Linzer was a good-natured man, reliable and kind-hearted, though somewhat long-winded. He was an old bachelor; something seemed to have gone wrong at certain crossroads in his life. Linzer had a grammar school education in Poland and even a couple of semesters at University, but eventually decided to join his sister's business in Genoa. On the surface he seemed contented enough but Henry sensed that his heart was not in commerce. He was a strange mixture of intellectual and businessman, not completely at home in either world.

Rumour had it that he had been involved in an unhappy love affair which culminated in a nervous breakdown. Now, at the age of forty, he had acquired various old-bachelor characteristics, among them the spinning of yarns, although he never uttered a bad word about anyone. He was always well informed but gave nothing away, except to Henry, whom he regarded as his protégé. He kept his ear to the ground and within a short time of his arrival was *au fait* with camp goings-on, so it was no surprise that he was the first among the provision buyers to get wind of yet another ham in the stores. After going through his usual routine of simulated indifference, he asked casually, "What on earth is that? A lamb's leg?"

"A lamb's leg?" protested Giuseppe. "This is one of the finest Calabrian hams!"

"That says it all!" retorted Linzer. "Who's ever heard of Calabrian ham? Anyway, *quanto costa*?"

Giuseppe bared his putrid teeth in a grin. "Three hundred and fifty lire."

Linzer gasped, genuinely shocked. "Three hundred and fifty? You must be mad!"

"Your comrade, the one who went away, Mr Altman, he paid me two hundred and fifty!" Giuseppe folded his arms in defiance.

Linzer dropped the matter. He would have done that whatever the price, but this time he dropped the ham like a hot potato, for this was sheer usury. Just the same, he reported the matter to his comrades. "I know the price is exorbitant, but Giuseppe told me that Mr Altman had paid 250 lire and considering how prices are rocketing ..."

"Who says Altman paid 250 lire?" snapped young Scholz. "Never! Giuseppe is a liar! He only paid a hundred and twenty!"

"It's true," Szafran broke in, "Mr Altman was a shrewd buyer. He could lick you, Mr Linzer, any time!"

Reimer exploded. "This ought to be reported to the comandante. It's extortion."

Henry observed that this would only result in anything worth buying disappearing from the stores.

"But that lying swine, Giuseppe," erupted Wolf, "he ought to be taught a lesson. Mr Altman was too clever. He would never have paid 250 lire for a ham."

"But he did," said a firm, low voice. Everybody turned round. It was Schindler, another Jew from Silesia, and a close friend of Altman.

"What do you mean, he did?" yelled Reimer, his flaming red hair matched by a red face burning with anger.

Schindler kept his calm. "I promised not to tell you. He didn't wish to offend you. But he did pay the difference out of his own pocket."

There was an astonished silence in the *camerata*.

"Now that I have broken my promise, I'll tell you more. If you, Mr Linzer, will check the accounts prior to taking office, you'll find there is a surplus of one thousand lire."

People listened open-mouthed in silence. For these beggars a thousand lire represented a fortune.

"I cannot believe it," said someone.

"Why did he do it?" asked Reimer, shaking his head.

Schindler smiled. "When his departure was confirmed, he put down a thousand lire in the 'Bank of Ferramonti' saying that it was the least he could do. He even played down his own generosity, saying the lira wasn't worth much abroad anyway."

One morning, during *appello*, Meiersohn did not respond when his name was called out. Tommasini, who was particularly short-tempered and impatient that day, lost his temper. "*Porca miseria*! Meiersohn! *Rispondi*!"

Everyone's eyes turned to Meiersohn's bed. He seemed still fast asleep and Wolf went up to him to nudge him gently. "Grandad! Wake up!"

But Mr Meiersohn could neither reply nor get up, for he was dead. He had died the way he had lived, quietly and peacefully, without any fuss, like a candle blown out.

Mr Meiersohn, the highly observant, orthodox Jew, was buried in the Catholic cemetery of Tarsia, about a mile's distance from Ferramonti. Only ten internees were allowed to accompany his bier, Librowicz and the three doctors among them. His body was laid to rest close to the wall, for in the eyes of the Catholic Church, Meiersohn was an outcast, a heretic. The strange and paradoxical thing was that Reimer, who had taken delight in baiting the poor old man, insisted on being among those ten who paid Meiersohn their last respects. The workings of the human psyche are indeed complex.

Chapter 16

Community spirit

Among the new arrivals from the Benghazi transport there was a strange pair; they were not married but could always be seen together. He was a smallish man with a rubicund baby-face and fine sensitive hands. She was much taller, at least fifteen years older and very bossy. Gossip had it that she was hell-bent on getting married to this younger and weaker representative of the supposedly stronger sex. Mr Klein was a watchmaker and his stoop had been acquired through endless hours at the bench. No sooner had he arrived in the camp than he began collecting watches for repair. Like Mrs Halpern, the camp's new laundress, he did the repairs for a pittance, because as Szafran remarked, "Who needs a watch in a concentration camp? Afraid you might miss a train?"

With the arrival of that large and active transport, a new way of life developed. Previously no one had expected to be paid for anything. Now people were prepared to work hard for very little, just to afford an extra pound of tomatoes, or stamps. The question was: where did the money come from? It was Szafran who gave the best answer to this puzzle, with what he called the 'Albanian Economy'.

"In Albania, the poor peasants survive by stealing the only village goat in turns. For a while they live on its milk until someone else steals the goat from them. That's our sort of economy here."

Henry's financial resources were dwindling. What little money he had might perhaps last another month. He still had gifts from his father and his beloved brother Mundek, a gold wristwatch and gold and ruby cufflinks, but these he wanted to save for an emergency. Bartering was going on over the barbed wire with the locals, so he could perhaps sell a couple of shirts, a pullover, or even a suit. For most internees, a suit represented life before Ferramonti and symbolised a hope for better times ahead. Henry had already lost a lot of weight and his probably no longer even fit him. The important thing was to survive. He could buy another suit one day if he ever got out of Ferramonti.

It was astonishing, what a softening and civilising effect the mere presence of women and children had on the general comportment of that originally exclusively male population. Shaving apart, other changes were more subtle and took longer to establish themselves: the brushing of teeth, the combing of hair, the covering of bare chests, the wearing of neckties and socks. But the metamorphosis of the everyday language was perhaps the most interesting phenomenon, with the gradual disappearance of obscenities and four-letter words from their vocabulary.

With the passing of time, the old and new population intermingled, fusing into one community. Flirtations and courtships sprang up, causing quite a few marriages to spring a leak. Married couples without children slept apart, which in itself had far-reaching psychological effects, since as the saying goes: many a marriage problem is resolved in bed. The solidity of marriage ties was also threatened by the sexual frustration of the original male population, who had spent so many months without women. Their sexual hunger was written all over their faces, with a disturbing effect on many a woman accustomed only to the humdrum attentions of her husband. Even the least attractive of fading damsels, the habitual wallflowers of old, had their heyday as they blossomed under the glow of the constant, subtle (and not so subtle) attentions of sex-starved masculinity. In this context Szafran, usually not prone to literary expressions, remarked, "The witch who doesn't fly here on *Walpurgisnacht*, never will!"

Added to this turmoil of aroused passions was an element of euphoria due to the unexpected success of British arms in North Africa. Though the press tried to minimise it, it was obvious that a much smaller British contingent had succeeded in routing the Italians. General Wavell had broken into Cyrenaica and was threatening Tobruk.

The contagious mood of optimism must have communicated itself to little Wolf, for suddenly the Muses added a new strain to his lyre:

Is friend Adolf going to yell?

When your army, you lousy nit

Gets bogged down in African shit."

Thus simply, a new song was born. As always, Wolf never tried to push his creations on others. He was a natural songster, like the birds in the trees, and sang his ditties to himself as he swept.

The Benghazi transport also brought some cultural diversions, including the production of plays, to prevent the 'rot of the soul'. Selecting actors, rehearsing, staging, all this indirectly brought together a large number of individuals.

Most members of the Benghazi transport were Zionists and not particularly interested in religion, but there was a nucleus of observant Jews who wanted a synagogue. Henry, as *capo* with some history of positive dealings with the comandante, was entrusted with negotiations, although he did not relish the role. As soon as he entered the office Henry noticed some changes in Signor Rizzi. First, he now wore a collar and tie, but still sporting his riding breeches and boots. Secondly, his play-acting and boisterousness had lost its original lustre; and even that bark, which had always been worse than its bite, seemed to have mellowed. Could it be that the Greek debacle, the Taranto disaster coupled with the recent reversals in Tripoli had undermined his cockiness?

"What can I do for you?"

"Signor Rizzi, I was sent here by my comrades to enquire if we could use an empty barrack as a place of worship."

Signor Rizzi looked genuinely surprised. "A place of worship? A synagogue? Why did it take so long before your people felt the need?"

A good question. Frankly Henry was at a loss.

"Signor Comandante," he proffered after some hesitation, "things have changed. We now have women and especially children who need some form of religious instruction."

"You say things have changed. What else has changed?"

Henry reflected for a moment, undecided whether it was prudent to reveal his thoughts.

"The other change is our conviction that this is going to be a long war and not a *Blitzkrieg*."

Evidently Henry had touched upon a sore spot because the comandante's brows contracted and his eyelids narrowed.

"Have you suddenly become a prophet then?" he asked mockingly, the old irony surfacing. When Henry did not reply, he asked, "What makes you think so?"

"The events of the war speak for themselves."

For an instant Henry regretted this remark which betrayed the internees' familiarity with current affairs, but by now Signor Rizzi was probably aware that newspapers were circulating in the camp.

Unexpectedly Signor Rizzi got up and looking directly into Henry's eyes he said, "I too believe this will be a long war."

His voice was weary and despite their respective situations, Henry could not help feeling a little sorry for him. It must be hard for someone who had victory in his grasp to see it elude him at the last moment.

"Well," the comandante resumed, "a place of worship might be considered in the spring when new barracks will be erected. Just now there are only two empty barracks and more people are expected."

He gave Henry a not unfriendly nod of dismissal. The interview was over.

Chapter 17

3 Milanesi

What the *comandante* said proved quite true: more and more people continued to arrive. Not in large groups but in a steady flow. The last three to settle in *camerata* 3 came from Milan and were quite remarkable individuals.

One of them, Mr Borstyn, was an elderly man, cultured, well-groomed and sophisticated. He was spotlessly clean and his big, friendly smile revealed an outgoing, generous personality. As soon as he arrived, he erected four wooden posts at the corners of his bed and spread a mosquito net over them.

The second, Mr Spitz, was a funny little man: small of stature, his bow legs were surmounted by a sizeable paunch. He very much resembled the statue of Morgante, the famous 'dwarf' in the Boboli gardens in Florence. There was a perpetual cigarette stub in the corner of his mouth and he always wore a hat; some said he even slept with it on. Spitz was a gambler who indulged in endless poker games, and to raise some cash he set about a business almost immediately. Of all the unlikely enterprises in a concentration camp, he chose to clean hats. What he did was quite simple. He soaked the dirty hats overnight in a kind of soapy solution. Next day he brushed the hats hard, filled the hollow with paper, packing it tightly, and then left the hats to dry in the sun, strangely enough with excellent results. He only asked for a minimal reward and odd as it might seem he found enough customers to keep him busy.

But the most unforgettable character of the three was Moishele Perlman, a heart-warming clown. He was about thirty-three years of age, olive skinned and suntanned, of medium height with a slight list to the right. Whether his limp was genuine or a mannerism was hard to say. Years of house-to-house peddling in the Italian provinces, selling raincoats, must have affected his feet and gait. His frame was lithe, his face thin and deeply furrowed, especially his forehead, which when wrinkled reminded one of a puppy. There was also a spaniel-like quality in his eyes; brown, large and melancholy.

This mellow tristesse never really left him, even when he smiled or roared with laughter, which he often did. A strange mixture of puckish mischievousness and profound sadness was about him. He had an eye for the girls and used to wink at his friends, outlining their curves with his hands and nodding approvingly. He seldom talked about himself but it was known that he came from Poland. Moishele had lived in Milan for several years, "if you can call it living," he used to say wryly. His travels, selling 'capotti and impermeabili', took him all over Italy and as a side-line he also bought skins from peasants for the furriers in Milan. He had a large stock of hilarious travelling anecdotes, intermingled with amorous conquests. He particularly liked to tell of an adventure when he lost his straw hat, braces and tie in a Godforsaken hamlet in Sicily.

When Moishele first arrived in Ferramonti he was looked upon as a greenhorn by the old hands but he soon proved them wrong. His long years of experience of peddling, his resilience to fatigue, the habit of irregular meals and make-shift sleeping arrangements, had produced in him an adaptability of the highest degree. He was a master of improvisation and ingenuity: roasted peas took the place of coffee beans, dried dandelion and mint leaves made a 'special blend' of tobacco. Even discarded shoes, skilfully trimmed, became useful sandals. This adaptability placed him high in nature's order of survival; like thistles and nettles he was tough and indestructible. His greatest asset was his sense of humour and a capacity for self-mockery. He arrived with a shabby suitcase and very little cash but what little he had he shared with others. When he was broke, he accepted the inevitable philosophically. "Why worry? Leave that to Hitler. He is the one losing this war." To those complaining of the starvation diet he'd reply, "Why should you grumble? You're living here on a pension of 5 lire, with plenty of sunshine, plenty of time, plenty of flies and mosquitoes, and you don't have to work. What more do you want, meshuggener?"

In spite of his many conquests, it was known that Moishele had had an enduring love affair with an Italian woman in Milan, to whom he was deeply devoted. He never spoke of her, but it was rumoured that she had betrayed him to the police. For many months he had attempted to evade confinement by an elaborate stratagem of precautionary measures. For a start he slept each night in a different place, using the most unlikely hideouts. During the summer he often slept in the open, but when it got cooler he took refuge in greenhouses and occasionally in the waiting rooms of railway stations — the 'Beggars' Ritz' he called them. Sometimes he took a chance and slept in the houses of Italian friends, of whom he had many. But when sterner laws about harbouring foreign Jews were promulgated, he did not wish to implicate them, and even kept away from his lady friend for long periods. Only by telephone did he keep in touch with her. One night, when the notorious Milanese fog rose from the surrounding rice fields and the cold began to bite, he took a gamble against his better judgement and went to Francesca, his woman friend. No one will ever know whether the neighbours or Francesca informed on him. But, in the middle of the night, both were roused from sleep and Moishele, still in his pyjamas, was arrested.

Chapter 18

Moishele's Tale

Over the months, Henry's relationship with Dr Bernheim grew closer. He was fascinated by the new dimensions opening up for him. Although Dr Bernheim had explained to him why it was so important to study mankind from the dawn of civilisation, Henry still found that approach excessive. So Bernheim tried again.

"Man's mind has expanded over the ages like a snowball — better still, like an onion — layer upon layer. So the older layers are buried under the younger and newer layers. These are suppressed and modern man has lost the memory of the meaning of certain archaic experiences. He sometimes thinks, feels and acts in ways quite foreign to his present state of mind. He has lost the key to unlock his age-old past. Much of what we call mental illness is due to this. That is why psychologists must be well versed in man's remote history, for patients may well be suffering from 'flashbacks' to primeval experiences without understanding what is happening to them."

One cold December evening, returning from an animated discussion with Dr Bernheim Henry found his *camerata* in euphoric excitement.

"Well John! What do you say now? Am I still a naïve optimist?" asked Dino.

Henry, who was still chewing over that evening's complex discussion, looked blank.

"I don't know what you're on about."

Dino looked at him half-astounded and half-annoyed.

"Don't you know anything? North Africa is falling to the British!"

Henry beamed. "But that's splendid news!"

"If you spent less time with that brainbox friend of yours," Dino muttered with ill-concealed spite, "you'd know what was going on in the world."

Here we go again, he thought, but refrained from responding.

"Besides," resumed Dino, "I cannot see how you even find the time to do your job as *capo* properly! You are hardly ever here! You have no idea what is going on these days."

This was a more energetic broadside with wider implications.

"Has anyone else complained?"

"Not exactly, but I still can't see how …"

"Look my friend," Henry broke in, "you can take over any time you like! This *capo* business means nothing to me. Extra responsibility that's all. If you think you can do a better job, be my guest!"

At this point Ossi intervened. "Stop it, both of you! No squabbling!"

Dino smiled and gave Henry a conciliatory pat on the shoulder.

"Let's not quarrel," said Dino. "The news is too good for that."

He was right of course, for this was a major blow against the Axis. Everybody felt happy and grandiose strategic plans were conceived and hammered out that night in *camerata* 3.

"There was a letter from my friend in Genoa," said Ossi suddenly, lighting himself a cigarette with his usual casual elegance. Ossi had lost a good deal of weight. Henry had not noticed it before, but it struck him now. Like his own, Ossi's money was running out fast. He liked his tobacco and what little reserves were still left were bound to go up in smoke.

"So what's the news?"

"There is a Portuguese ship sailing from Genoa in 2 months. It's carrying some clerics and diplomats from neutral countries. We have a fair chance."

"What do we have we to do?"

"Nothing. If the ship's captain is willing to sign us on, he has to apply to the Italian Ministry for our release. My friend is working on it."

Ossi blew the smoke out through his nostrils, slowly and deliberately. Henry watched, feeling a great urge to smoke too but he was trying hard to stick to his self-imposed ration of three cigarettes a day.

"In two months anything can happen in times of war," said Henry. "Do you really think your plan will work?"

"I sincerely hope so," replied Ossi calmly as he picked up a book. But suddenly he slapped himself on the forehead. "I nearly forgot. That girl, the one with the blonde plaits, she was looking for you."

"What did she want?" asked Henry as casually as he could.

"I don't know. She spoke mostly with Dino."

As the evening roll call was due, Henry resolved to find Yadranka in the morning. However, in view of Ossi's news, it was high time he informed Mona of the latest developments. It was only fair.

1) *"Dear Mona! Excuse the long silence. There was nothing*

2)   *to report. There is some news now. I have hinted at it*

3)   *before without details. The fact is I may be taken*

4)   *on board a ship as a deckhand and leave the country.*

5)   *It would be legal and above board, as the Italian*

6)   *Ministry would have to sanction it. An official application*

7)   *would have to be made by the ship's captain.*

8)   *Should I get away, this is not the end. We would meet*

9)   *again after the war and start afresh. After all we*

10) *are separated now, so what's the difference? Wish me*

11) *luck. I realise your position and the pressure from*

12) *your mother. Keep your chin up. Courage! Love Henry."*

Henry was glad to have made the effort. Squeezing some sense into twelve lines without offending the censors was a disagreeable, laborious task. Up to a point he could sympathise with Mona's mother. In the golden pre-war days, as a newly qualified doctor, he was a most welcome guest, a good catch. But with the racial laws things began to change and had reached a critical point when Mona — dreamy and romantic as she was — had tried to run away from home to be with him in Genoa. How much more must Mona's mother resent her daughter's plight now that he was in a concentration camp? He certainly was far from the ideal son-in-law.

Mr Borstyn beckoned Henry to his corner. As usual he was clean-shaven, wore an impeccable white shirt and a warm expression.

"Dr Raupner, would you and your two doctor friends care to share a bottle of Asti Spumante to celebrate the news from Egypt? Apparently a great defeat!"

"A bottle of Asti?" repeated Henry, "I'm sure they'll be delighted." And so they were.

"How did you manage to keep it so long?" Dino enquired.

"I kept it just for such an occasion as this. And there are two more. The last one's for victory."

Henry looked at the distinguished, lean figure of the elderly man sitting on his four-poster bed. He suspected that Borstyn's invitation to the three of them was not only to celebrate some good news, but also to re-establish friendly relations. He had witnessed Henry's little skirmish with Dino and sought a tactful way to repair the damage. Filling four glasses he called out, "*L'chaim.*"

Split in four a bottle of wine does not go far, but on an empty stomach and in good company it can go far enough to lift the spirits. Soon all four of them were chuckling away for no good reason and when Dino put on his gorilla act they were helpless with laughter.

Amidst the jovial atmosphere the door opened and Moishele Perlman walked in.

"So somebody is celebrating, eh?"

"Come Mr Perlman," Borstyn said jovially, "you are most welcome. Help yourself. Only there isn't much left in the bottle."

Moishele had no need of wine to make him merry and soon had the whole *camerata* roaring with laughter when he began telling them about his salesman's exploits and adventures.

"Tell us the story about your straw hat and silk tie!" Szafran called out.

Moishele looked embarrassed, indicating with a side-glance at Mr Borstyn that this was not the kind of story to tell in his presence, but Borstyn's perceptive eye caught his gesture and he smiled mischievously.

"Don't be shy! I could tell you a few Russian tales that would make you blush, young man!"

"Well then, if you insist," began Moishele, crossing his legs and clasping his knees.

"Well, it happened in Sicily on a very hot day, in a village so poor and remote even the devil would not bother to call there. But I — being a *shlemiel* — did call. It was so hot you could fry eggs in the sun. I had been peddling for hours and wanted a rest. There was this tumbledown shack, so I knocked at the door. There was no answer. You know me. No one gets rid of Moishele Perlman that easily. So I knocked again. This time the door opened; a pretty young woman peered out.

'What do you want?' she asked and when I showed her a raincoat she almost slammed the door in my face.

'I am a widow,' she called out. 'I've hardly enough to eat never mind luxuries!'

But I put my foot in the door. I'm used to people slamming the door in my face.

'Not so fast!' I told her. 'I also buy! Anything to sell? Sheep-skins?' You know, I used to work with furriers in Milan. The bastards paid me a few lousy lire and then they dyed the sheepskins and sold them for Astrakhan. Never mind those bloodsuckers, let's get back to the story. As soon as I mentioned the sheepskins, she cocked her ears. She seemed interested but still in two minds, so I said 'I pay well, if the skins are in good condition'. For a moment she seemed to hesitate then she said, 'I have a few skins in the barn'."

At that moment, showman that he was, Moishele looked at his watch. "It's getting late, I must go back to my *camerata*."

"Stop clowning, you *meshuggener*! Get on with it!" Szafran said, digging his elbow into Moishele's ribs.

"Well, if you insist ... Where was I? Ah, yes. She opened the door and let me in. The ice was broken. 'It's terribly hot,' I said and she looked me over from top to bottom. I was perspiring like a pig. The sweat was running from me like a waterfall. My worn-out shoes were covered in dust. I must have looked a real *nebbich*, but she smiled and said, 'That's a nice straw hat you're wearing'. You know I had got myself a new straw hat especially for the Sicilian job to protect my face from the sun, and also a silk tie, to look respectable. If a salesman looks like a *shnorrer*, they throw him out before he can open his mouth.

'Want to wash your face?' she asked. I nodded and so she brought a basin of water. I took off my hat, washed my hands and face and felt like a new-born baby.

'Can I have a glass of water?' I asked.

She smiled again. 'You don't drink water in Sicily. Want a drop of wine? *Vino* Siciliano?'

So I sat down. In a rocking chair. Never seen the like of it before. It must have come out of Tutankhamen's tomb, creaking and straining at every rock. But it was like paradise just to sit there and rest. I drank the wine. I was so thirsty I could have drunk a barrel of dishwater. The wine must have gone to my head because I began to feel drowsy. It was so quiet outside. Just a few sheep bleating, some birds twittering... My head was beginning to nod. I was so tired ... and with that *vino* I could have slept for a week.

But the young woman prodded me in the chest.

'Hey you! A fine salesman! Going to sleep?' I opened my eyes.

'Sorry, I'm not used to this heat'.

I got up and put my hat on.

'Have another glass of wine and I'll show you the skins in the barn'.

I wondered what skin she was going to show me. Anyway I drank and again she drank a glass too. Then she led the way to the barn and I followed. My knees were shaking. Not only from the wine. It was dark in the barn and the hay smelled good. She smelled even better. So, I put my arm around her shoulder.

'Let's have a rest here. It's so peaceful and cool.'

She shook my arm off. 'You must be mad!' she said.

So, I let myself fall in the hay and pulled her down with me. We were both flat out on the straw wrestling, but not for long. She wasn't a hot-blooded Sicilian for nothing, and a widow at that. I didn't dare to undress, in case someone came in. I only pulled down my trousers and took off my straw hat and tie. And.....well I am sure you can imagine the rest."

He let the story tail off as the audience sniggered and nudged each other trying to conjure up the image and relishing its lasciviousness.

"When I woke up, I searched and searched but couldn't find either my hat or my tie."

"What happened to them?" asked young Scholz, eventually.

"Her donkey had eaten both! I hadn't seen him in the dark. He must have had a bloody good nosh."

The *camerata* burst out laughing and Moishele joined in, as if hearing the story for the first time.

Chapter 19

Analysis

Next morning Henry went across to Yadranka's barrack.

"I was told you were looking for me."

"Yes I was," she replied rather coolly.

"Anything special?" Henry asked, surprised at her frosty reception.

"Nothing in particular. Only my mother wondered whether you'd like to eat with us last night."

"Oh! What a pity!" Henry was genuinely upset at the thought of missing out on some extra food not to mention home cooking. Hunger was his constant companion and the watery concoctions from the kitchen left his guts churning. The bitter chill of December in the Crati valley made the thought of extra hot food very inviting indeed.

"I was surprised you did not bother to come and find out."

She seemed offended and Henry hastened to explain.

"It was late when I found out you had visited, and after *appello* it is unwise to visit female barracks."

Yadranka did not reply and there followed an embarrassed silence.

"Would you like to come out for a stroll?" asked Henry in an effort to appease her.

She hesitated. "I really ought to help mother, but I suppose I could spare a few minutes." She fetched her warmest coat and scarf.

So they walked in silence for a while looking at the cold hard ground with the shroud of heavy morning mist hanging over them.

"Why do you spend so much time with that egghead?" she burst out eventually.

Henry had to laugh. "Ha! You've been gossiping with Dino!"

She looked uncomfortable. "Yes, but you haven't answered my question."

"He is very intelligent. Well read. A psychotherapist and very interested in ancient civilisations. I enjoy talking to him. There are so few..."

"Ancient civilisations?" she interrupted. "So why don't you talk to me? I was studying history, you know before the war."

"Ah Yadranka, it's not the everyday aspects of history I am talking about. What I am discussing with the 'egghead' as you call him is how human desires, taboos and morals have crystallised into mythology and these mythological precipitates are a goldmine for a student of psychology. In fact I hope to take up psychiatry one day."

Yadranka gave him a sideways glance. She seemed to be turning something over in her mind. She stopped walking and asked him directly in her unconventional way.

"Is something bothering you?"

Henry, surprised by her question, was wary. "Why do you ask?"

"I find your preoccupation with psychology a little strange. Do you have a problem?"

"Who hasn't?" Henry replied, as evasively and light-heartedly as he could.

"I mean specific problems."

Had anybody else asked the same direct questions he would have told them to mind their own business but the way Yadranka enquired had something disarming about it. One could not call it indiscreet or nosy; child-like or innocent would have been more appropriate.

"I'd like to know myself better but then, maybe everyone should? The problem which is foremost in my mind is: How can a Jew, living in a hostile gentile world, remain true to his deepest roots without isolating himself from the environment in which he lives?"

She contemplated this point as they walked in silence.

"It's almost like trying to square a circle," observed Yadranka finally. "Mind you, this was less of a problem to me. We didn't have much anti-Semitism in Yugoslavia, least not that I noticed as a young girl. Still, I had different problems."

"And what were yours?" asked Henry, adopting Yadranka's blunt approach.

"Oh…" her voice trailed off as she sifted through her thoughts, hesitantly. "They were of a different kind altogether. Less philosophical. More personal I suppose."

"Go on," Henry prompted gently giving her time to collect her thoughts as they sauntered.

"I miss my father! He died when I was five and I hardly remember him. When other children's fathers attended school events I used to feel envious and sad. It must be nice, I thought, to have a strong man behind you, to feel protected." At this point she blushed, realising how her words might appear to the older Henry.

They were getting close to the camp limits on their stroll; the barbed wire and sentry box in all its striped glory loomed.

"Well, I'd better be going back now. My mother will be looking for me. *Arrivederci, shalom.*"

Back in his *camerata* Henry chewed over their conversation. He had to tread carefully. Yadranka was still half a child, one apparently in need of a father figure. She was a lovely girl, simple and direct, but it would be unfair to encourage her, considering he was not free to do so. Her mother's invitation to dinner sat uneasily with him despite the temptations of an extra meal. Before he had met Mona, he used to get panicky whenever parents appeared on the scene. He liked to keep at a safe distance lest they got the wrong idea. The same had applied even to Mona's parents before he'd got more involved. Sometimes now he wished he had kept to this golden rule.

In the afternoon, when he met Dr Bernheim, he soon forgot his qualms as he listened to the theories and expositions of his mentor.

"You see the tragedy of life lies largely in the dichotomy between thinking and feeling. We may realise intellectually that something is wrong yet be unable to make ourselves feel that way. Reason pulls in one direction, emotion the opposite way. The endless battle between head and heart."

Their discussions, first merely of an academic nature, gradually assumed a more personal colouring, until Dr Bernheim remarked one day, "I've been thinking. You want to take up psychotherapy one day. Then why not have a training analysis with me? You would gain more insight, which would benefit you professionally some day and it would stop me from getting rusty."

Henry accepted immediately. He had been secretly hoping for this to happen but had not had the courage to ask for it. He was exhilarated, for such a training analysis would enable him to turn a seemingly wasted period of his life here into valuable experience.

Dr Bernheim, noticing Henry's enthusiasm, thought it advisable to assuage his eagerness.

"But I must warn you. Analysis is no picnic! You will gain some insight, as well as many bitter truths about yourself. At times you may also feel depressed, when you discover unflattering facets of your personality. This does not apply only to you, but to everybody. But you will get over it for the purpose of analysis is to bring about change and healthy reactions to one's shortcomings, not to bemoan them."

Chapter 20

Alone

Henry had spent 7 years as a medical student on the Liguria. Wrapped in his thick tweed coat and scarf, a winter stroll along Bordighera's *lungomare* with his sister Helena had been a great pleasure; they would sit on the rocks at Capo Ampeglio, gazing out into the blue infinity of the Mediterranean, deep in their own particular reverie. But the bone-piercing cold in Ferramonti, in that valley of chilled mist was a very different kind of cold. At night, the hovering icy damp penetrated through the allotted two thin blankets; the wooden bed frames and straw-filled palliasses gave neither warmth nor comfort during the bitter winter months. But not all the internees were as hard up as Henry; he had arrived in the July heat with little thought of warm clothing or even of winter. Now he wore his few warm clothes all day and often at night just to keep from freezing. The only good thing was there were no flies!

In January it was Henry's 28th birthday. He didn't celebrate or even tell anybody about it. A birthday in a concentration camp was no cause for jubilation. Besides his old money was running out fast and he couldn't afford to squander it on trivia. True, there was the possibility of his leaving the camp with Ossi but deep down he doubted very much that this would happen. The regular trafficking through the barbed wire was in full swing during the winter months. Woollens and other kinds of warm clothing were very much in demand with the rural population. The trouble was the peasants took advantage of the internees' helplessness to exploit them utterly. Even so, Henry parted with a much-needed woollen vest and pullover, exchanging them for a bottle of olive oil and a few sausages.

Sometimes he wondered why Mona never sent him a food parcel. Dino and other internees received regular bounties, which proved that it was possible to send them. Mind you, despite her intelligence, Mona had her head in the clouds. How utterly impractical she was transpired from the moment she'd chosen for her escapade. Badgered by the police as he was forbidden to practise medicine, it was a miracle that he had been able to keep body and soul together. No doubt her elopement plan had not been a mere theatrical gesture, but an honest attempt to stay with him; but how did she expect him to provide for her under those circumstances? No wonder her mother was furious! Henry received a telegram threatening expulsion from Italy unless Mona was sent back immediately. He knew of Mona's loyal and defiant intention to come to live with him but still, he had been stunned to see her, for this was no time for romantic elopements. Yes, Mona was very sweet but devoid of any common sense.

As the days went by, Ossi and Henry waited impatiently for some positive news from Genoa. Things were allegedly 'progressing' but there was no evidence of it. He spoke to Yadranka about his hope, but her response was non-committal. In fact Henry had the impression that she was not enamoured with the idea.

"I wish you luck," she said half-heartedly, "but a sea voyage in time of war is very risky. Why not stay here? Better the devil we know. Why not do something useful in the camp?" she added.

"I try my best as *capo camerata*."

"That's not enough. I for example have started teaching history to the children. You could take some interest in the school too."

In fact the school was yet another factor which had brought new life to Ferramonti. Mrs Feinberg, its chairman, kept a watchful eye on its smooth running. Strange how despite her stern ways the children clung to her, though in truth they were also a little scared. Whenever in trouble, they usually ran to her first.

"Do you know why Mrs Feinberg has no children of her own?" asked Henry of Yadranka one day.

"I suppose she was too engrossed in her studies and married late. As a lecturer in Jurisprudence there'd be even less time for rearing children."

"Well she is still young enough to have a child."

Yadranka giggled. "Where would she find a sire? Miraculous conceptions don't happen anymore. Her husband is dead you know."

"No need for miracles. There are plenty of men here, and very willing ones too. She could easily find a partner."

Yadranka laughed. "Good! That gives me a chance too!"

"Why? Do you want to get married?"

Yadranka nodded, half in jest and half in earnest. "Oh, yes, if I found the right man. Sometimes I feel very lonely and ... I love children."

Henry seemed surprised. "Children? You're still half a child yourself. Besides, you said you wanted to remain 'Yalda', just a girl, for ever."

"True, but sometimes we say things we don't mean." Her words hung in the air.

When Henry got back to the *camerata* he found a poker game in full swing. Moishele Perlman, Spitz the hat cleaner, Szafran and two others he did not know, were at each other's throats.

"Get a move on Einstein! No use racking your sparrow brain!" Moishele cried, thumping his cards on the table. None of them had any cash so the gamblers used cigarettes, crusts of bread, or pieces of soap as stakes. Henry loved to watch Moishele at poker because all his characteristics — good and bad — emerged at once. He could be flamboyant, cunning, needling, provocative, tolerant, bluffing and generous. Sometimes, regardless of his boisterousness, a passing sadness would come over him, a sudden frown, like the brief shadow from a cloud. His spaniel eyes would dim, but he would soon spring to life again. More than once Moishele refused to accept his winnings, as he did now.

"Who wants your bread, you scarecrow! Look at him, the *shlemiel*. He needs a prop just to stand up!"

Amused by Moishele's antics Henry walked over to his palliasse, where to his surprise he found a letter. It was enclosed in a bluish envelope, not oblong like Mona's but rather squarish and of rougher texture. He saw the postmark: Viareggio. Eagerly he opened it but his spirits sank when he saw the unfamiliar handwriting. The letter was from Mona's mother.

'Dear Dr Raupner,

As Mona does not feel she can write, it is my unpleasant task to do so. You plan to leave this country and leave Mona behind for God knows how long. No one can tell the duration of this war. It may go on for years. I am a mother and Mona is my only child. I cannot allow her to ruin her life, waiting for years until this war is over. By that time both of you may have changed. Time can do strange things to people.

To come to the point, I have persuaded Mona to accept a proposal of marriage from a decent young man. I am truly sorry it had to end this way but we have to be realistic, not bury our heads in the sand. I wish you all the best and hope you will find much happiness once this war is over.

Yours sincerely, Margherita Silvani.'

Henry was stunned. A host of contradictory emotions rose within him and struggled against each other: hurt, contempt, anger, disappointment. He slumped on his bed as he re-read the words. He imagined Mona's tears and protestations at such an idea; he felt the pain and jealousy of the easy transfer of her affections to the "decent young man" who had proposed. He stared around the dismal *camerata* at the pin-ups on the rickety walls or the family photos adorning the wooden tables; those connections with the outside world and those we love. Then slowly, but strangely, a new feeling started to sweep through him: a feeling of relief. What hurt and disillusioned him most was Mona's lack of courage in not writing herself, choosing to hide behind her mother's skirts. His heart was also saddened by the realisation that there was now not a living soul in Italy to whom he could write, or who would write to him. His brothers and sisters were scattered in various continents following the racial laws, and did not even know his whereabouts. As for her mother's letter, he had no quarrel with it. In fact the letter seemed decent enough. It was surprisingly fair, devoid of malicious overtones. He could understand her point of view. He read the letter again and then folded it and put it in his wallet, which contained documents, letters and other things of sentimental value. Then he buried the wallet at the bottom of his suitcase. Something inside him went numb; a flickering flame died. Another chapter of his life had ended. Despite his state of malnutrition he did not feel like eating. In fact he did not eat for a whole day.

Chapter 21

To work!

It had to happen sooner or later and now that time had come. Henry did not have a single lira, not even a centesimo. True he had been in such a situation many a time during his student days, but that was different. All he'd had to do then was tighten his belt temporarily and wait for his father's cheque. Or he could have borrowed from friends. Now there was no hope of any cheques and as for borrowing, this was out of the question; most of his pals were in the same boat. Ossi was broke and he was not going to borrow from Dino who was not short of money. His pride would simply not allow it.

'*Arm wie eine Kirchenmaus*,' he thought, and smiled ruefully.

He wistfully remembered his brother Mundek's advice about shaving his head in the summer as this was supposed to invigorate the scalp and ensure a luxuriant growth of hair. Now, although it was only spring, he did the same.

Wolf shaved his hair for him and did it with great relish.

"*Capo*, your head looks like a twisted billiard ball," said Szafran.

Others were less complimentary. "More like a naked arse!"

Throughout the many months of his confinement Henry had been able to supplement his diet a little, but now that his cash had gone, hunger began to bite. He had by now lost a good deal of weight; although in good shape on arrival he was now, some eight months later, very thin. For two weeks or so he took it philosophically, but then he decided to act. Dr Bernheim, during his analysis, repeated frequently that one had to 'test reality day by day' and react accordingly. Well, his reality now was hunger, so he was going to do something about it.

Since early March, a voluntary working party of internees had been going out into the woods to work for a pittance. Henry envied them not so much for the little money they earned but for the privilege of getting out of the camp. Others looked down on them for 'helping the enemy's war effort' but now that his innards began to play him up, with his stomach

grumbling and his guts griping, Henry enquired what it was
the men did to be accused of helping the enemy. It turned out
that they collected brushwood and sticks and tied them up in
bundles. Theoretically they did help the enemy, but their activities were hardly likely to alter the course of the war. So,
Henry decided it was unrealistic to stand on far-fetched principles with an empty stomach and opted to join the working
party as soon as a vacancy appeared.

Ossi refused. "I will not work for them," he said flatly.

Henry shrugged his shoulders; he thought the whole thing
too trivial to make an issue of it and registered with the camp
police who instructed him to present himself next morning at 8
o'clock sharp at the front gate. Henry was excited! Since the
day of the marsh inspection with Dr Sabatini back in July, and
Meiersohn's funeral in October, which had been an event of
great sorrow, he had not left the camp.

Next morning a small group of internees assembled at the
front gate. Soon two agents, revolvers dangling casually from
their holsters, emerged from the *questura* and they all passed
through the gate to the outside world.

It was a glorious spring morning, not a cloud in the sky;
the air was fresh and warm. After a few minutes' walk, the
marshes Henry knew already came into view. The green of the
grass was bespangled lavishly with blues, reds and yellows;
cornflowers, poppies, wild flowers everywhere, a feast for the
eye. He was glad to be alive on this lovely morning despite his
forced captivity.

After a mile or so they turned inland from the river and
marshes. Here the landscape changed completely. A narrow
path led into a pinewood which grew denser and darker as
they went on. Eventually they came to a clearing where many
trees had been felled recently and where branches and twigs
lay scattered in the brushwood. There they came to a halt.
Watching the others, Henry soon got the idea of the work involved and started to gather sticks and branches and tie them
into bundles. The work, being light and simple, made no demands on his concentration so he was able to look about him,
but apart from the sandy soil and the majestic pines he could
see very little as the thick forest hid the rest of the landscape

from view. The air was filled with the penetrating resinous scent of pines, which almost hurt his nostrils.

Henry gave a deep sigh for no specific reason. It was the first time in months that he'd been able to enjoy a measure of privacy, since they worked at some distance from each other, and as for the agents they kept well away from the internees. How different from the cooped-up conditions in the camp, where people even had to defecate in full view.

Henry was in a reflective mood; most of life's situations, he pondered, have potential gains and losses. The hardest to bear, he found, was his deprivation of freedom, and yet to a large extent this was offset by the loss of responsibility. In situations of helplessness one has to accept the whims of Fate, and in such a passive resigned attitude there is often more peace of mind than one ever knew in the turbulent days of freedom. *True,* he thought, *this may be the peace of mind of a slave but perhaps even slavery has its compensations.*

"So you're a newcomer? What made you join the 'enemy's war effort'?" the man working nearby called out to Henry.

"An empty stomach, I suppose."

There was little shade in the clearing and as the Calabrian day got warmer, Henry's shaven pate began to feel the sun — and the day was still young. The oozing resinous gum evaporating in the growing heat increased the intense fragrance, which brought back memories of the pine forests in Austria, then of the pineta in Viareggio and Mona. *Strange how certain scents can recall long-forgotten episodes of one's life and the intense emotions that accompanied them,* he thought.

Immersed in his reflections, Henry added bundle upon bundle to the heap which was gradually piling up in front of him.

"What do you think you are doing? Building the tower of Babylon? You work too fast! Take it easy!"

Evidently this man, a Mr Garfunkel, did not approve of Henry's enthusiasm.

"They only pay us two miserable lire," he continued, "so don't overdo it!"

Henry slowed down. It was getting quite warm so he took off his shirt. It was almost midday and Henry felt both thirsty and very hungry. All he had with him was a piece of bread, a thin slice of cheese and an apple, which Lubicz had given him instead of lunch, and even that was rather generous. The two agents sat in the shade, a straw-clad Chianti flask between them. When their bottle was empty they stretched themselves out and went to sleep.

A strange way to guard a prisoner, Henry mused.

A faint ringing became audible. Henry strained to identify the sound; there was no mistaking it, it was the silvery tinkling of a little bell.

"Here they come!" called out Garfunkel.

A small donkey, the bell dangling from his neck, came into view. He was loaded with a calabash on one side, a barrel on the other and was followed at some distance by a young woman bearing a large terracotta bowl on her head. She held herself erect; her walk was lithe and supple. *Ruth coming to the well*, thought Henry.

"*Finalmente!*" said Garfunkel. "I thought you were never coming today, Maria."

The young woman smiled, removed the bowl from her head and put it on the ground. "Have you brought anything for me?"

Garfunkel winked and beckoned his pals. "*Si*, we have things."

Henry looked at them, puzzled, when Garfunkel addressed him. "Have you brought anything?"

"What was I supposed to bring?" he asked, bewildered.

Garfunkel shook his head. "You are a funny man, *Herr Doktor*. You surely don't think we only come out here for the beggar's pay they give us!"

"I still don't follow you."

"Then you must be very naïve. We bring various articles in exchange for food or money. The *chappers* are in on it and get their cut."

With these words he took from his pocket an old watch and a lighter and the others produced their wares too. Most of it was cheap rubbish, a worn-out necklace of glass pearls, a cigarette holder, a leather purse, a small bottle of cheap perfume and other such trinkets.

"*Che roba*! What rubbish!" protested Maria. But this was routine. She would have uttered the same deprecatory remarks had they brought the crown jewels. Then the bargaining really started. Three eggs for the lighter. Garfunkel wanted four. A pound of flour and a piece of mortadella for the watch. Garfunkel wanted more than double. So the haggling and bargaining went on, but all in a friendly spirit, until at last agreement was reached.

"And you?" She suddenly turned to Henry, who stood aside. "Have you nothing to sell?"

Embarrassed, Henry shook his head. Maria smiled at him and reached into her bowl. "Here then. You have this," and held out an egg.

Henry blushed to the roots of his shaven bald head. Never before had he felt so humiliated — almost like a beggar. Maria, though only a simple peasant, sensed his shame.

"Not to worry. You'll bring me something next time." With these words she removed the water containers from the donkey's flanks, deposited them on the ground, mounted the donkey and departed. "*Arrivederci …domani!*" she called out.

As soon as she had gone they seized the calabash, held it up and after removing the plug let the water trickle directly into their mouths. Henry drank greedily to quench what seemed an unquenchable thirst, and then joined the rest for the midday break. Garfunkel began to dig a hole in the sand. "Who wants them cooked?" and then addressing Henry he asked, "Do you want yours cooked, Herr Doktor?"

Again Henry was at a loss. Garfunkel smiled. "I forgot you are a greenhorn. Give me your egg."

He placed about a dozen eggs in the hole, covered them with sand, put a few dry sticks on top and lit them. For a few minutes he continued to feed the fire and then he dug the eggs out. "Here you are."

Henry was fascinated by this novel method of preparing hardboiled eggs without water. He ate the egg and his cheese with great relish, for it had been ages since he had a whole egg all to himself. If for nothing else, this egg alone had been worth the morning's toil.

As he stretched himself out in the grass he felt at peace with the world, listening to the cheerful chatter of the birds in the forest.

Resuming his work under the cloudless sky Henry sprinkled some water over his bare chest and pate. His scalp was burning and he regretted having shaved off his hair at the wrong time. The hours began to drag and he looked forward to their return to the camp. A warm breeze stirred in the bushes as they set off back for the camp; the atmosphere was brilliantly clear now and every object, every flower, was sharply etched out in the crystal air. The colours, pastel hued in the morning mist, now sang out loud and dazzlingly vivid.

Back in the *camerata*, Henry met alarmed looks from his pals. "What is the matter with you, *capo*? You look like a lobster!"

In fact, when Henry caught sight of himself in a shaving mirror he got a shock, for he was scarlet all over. However, it really looked worse than it was, for Henry's skin had become conditioned to the Italian sun over the years. Just the same he applied some olive oil to his skin and a wet towel to his forehead before he flopped onto his palliasse. He was exhausted, his skin was tingling all over, but there was joy and contentment in his heart. After so long a confinement in so narrow a space, this outing with its wealth of impressions was like a new lease of life and he allowed himself to savour the feeling that comes at the end of a day's work, admittedly not a particularly hard one.

As the weeks went by Henry became a seasoned outdoor worker. His skin tanned all over. His moustache, eyebrows and eyelashes turned straw-coloured. Even the stubble on his scalp, which had grown an inch or so, was bleached by the sun. Physically he felt in great shape. The exercise and additional nourishment had worked wonders.

Chapter 22

Sonia

One day as they were coming in from work, the oddest sight met his eyes. As he passed the sentry box into the *piazza*, there stood an impeccably dressed young woman, provocatively looking about her with open curiosity and almost supercilious amusement. She wore beautifully cut slacks with an elegantly tailored blouse; her shoes and belt spoke of elaborate craftsmanship. Beside her stood two little girls also dressed in finery. This group's unusual attire contrasted sharply with the miserable surroundings, being more suited to Biarritz or, as Henry recalled from his own medical student days, similar hunting grounds of the *Côte d'Azur*. Henry could not conceal a look of surprise as he passed and nor did he try. For a moment blue eyes met his and then her gaze travelled swiftly upwards, an inch or so above his head. She was blonde and buxom, with an ample bosom and broad hips.

Why on earth would anyone dress up like this in a concentration camp? he mused.

He saw the two agents nudging each other, as well as nodding their heads approvingly.

"*Perbacco! Che pezzo di fica!*" they murmured *sotto voce*, almost licking their lips.

After a day's work in the sun, Henry could hardly wait to throw himself on his bed. Dino, always in the same good-humour, greeted him with a mighty slap on the back.

"Well John, how was the convict labour today?"

Henry smiled, took off his sandals and lay down. "It's easy for you capitalists. You can afford to be idle." There was no reproach or malice in Henry's words, just a jocular statement of fact — unless, of course, there was more to his joke than met the eye; in every joke there lies a grain of truth, it is said.

"I hear we have some new arrivals in the camp," said Wolf.

"And what arrivals!" exclaimed Szafran with emphasis.

"They say there is a very interesting woman among them," remarked Reimer.

"Interesting?" Szafran echoed ironically, "More like tasty! A real cock-killer!"

"Where is she?!" Dino called out promptly, licking his lips and beating his chest as if he were on heat.

"I think I have seen her already," said Henry calmly.

"How could you?" Dino asked, astonished. "You only just came in from work!"

"It shows he can pick them out from any distance, our *capo*," joked Szafran.

"Really John..?" interrupted Dino, "Where did you see her?"

"She was standing in the *piazza* with two little girls."

"Well, what's so special about her?"

"She is dressed to kill."

"Is that all?" Dino asked, visibly disappointed. "What does she look like?"

Henry was amused by all the commotion. He grinned. "Not bad, not bad at all, but what a show off!"

At this point Ossi joined in the conversation.

"Not necessarily. Some English Lords dress for dinner to dine alone in the middle of the desert!"

"Then they're eccentric," retorted Henry.

"Eccentric they may be, but not necessarily show offs."

"She must have plenty of dough," said Szafran. "They say her husband is a furrier in Milan but they really come from Frankfurt."

Little Wolf, who had carried on imperturbably with the sweeping up, planted himself squarely in front of Szafran.

"Hey you! You've gone to a lot of trouble to get information about that woman. Why this sudden interest?"

Szafran gave a low sheepish chuckle. "She really is something, I'm telling you. Her name is Sonia Heller."

And that was the end of the conversation. But thoughts of Sonia Heller continued to amuse and perplex the inmates of *camerata* 3 in their quieter moments.

Henry continued to enjoy his work in the woods despite the increasing heat of the Calabrian sun and had become an important supplier of food to his *camerata*. Considering that most edibles had been rationed by now, even for Italians, little

was left in the camp stores. For this reason Henry's contact
with the outer world proved a real Godsend for his *camerata*,
especially as its occupants knew they could rely on their *capo*'s
honesty. Money they did not have; most of them had something to barter for food although after almost a year of captivity, only the most cherished items remained and the thought of
parting with these was painful.

By now, Henry had established an excellent rapport with
Maria, who had so generously given him that precious egg; it
seemed she also had a soft spot for him, treating his merchandise with a certain magnanimity. Every day the working
party waited impatiently for the tinkling of the bell heralding
the approach through the woods of Ciuccio, her little donkey.
He was so appealingly shaggy in his straw hat with little ear
holes that Henry would spend much of his rest time stroking
him, occasionally sacrificing a precious piece of bread to watch
those powerful mandibles grinding away. Maria, her little
business prospering, treated herself to a new blue head scarf
and looked very pretty.

As a result of his work, Henry had to neglect his analysis.
On most days he was too tired for such exacting mental exercises. He also saw very little of Yadranka, though this was
more by design than lack of opportunity. Somehow he seemed
to avoid her, which was rather paradoxical considering that he
was no longer engaged to Mona. Perhaps he had a temporary
aversion to women as a whole. As for their hiring by the Portuguese ship, nothing had come of it in the end. Ossi's Genoese friend wrote a long letter full of apologies explaining that
there had been a 'technical hitch' at the last moment. So that
was that and the prospect of an early escape bit the Ferramonti
dust. Ossi insisted that the plan was still good; they just had to
bide their time.

The month of May 1941 was nearing its end, foreshadow-
ing a second scorching summer in Ferramonti. Things were
not going too well with the British, who still stood alone. After
the German invasion of Yugoslavia, British troops in Africa
were diverted to Greece with the result that General Rommel
counter-attacked, driving the British back. Out of the gloom,

rumours, largely based on wishful thinking, of an impending German attack on Russia began to circulate.

"Even Hitler, mad as he is, could not possibly be so nuts as to fight a war on two fronts," opined Szafran.

But Borstyn had different views. "There is no knowing what a madman can do. Megalomania is often a Godsend."

Henry was bored with the never-ending rumours, speculations and prophecies of the internees and glad to escape every morning into the quiet of the woods. On his return from work one day there was a blonde woman sitting next to his bed and chatting with Ossi.

"Let me introduce you to Mrs Heller," said Ossi. "In fact she has really come to see you."

Henry raised his eyebrows. "To see me? Why?"

They shook hands and Mrs Heller remarked with a smile, "We have seen each other before, in the *piazza*, I believe."

Henry reciprocated her smile. "Yes, I believe we have. What can I do for you?"

Mrs Heller came straight to the point. "You will have noticed my two daughters. I must feed them and they are not used to this rubbish they call food here."

"Neither are the other children," Henry replied coolly.

"I know," said Mrs Heller apologetically "but this does not alter the fact I must do my best for my children."

Henry made no reply, but after a moment's pause he asked, "And why have you come to me?"

"Mr Linzer advised me. He mentioned you're working outside and ..."

"I see." Henry cut her short. "And what do you need?"

Mrs Heller, glancing at Henry's rucksack, full to bursting point, gave a throaty laugh.

"I bet I could use all of it. How much for the lot?"

Henry gave her an icy look.

"Mrs Heller, I'm not a black-marketeer. All this has been brought for my comrades. It's not for sale." But seeing her face drop he added, "If there are a few things you need for the children I am sure we could find you some between us."

Her face brightened again. "Thank you, doctor..."

"Raupner."

"Sorry, I forgot. You tell me what I can have."

That's better, thought Henry. He took out an egg, a pound of flour and a piece of cheese.

"You can have these. I have exchanged them for an old woollen vest, for myself."

Sonia looked Henry in the face with a strange expression in her eyes.

"And what about yourself? I wouldn't want to deprive you …"

"Never mind," responded Henry dryly. "I don't need anything today and I can get something else tomorrow if I want to." This was not true but his pride would not allow him to admit his hunger.

Sonia Heller began to fidget with her purse and took out a hundred lire note. Henry looked at the banknote with amused fascination.

"Good Lord! It's ages since I saw such money!" Mrs Heller was so embarrassed, she blushed.

"No, Mrs Heller, I don't want any money. I'd rather you gave me something like the woollen vest I exchanged for these articles."

Ossi found this idea absurd.

"Henry, use your loaf! Where would Mrs Heller get a man's woollen vest from?"

Dino, who had just come in and had caught the last part of the sentence, remarked mockingly, "She could give him a pair of woolly knickers."

Mrs Heller's eyes narrowed and she gave Dino a frosty look which had the desired effect. He piped down immediately.

Regaining her composure, after a moment's reflection Sonia Heller opened her purse again and took out her powder compact.

"Would this do?" she asked hesitantly.

"Hardly," said Henry, whose expression hardened. "Mrs Heller, this is a concentration camp and the things we barter for food go to peasants." He was beginning to lose patience with her.

Again an expression of discomfiture mingled with apology invaded her face.

"I really don't know what to give you. Why not come to my place and choose something. Please, Dr Gerber, you come too. You have been very helpful."

Tired as he was, Henry could not resist the temptation of having a peep at this woman's set-up and particularly her wardrobe so he accepted her suggestion. Her family hut was at quite a distance and on their way they met with some curious and almost hostile glances. They must have made a strange trio: Sonia, all dressed up, flanked on her right by Ossi in simple but neat attire, and on her left by Henry, looking like a tramp in his working clothes and worn-out sandals. The small wooden hut, situated at the lower end of the camp, was close to Pasquale's sentry box. Her two little girls were digging in the sandy earth nearby.

"Come here children. I want to introduce you to the doctors."

The little girls left their spades in the soil and hurried to greet their mother.

"This is Susan and this is Deborah." Both children were dressed in pristine white, or rather had been before they'd started digging.

Ridiculous, thought Henry, *to allow children to play in such clothing.*

The girls were of much darker complexion than their mother and very pretty.

"They are the spitting image of their father," said Sonia, "and also have his good looks."

"Fishing for compliments, Mrs Heller?"

Sonia looked at him calmly. "You seem rather aggressive, Dr Raupner. You don't like me, do you?"

"I neither like nor dislike you, Mrs Heller. I hardly know you."

"Enough, enough!" interjected Ossi. "No need to get personal. What my friend meant was that their mother is beautiful enough to account..."

Sonia seemed amused and smiled. "Thank you, Dr Gerber, for the compliment. Did you mean it that way, Dr Raupner?"

Henry shrugged his shoulders, but did not reply.

The tiny family hut consisted of one room and a recess containing rudimentary cooking facilities. Larger families had more spacious accommodation. Considering Sonia's tiny room served all purposes it was not surprising that it was in great disorder, crammed to the ceiling with suitcases, boxes, toys and other paraphernalia. In addition to all this, there was a camp-bed for Sonia and another for the girls protruding halfway from the recess. Coat hangers with their respective garments hung from long nails in the walls, adding a bohemian, not to say chaotic, touch to the whole muddle. On top of all that, there was a table and three stools in the centre.

"I do apologise for this mess, but you will understand…"

"Certainly we do!" said Ossi, sensing her discomfort.

The two men felt clumsy and hemmed in by the cramped space and also embarrassed because Sonia's silk lingerie was lying in full view across her bed. She removed it deftly as she asked them to sit down. One stool was piled up with washing and the two remaining stools, probably the children's, seemed too fragile for a man's weight.

"Sit on the bed," suggested Sonia. Ossi obliged, but Henry remained where he was, fearing the bed might collapse. Sonia, sensing Henry's impatience, began rummaging among her garments for something Henry might accept. But most things were in excellent condition and she was on her guard not to provoke another of Henry's sarcastic remarks. Suddenly she stopped. "I've got an idea. Suppose I give you something more valuable than your woollen vest. You can get your victuals back with it and any surplus you can pass on to me. How's that?"

"I think it's an excellent idea," said Ossi. "It kills two birds with one stone."

She took out a woollen jumper. "Will you take this? Please do, and get some more provisions for me too."

Henry agreed. At that moment the piercing sound of a whistle hit their eardrums.

"*Appello*! We'd better be going," said Henry, and shook hands with Sonia. Not Ossi. He bent over and kissed her hand, continental-style.

As they were about to leave, Sonia barred Henry's way and looked him boldly in the face. "Will you satisfy my curiosity?"

Henry measured her with suspicion. "It depends."

Sonia grinned, her eyes shining mischievously. "Why on earth do you shave off all your hair, Dr Raupner?"

Unprepared for this kind of question, Henry needed a second to gather his wits about him. It was a very personal question which he resented, so he over-reacted.

"I'll satisfy your curiosity, if you satisfy mine. All right?" He paused for a moment to lend stronger emphasis to his words. "Mrs Heller, why do you dress up in a concentration camp as if you were going to a ball?"

With a wave and a smile, and clutching the woollen jumper, he began running towards his *camerata*, reaching it just in time. Ossi arrived a little later, out of breath from the long walk.

"Why did you have to be so rude to Mrs Heller?" he asked as soon as the roll call was over.

"I don't like snobs. That's all."

Chapter 23

Discoveries

Henry continued his work in the woods. His skin burned darker until it became almost black. He looked lean and slender; even his scholar's stoop straightened out. Physically he felt really well; the extra provisions, a few eggs, some local sausages and bread, made all the difference to the meagre diet. Mona was a fading memory of the past on whom his thoughts seldom dwelt and when they did there was no pain, just warm memories of Viareggio, the pineta and happy days on the beach.

On his return from work he had by now got used to finding Sonia in Ossi's company, waiting for her share of provisions. They seemed to really hit it off. In his student days Ossi used to dress meticulously and now, under Sonia's influence, he began to display his dress sense again; garments he had stowed away for better times were dragged out into the light of day. Sometimes Henry felt regret at the ill-timed metamorphosis that had overtaken Ossi, probably against his better judgement. But he never made any remarks to that effect, and besides he spent only a fraction of the day in the camp now.

Meanwhile away from the *camerata*, the agents accompanying the working party took their cuts in the internees' transactions. Their surveillance was anything but strict. This encouraged Henry to take occasional liberties. Thus, one day, during lunch break, he decided to explore deeper in the forest where the sandy ground became softer under foot. The coniferous trees were gradually replaced by elms, planes and oak and, further on, the soil became almost marshy until unexpectedly he came upon a little pond in a glade. It was irregular in shape, surrounded by brushwood and briar, and from its surface protruded moss-covered rocks. Henry stood there mesmerised. Rivers, lakes and ponds had always held a special fascination for him, rooted in his childhood fishing days with his brother Lonek. Air bubbles rising and concentric rings forming on the pond's surface proved that there was life in the water, perhaps even fish.

Henry was seized by a sudden desire to sink a line and hook into this unknown water, anticipating a bite from some strange species of Calabrian fish. Throughout the rest of that working day he could not free himself from the excitement which only passionate fishermen can understand. His thoughts revolved around this sole topic as he continued tying up his bundles of sticks. A fishing rod was no problem; he could cut himself a springy branch from a hazel tree. Strong cotton would do for a line and a bottle cork could be easily adapted to a float. The only problem was the hook. Then he suddenly remembered his old wallet, the one where he had stowed away that letter from Mona's mother. It contained all sorts of relics, some of importance, others of sentimental value. If he was not mistaken, there was also a small greaseproof envelope containing hooks, a memento from a happy fishing trip. He could not be sure, but would check as soon as he got back to camp. The end of the work day could not come soon enough.

No sooner had he entered the *camerata* than he got out his suitcase and started turning its contents upside down. Ossi and Sonia watched him in bewilderment.

"What is it Henry? Got a train to catch?"

It was no good trying to explain. He found the old wallet and started examining its contents. Yes! There it was, the little greaseproof envelope, tucked away between documents and letters, holding three hooks of different sizes. He was overjoyed and a broad grin lit up his face.

"What have you found?" asked Sonia.

"Nothing much."

"Then why all this frantic performance?" enquired Ossi.

"Never mind, you wouldn't understand."

"I bet he was looking for the address of an old flame," said Sonia with a smile.

"You could say that in a sense. Only this old flame was not a woman."

With this remark Henry grinned and dismissed the matter. Sonia picked up Henry's rucksack. It was empty.

"Why Henry! Haven't you brought anything today?"

"I'm sorry. I missed Maria."

There was both surprise and reproach in Sonia's voice.

"How could you have missed her? She comes every day, doesn't she?"

"Yes, she does, but I was off, exploring the forest."

Sonia looked at him in silence, a strange pensive expression in her eyes.

To avoid further questioning, Henry changed subject.

"Any news in the camp?"

"There are all sorts of '*bonks*' circulating," replied Ossi, eventually.

"What are *bonks*?" enquired Sonia.

"A *bonk*," explained Ossi, "means a bumblebee in Polish. It buzzes like a rumour."

"Well, what sort of rumours are there?" asked Henry.

"Something to do with Germany and Russia."

"Is that all? If our strategists had their own way, Russia and Germany would have been at each other's throats ages ago."

With this, Henry took off his sandals and was about to lie down when Sonia suddenly addressed him.

"Would you like to come over to my place for a bite to eat? Ossi is coming."

Before his working days when he was half starved he would most likely have declined, but now that he could provide for himself, he accepted. So he went out to wash, got out of his working garb, put on a pair of shorts and a clean white shirt and re-joined Sonia and Ossi, who waited for him under the oak.

"You look a picture when you've washed your face," said Sonia. "With that tan you look like the very devil!"

"Is that meant to be a compliment?" Henry asked, smiling.

It was true. The white shirt only accentuated Henry's dark tan. His hair, now two inches long, was bleached by the sun and his crew cut fitted his present outdoor personality well. He looked handsome and virile. They set off for Sonia's hut.

"Can we go out to play?" asked Susan, the youngest child, seeing her mother returning with guests.

"You can, but don't be too long. Supper will be ready soon."

The children darted off; Sonia put on an apron and Henry watched her with a strange twinkle in his eye.

"What is the matter?" she asked, smiling.

"I somehow hadn't pictured you in such matronly *Hausfrau's* attire.

Sonia looked at him, taken aback. "You must have some very strange notions about me, Henry," with which she retreated into the recess-cum-kitchen to heat up the meal she had already prepared. The men sat down on two strong chairs, apparently new additions to her household. Ossi seemed a bit glum.

"Why do you always have to make such caustic remarks?" he whispered.

Henry put a reassuring hand on Ossi's shoulder. "I don't mean anything really. Just my way of talking."

Before long, they were all tucking into a rich and spicy Hungarian goulash. It had been so dreadfully long since Henry and Ossi had tasted anything tasty or filling, though this was mostly vegetables and dumplings. Each mouthful was savoured amidst a good deal of lip-smacking and sighs of pleasure until the plates were scraped clean. This was followed by pancakes with jam and to round off the meal, coffee — real coffee — the aroma of which was bliss in itself.

Henry was in ecstasy. He smiled, sighed and patted his belly.

"I must compliment you, Sonia. This goulash is probably the tastiest I have ever eaten. As for the pancakes...and the coffee..." Henry was half-swooning in delight at the memory of the sweetness of the pancakes and the lingering aroma of the coffee which permeated the small room. And how long since he had tasted jam!

"Thank you, Henry. Mind you, it's not that difficult to satisfy the palate of half-starved men."

To crown it all, Sonia conjured up a fiasco of Barbera proving that if you had the money you could obtain almost anything in an Italian concentration camp. Sonia poured everybody, even the children, a small glass of wine.

"*L'chaim*! To Life!" They clinked glasses, drank and filled up again. Then Sonia proposed a toast. "To Henry, who brings all these good things for us."

There was a counter toast from Ossi.

"To our generous hostess."

Gradually the wine began to go to their heads. It was a large flask and there was still plenty left in it. The children, taking advantage of their mother's distraction, scampered away to play outside. Ossi had his gaze fixed on Sonia. He only had eyes for her. Before his arrest he had lost his heart to a pretty young blonde in Genoa, with whom all contact had since dried up, much to Ossi's consternation; Henry had seen photos of them together in happier times, holding hands, strolling along the *lungomare*. Now at last Ossi was re-kindling those feelings which had laid dormant for so long. Without doubt he was in love. A dreamy expression suffused that fine, handsome countenance as he watched Sonia's every move.

Henry felt his eyes getting heavy and his head swimming a little. His thoughts returned to the pond, his fishing hooks and the anticipated excitement of tomorrow. *God knows what these Calabrese fish will look like.*

Ossi began to sing "*Parlami d'amore, Mariu!*" He was definitely tipsy, but pleasantly so. Henry watched him, smiling. He had a very warm regard for Ossi; he also remembered fondly from his own adolescence, those first darts of Cupid's arrows and the pleasure-pain when they found their target.

Sonia beamed, glad to have hosted such a pleasant evening in the God-forsaken place. Her face shone with contentment for she was fully aware what this meal meant to the men. After all, they had been imprisoned in Ferramonti for almost a year. Suddenly Sonia poked Henry in the chest.

"You still owe me an answer, you know!"

"I don't understand," Henry replied blankly through the fumes of wine.

"You've never told me why you shaved off your hair."

Henry burst out laughing, his hilarity much in excess of his habitual response.

It's that vino all right.

"And you haven't told me why you dress up in this dump as if you were on the Promenade des Anglais in Nice."

"All right! I will. But you first, OK?"

Ossi, his raven hair in disarray, looked slightly alarmed.

"Oh please you're not going to argue, are you?"

Sonia's question had a sobering effect on Henry. He straightened himself up in his chair, screwed up his eyes, giving her a sharp look.

"Before I answer your question, may I ask you why you want to know?"

"Because it intrigues me that a handsome young man should disfigure himself, unless he has a good reason. Or wanted to punish himself?"

Henry seemed lost in thought as well as for words.

"To be truthful, I never thought about it. But I will try to explain it to you and to myself."

He took another gulp of *vino* to lubricate his throat and mind.

"Let me start three months ago. I had a distressing experience. Never mind the details. Soon after, our hopes of leaving this damned place as deckhands were dashed. A month later, the Nazis invaded Yugoslavia and Greece and to rub more salt into the wound, Rommel pushed the British back in North Africa. To add insult to injury, this was the very moment my money chose to run out. So you can see that by March I was not exactly in a happy frame of mind." He helped himself to a cigarette and went on. "In my student days, when broke, I used to wire home: 'Dear money, send father'. I didn't know what it meant to be destitute. So when I could not find a single coin in my pocket I must have got scared. I must have felt that my light-hearted youth had come to an end and was buried and so following the Hebrew tradition of mourning, I symbolically cut my hair as a sign of bereavement." Henry brushed his forehead as if to dispel the fumes of wine.

"There could be another explanation," he continued. "When still adolescent I used to shave my head during summer holidays. So perhaps by cutting my hair I was subconsciously trying to conjure up that golden age of irresponsibility when I felt secure and protected. Psychologists call it regression."

A sudden idea must have crossed his mind for he looked surprised. "Yes! Now that I come to think of it, there could be a third reason. There is a young woman in the camp. I liked her, but may have been afraid of getting involved. So I cut my hair, to lessen my chances." Henry folded his arms across his chest, threw back his head and smiled. "There you are, Sonia. Take your pick."

Sonia, who had been listening to him intently, seemed particularly interested in his last disclosure. "Who is this young woman?" she asked with undisguised curiosity.

"Never mind. It doesn't matter anyway."

But Sonia did not give up so easily. There was a curiously enigmatic expression on her face and a fleeting twinkle in her eyes when she asked, "And why are you so afraid of getting emotionally involved?"

He laughed and responded good-humouredly.

"I agreed to some explanation but not an interrogation! Anyway it is your turn now."

Ossi was sitting on pins, afraid that tempers might get frayed. But Sonia, following Henry's example, poured herself a glass of wine and drained it almost in one gulp.

"I could simply answer your question in one sentence: I just haven't got any rags! But that wouldn't satisfy you. So this is the truth. We had to leave Frankfurt in 1937 because of my husband's big mouth. He had talked too much, too loud and too long and one day we were tipped off that the Gestapo was after him. Though we had a good furrier's business we had to leave overnight with literally nothing but the clothes we stood up in. The Jews in Milan wouldn't accept the reason for our hurried escape at that time; they thought us imposters and gave us the cold shoulder." She paused, eyes glazing over as she relived the experience.

"We lived first of all in one room and a kitchen. I washed, scrubbed the floor, sewed all the children's clothes and evenings I worked as a waitress. Gradually we worked our way up for despite his loud mouth my husband is a first class furrier. In 1938 things improved rapidly. I became pregnant and had a baby boy, but he died at five months and I became terribly depressed and ill. On top of all this came the racial laws and our conviction that we had jumped from the frying pan into the fire. My depression grew." The memory of these days must have been very painful, for her eyes had the sheen of unshed tears. "You're interested in psychology, Henry, so you ought to know there is nothing can raise a woman's morale like a new hat and clothes. The worse I felt, the more clothes I bought, and I also wanted to give those Italian Jews one in the eye for having cold-shouldered us when we arrived. Not very noble I know, but very understandable. All my old clothes I gave away to my daily help. I didn't want to see them ever again, nor be reminded of that first miserable year."

She stopped to gain control of her emotions, which seemed to run away with her, now that the wine had loosened her restraint. "The *coup de grâce* was still to come: Italy's declaration of war. I didn't know what to expect. The war went on but the Italian authorities left us in peace. Then one day they came to arrest us. My husband was away. In haste I packed what I could. Did you expect me to buy special outfits of rags for a concentration camp? Besides, I didn't know where they'd send us. Did you?"

Henry listened to her but was not totally convinced by her arguments for there were many women in the camp who despite similar experiences had reacted differently.

"Is that all?" he asked. "No other reasons?"

"Weren't there reasons enough?" She seemed to hesitate. "There is one further reason, but I'd rather not talk about it just now."

Henry felt a little annoyed, because she seemed to be holding back.

"Couldn't there be a simpler explanation? Such as vanity?"

Ossi's eyes flashed ominously. "Henry, you are disgusting!"

Clearly Sonia felt insulted.

"I was only joking," he said, backtracking. "I didn't mean to be rude to such an exquisite hostess. Not after so delicious a meal. So please don't be cross with me."

That night Henry turned and tossed on his camp-bed, unable to get off to sleep. The day's events, the discovery of the pond, that hearty and palate-warming meal, the Barbera and the mutual confidences, all this had unnerved him. Why was he so rude to Sonia, he wondered, especially as it always upset Ossi, whom he liked? There he lay to his right, fast asleep, with his face as usual covered with the blanket, except for his forehead and his shock of hair. By moonlight that raven-black hair contrasted even more sharply with his forehead's pallor, which had a translucent, almost ghostlike appearance.

Romantic old Romeo, he thought, smiling in the dark. His own efforts to fall asleep were fruitless. On top of it all there was this damned mattress pricking his behind. Tomorrow without fail he really was going to refill that bloody bag of straw, once and for all!

Tomorrow, he suddenly remembered, *tomorrow I'm going fishing*! And on this happy note he fell asleep.

Chapter 24

Hope Springs Eternal

Henry woke at dawn despite his restless night, swiftly wrapped up his 'fishing gear' – a spool of cotton, a bottle cork and the hooks—and put it in his pocket. It was a fine June morning, with blue sky and the promise of heat still to come. He enjoyed the early morning brisk walk to freedom more than ever as he imagined the thrill of casting out and feeling that longed for tug on the line.

Impatiently he waited for the midday break, and finally, he stole away unobtrusively. In no time he'd cut himself a whippy rod from a hazel, tied the thread to the tip, pushed the cotton through a hole in the bottle cork, attached the hook to the end of the line, and—hey presto—all was set.

In the moist humus surrounding the cooling shade of the pond he soon dug up a fat worm, put it on the hook and cast his line, thrilled with anticipation. He looked briefly around him taking in the coolness of the trees and the water so refreshing after the dryness of the camp. Then, eyes fixed with a hypnotic stare, he watched the float, waiting for signs which would justify his expectations. He watched and waited, one minute, two minutes. All his muscles were contracted, ready for instant reaction, and suddenly the float wobbled, began to tremble, gave one quick quiver and slid under the water. With a quick jerk he struck and felt the unmistakeable resistance of the weight at the other end, that weight which quickens every fisherman's heart. He'd never expected it to happen so soon. As he had no reel to wind his catch in he had to pull it out with a mighty jerk of the rod. And up it came, flying through the air, something plumpish, greeny-brown and almost immobile. He ran to the spot where it had fallen. What strange kind of creature was this? He squatted on his haunches to examine his catch. This was no fish! It was a tortoise or more correctly, a freshwater turtle. Whatever catch he might have expected, it wouldn't have occurred to him in a thousand years that he'd land a turtle! Luckily the hook had not been swallowed, but was embedded in the turtle's horny upper lip and easily came out.

Henry inspected his catch with tenderness and admiration. It was a small turtle, not more than two pounds in weight. The horny shell was greenish-brown and its head, when protruded from the protective coat of mail, was supported by a long wrinkled neck. It had two lovely black eyes, moist and shining. Henry picked it up and tried to stroke its head, but the turtle retracted it immediately.

He was dying to show her to his workmates; his appetite for fishing had gone completely for fear of injuring another turtle with the hook.

"Perbacco! Una tartaruga!" exclaimed one of them.

"Well," said Garfunkel, "now we can have turtle soup."

"Not likely!" retorted Henry. "This one will be a mascot for *camerata* 3."

Just as he had been eager that morning to get off to work so he was now impatient to get back to camp to show off his new pet. The news of his extraordinary catch soon spread throughout the camp and as usual its sensation-starved population seized on anything new as a most welcome diversion. Henry was bombarded with questions as he patiently recounted the same story over and over again. *Camerata* 3 was most proud of their newly acquired mascot.

"*Mazel and Broche!*" said Szafran. "Let's hope she'll bring us luck!"

Wolf took charge of the turtle right from the start. The cranky little man was badly in need of affection and since he could not seem to get it from humans he was ready to bestow it on anything incapable of raising objections.

"What shall we feed her?" he asked.

"I don't know," replied Henry. "We had a tortoise when I was a child. We called her 'Grannie' because of her wrinkled neck...anyway, we fed her on lettuce and fruit. But this one took the bait so she must eat worms, I suppose."

"Let's give her macaroni," said Reimer jokingly. "They look like worms."

But little Wolf was in no joking mood. "You shut up, you carroty *yekkisher shmock!*"

It was strange how these two were still at each other's throats after breathing the same air and sharing the same *cam-*

erata for almost a year. But despite the seemingly overt animosity between the German and Polish Jew, there was really no depth to their hostility; it was more needling than stinging, more barking than biting, as if both were driven by a compulsion to get at each other for the sake of a skirmish. Besides, Reimer had mellowed a good deal during that year.

They put her down on the concrete floor and she began to crawl. From time to time she stopped, stretched out her neck, moving her head from side to side, as if undecided where to go.

"What shall we call her?" asked young Scholz.

A great many names were proposed; some glamorous, some eccentric, some plain stupid.

"Let's call her *Tikvah*, Hebrew for Hope," suggested Borstyn, and this name was unanimously accepted, for Borstyn, whom they called 'Batyushka', little father, was highly respected.

At this moment Sonia, holding hands with Ossi, entered the *camerata*. "Whatever's this?" she asked, and quickly added, "May I have it for the children to play with?"

"No. Sorry. This isn't a toy. It's a living creature, our mascot."

Moishele's deep voice reverberated through the *camerata*.

"Where is the creature?" he yelled. "I'm told you caught a crocodile!"

"Stop clowning!" said Wolf. "Here she is, but you mustn't touch her."

"Mustn't touch her?" Moishele put his hand on Wolf's bald pate, which he often did to the latter's annoyance, and rubbed it. Turning to Sonia he continued, "Do you hear that? I can't touch her. The Koh-I-Noor, the Crown Jewels?" Then picking the turtle up, he pressed it against his cheek. "Come to daddy, you little beauty." Changing the subject, he addressed Sonia. "Well, haven't they caught your *shlemiel* of a husband yet?" Moishele knew Sonia's husband well. He used to sell him his sheepskins.

No one knew exactly whether turtles were entirely aquatic or amphibious creatures, so as a compromise *Tikvah* was put into a bucket of water containing large stones for her to climb on if she wanted some air.

"Goodnight, little *Tikvah*," said Wolf lovingly as he put the bucket in a corner.

After escorting Sonia back to her quarters, Ossi lay down, looking dreamily at the ceiling. Henry did not wish to disturb the languid visions of his friend and left him in peace.

Henry proposed a game of chess to Dino, who happened to be sitting beside him, fidgeting with his accordion. Dino had gradually drifted from the Triumvirate. The detachment had taken place by degrees, over a period of months. It had started with his objection at Dr Bernheim's intrusion and became more pronounced after the cross words over Henry's alleged neglect of duties as *capo camerata*. Then, when Henry had joined the working party, his contact with Dino had become even more distant and tenuous, especially as Dino had no need of Henry's supply of victuals.

Nevertheless Dino was as ever, good humoured and never bore malice. This was the source of his enduring charm. Henry and Dino were soon immersed in a complicated game which dragged on for hours and continued long after the roll call and eventually they had to play by candlelight.

Most people were asleep already and everything was quiet in the *camerata* when suddenly an unshaven, disordered man burst excitedly into the stillness of the room.

"Have you heard the latest?" he yelled at the top of his voice. "Hitler has attacked the Russian bear!"

It was Funk who brought these good tidings. Everybody jumped out of bed. At first people did not believe it, but when Funk emphatically assured them it was true, real pandemonium broke loose. People began to clap, sing and yell their heads off. None of them was a war-monger. On the contrary, they were the most peace-loving people, but the clash between the two colossi meant that Britain was no longer alone; she now had a powerful ally.

"*Mazel Tov! Mazel Tov!*" they shouted. "He's done it, the idiotic corporal!"

Despite Funk's unpopularity, people ran up to him, patting him on the shoulder as they bombarded him with questions.

"Can't stop now," he said, grinning self-importantly. "I have to tell the others!" And he was off.

Strange, thought Henry, that such sweet tidings should come from such a foul mouth; but what did it matter whose mouth it came from? The great historical event, the strategic folly had taken place: Hitler had voluntarily chosen to fight on two fronts.

"Well, the painter and decorator has put his foot in it!" exclaimed Wolf. "He'll get his balls fried all right."

No one was more exhilarated than Batyushka Borstyn, who originated from Russia. His face was aflame, his eyes shining. In his snow-white nightshirt, with his distinguished gentle features, he was a truly patriarchal figure. "Come here my friends! Let's celebrate!" He got out a bottle of vodka from his large suitcase and poured out a little aquavit in each mug. The drop of vodka was symbolic, for no one required any stimulants to feel exalted.

"*L' Chaim…Nazdrovja!*"

Wolf lifted the turtle from the bucket.

"I told you she'd bring us luck."

Borstyn, looking like a prophet inspired, raised his glass.

"Gentlemen! This is a historical event which our children's children will remember. God does not let trees grow to heaven. He has His way of cutting them down!"

The children of Israel sat up that night, discussing and formulating strategic plans. There was, however, one discordant note, one chalice of bitter gall, which had to be swallowed along with the sweet tidings.

"What will happen to the millions of Jews in Poland and Russia if the Nazis break through?"

This secret undercurrent of fear and anxiety ran parallel with their euphoria, but Batyushka Borstyn tried to dispel their secret dread.

"It won't come to that. The Nazis won't get that far. The Russian steamroller will flatten them before they start!"

"Amen!" said Szafran. "From your mouth to God's ears!"

Chapter 25

The Match

The first news to reach them was catastrophic, with Russian withdrawals and encirclements everywhere. The extent of the débâcle could be inferred from the way the *chappers* again strutted about the camp. However the internees tried to reassure themselves with Russia's well-tried strategy of withdrawing deep into their own territory, to extend the enemy's supply lines. Therefore the alleged German successes did not unduly alarm them or dampen their optimism.

To mark the dramatic turn of events the internees decided to hold a football match, to which the camp authorities did not object. The German successes swelled their heads and made them magnanimous; besides Italians loved soccer.

Because of the preponderance of Polish Jews, it was agreed that 'Poland' should play 'The Rest'. The young were eager to prepare a football pitch of some sort. The only sizeable piece of land sloped steeply toward the Crati, but this did not matter because the teams changed ends at halftime. The pitch was cleared of stones and countless buckets of water softened the ground until its unyielding crust gave softly beneath their feet. Chalk was found to outline the confines of the pitch; two uprights were rammed into the ground as goalposts and the problem of crossbars was solved with a length of string. It was quite amazing what teamwork and enthusiasm could achieve.

Despite 'Poland's' superiority from which to select a team, the opposition was no pushover, as it consisted of Czech, Hungarian and Austrian players, all with a high reputation for soccer artistry. Dvorak selected the Polish team, but apart from Feuerroth, Pomorski and himself, who were in a class of their own, there were no players of outstanding talent. Henry did not consider himself good enough to be included. Sonia and her husband were reputed to be enthusiastic football fans. They'd hardly ever missed a match as fanatical supporters of Milan and Juventus.

Ossi was well aware of Sonia's love of soccer. Understandably he wanted to please her as well as to shine. On medical advice he used to only play in goal as a child so he'd acquired considerable expertise in that position and now he offered himself as goalie. Dvorak was not impressed but as there was no one better, Ossi got the job.

Both teams trained passionately, which considering their extreme malnourishment, was quite remarkable. It was truly a case of mind over matter.

While all these feverish preparations were taking place the German troops had not been idle either. They seemed to go from victory to victory. Lvov, where Henry's parents and siblings had taken refuge after the *Anschluss*, had fallen. Worried and anxious as he was about their fate, he was aware that he was not the only one whose family was in danger. Besides, the internees were all trying hard to reassure each other that during their campaign the Germans had weightier things on their minds than to bother themselves with Jews. Some optimists opined that there was no reason to worry as the German invaders would be repulsed anyway in no time. But calamitous news continued and suddenly, now that they were triumphant, newspapers became officially available at the provision stores. Eye-catching headlines in fat print announced boastfully: 'Pincer movements close on hundreds of thousands of Russian soldiers'; 'Over two thousand aeroplanes destroyed on the ground'; 'Thousands of Russian tanks knocked out'. The agents had become arrogant and self-important; the internees crestfallen and downcast. Batyushka Borstyn did his best to reassure them.

"Gentlemen! Why so little faith? Napoleon even occupied Moscow and you know what end he came to!"

Camerata 3 soon suffered a loss of a different kind; little *Tikvah*, their mascot and 'hope' had died five days after her capture. No one knew why she had died for she had accepted food the day before, some lettuce and a worm. Wolf was heartbroken.

"I did all I could for her," he cried, wiping a tear from his sad eyes.

Henry tried to console him.

"I'm sure you did. The truth is this damned place is hardly the *Garden of Eden*."

Despite his shrug of acceptance, Henry felt stabs of remorse at having removed the innocent little creature from the dark cool waters where she had swum freely to her untimely death in a small camp bucket. With her head deeply retracted in her coat of mail and her eyes closed, she looked so pathetic in death. They buried Tikvah—Hope—under the oak, with heavy hearts.

Life goes on and hope, as they say, springs eternal. After all, what is left without it?

Finally the big day of the football match arrived; people were glad to forget their worries. They dressed up for the occasion and flocked to the pitch in good time 'to get a good seat'. As usual the elegant Sonia outshone all the other women. She wore a light blue suit, white sandals with a wide-brimmed hat, her eyes covered by a pair of large dark glasses. She attracted so much attention that Henry felt conspicuous sitting beside her.

"My husband would have been so excited if he'd been here."

Henry had wished to ask the pertinent question for some time, but had refrained for reasons of tact.

"Why is your husband not with you?"

Evidently Henry had touched on a delicate spot, for she coloured as she replied, "He's hiding. His Italian friends protect him for their own selfish reasons. He is good for business."

"But what about you? Wouldn't you rather have him here?"

Sonia looked the other way, waving at some people to collect herself before she replied.

"It doesn't matter what I want. Evidently his business comes first," and after a pause she added, "besides, he could not provide for us if he were here."

The footballers came out on to the field. Ossi was immaculate in dark blue shorts and white shirt. His jet-black hair could be easily spotted from a distance. Ossi's eyes seemed to range through the crowd, until they found the object of their search; he smiled and waved and then he came over to greet them.

"You look fine, Ossi," said Sonia, putting her hand on his shoulder.

He looked deep into her eyes.

"See you after the match, Sonia," and then turning to Henry he implored, "please don't quarrel with her!" and left, as excited as a knight wearing his lady's colours.

The game began erratically and for the first ten minutes many a pass landed among the crowd.

"Hey Dvorak! Forgotten your specs?!" yelled Moishele.

The referee seemed rather whistle-happy for he blew the damned thing at the slightest pretext. It seemed the game would never get into second gear with passes going nowhere and no one prepared to take a chance. People gradually got fed up with the lack of progress and continuous stoppages of the match.

"Hey ref! Get yourself a lollipop and leave the bloody whistle alone!"

Then suddenly Pomorski got the ball. He was a first-class winger, had perfect ball control, a turn of speed and knew how to ride a dirty tackle. Pomorski accelerated and centred the ball with precision into Feuerroth's path, and he slammed the ball with a beautiful volley into the goal! 'Poland's' supporters went frantic.

"Bravo Pomorski! Bravo Feuerroth!" they shrieked.

But their jubilation was not to last long. Trebitsch, the Austrian sportsman, determined to retrieve the honour of his team, made a solo run, beat one defender, chipped the ball high in front of the goal and Horvath, a Czech, nodded the ball in, as simple as that. It was not Ossi's fault as his view had been obstructed. This time a hysterical outburst came from those supporting 'The Rest'.

For a time the game fluctuated, but gradually 'The Rest' seemed to gain the upper hand. Trebitsch, Dino and Horvath each had a shot blocked by Ossi's clever goalkeeping. On one occasion, when the situation seemed desperate, Ossi had to throw himself at Horvath's feet to prevent a goal and was kicked in the chest. It was a hefty kick and must have hurt. Henry was very impressed. He'd never expected Ossi to perform so well.

"Isn't he good?" asked Sonia, smiling.

"He certainly is." *He's playing like the knights of old, for his Lady, La Belle Dame sans merci,* observed Henry to himself.

The referee blew his whistle for halftime. One all. The teams changed ends. Ossi sat down by a goalpost and rested his back against it. He looked rather pale, occasionally pressing his hand against his chest. That kick must have hurt; Henry admired his spirit and waved at him encouragingly.

The Poles started the second half refreshed and with fire in their bellies; they intended to beat 'The Rest' into submission before they knew what had hit them. They were all thunder and lightning. Pomorski and Feuerroth dominated the field, playing havoc with the opposition. Young Scholz had to make several spectacular saves and earned hearty applause from both sides. Pomorski, lithe as a hare, weaved his way unerringly towards the goal, but this time he was unable to ride the crude tackle of a defender, who chopped his legs from under him. There was a loud cry of indignation from the Polish partisans as poor Pomorski writhed in pain on the ground. A free kick was awarded, but it was no compensation for the loss of a player of Pomorski's class. Dvorak, the captain, had to rearrange his team. A hobbling Pomorski was no good on the wing, but since he was an all-rounder, capable of filling most positions, Dvorak decided to play him in goal. Ossi was not much of a winger, but even he might be better than an injured, limping player.

With the threat of Pomorski eliminated, 'The Rest' grew bolder and piled pressure upon pressure, until Trebitsch scored with a fine first time drive. Two to one for 'The Rest'. Their supporters went frantic and yelled themselves hoarse. There were only ten minutes left for play and 'the Rest' seemed to have victory in the bag. Their supporters spurred them on with electrifying yells and exhortations. No one bothered about Ossi on the right wing, as he had neither Pomorski's speed nor his skill so they could afford to throw all their defenders into attack. But unexpectedly a desperate kick from a Polish defender found Ossi completely unmarked. Sensing his great moment, he ran as he had never run in his life before. There was no one to obstruct and so, from a few yards he shot at goal. His luck held. The ball, after hitting a post, rolled slowly over the goal line. The ensuing uproar of howls and screams was indescribable. Ossi had retrieved the honour of the Poles minutes before the final whistle and the result, a draw, was most satisfying to all. Good old Ossi had saved the day for Poland! After the usual exchange of sporting niceties, amid back slapping and cheering, the crowd, in great spirits with no winners or losers to mar the atmosphere, began to disperse. They had truly had their money's worth, especially as they didn't have to pay anyway.

Sonia looked for Ossi but couldn't find him. "Where is he hiding, our hero? Anyway, I have to get the children's supper ready...see you later," and she hurried away.

As Henry was going back to his *camerata*, he bumped into Yadranka.

"Long time no see." Her voice had an icy inflection.

"You know I'm working and out of the camp most of the day."

Yadranka had a would-be enigmatic smile of her lips. "I saw you sitting just now with a very smart woman."

"She's a friend of my pal's."

"Is that so?" she said, this time her voice laced with irony. "You must be a very trustworthy friend then. Well, see you some time," and she turned away and left.

Her snub hurt a little, but he brushed it aside, eager as he was to find Ossi and congratulate him on his fine performance. But no matter where he looked, he couldn't find him anywhere and so he went back to the *camerata*, where to his surprise he found Ossi stretched out flat on his palliasse.

"Where the devil have you been? Sonia and I have been searching everywhere for you!"

Ossi did not reply, but kept staring at the ceiling. Then he stretched his palm onto his chest.

"I have such a pain here. That blessed idiot kicked me so hard."

"Well," said Henry reassuringly, "I'm sure it will soon pass," and stretched himself out too. "How does it feel to be the hero of the day?"

Ossi seemed to take little notice of his remark.

What is the matter with him? thought Henry. *Have I offended him in some way?*

Unexpectedly Ossi got up. "I am going out for some fresh air. I can hardly breathe in here," he muttered.

Henry was puzzled. *What's going on? Have I upset him?*

However he didn't mind being left on his own for a while. After the excitement of the match he felt in the right frame of mind for enjoying a cigarette in peace. He rested his head in the crook of his arm, inhaled deeply and watched the bluish trail of smoke spiralling up. Pity Yadranka was upset with him. He didn't mean to hurt her feelings.

Suddenly Dino rushed in, distraught and panic-stricken.

"Henry! Henry! Quick!" His voice trembled. A strange apprehension crept over Henry. This was the first time Dino had ever called him by his proper name. "Quick! Come quick!" Dino yelled. "Ossi has collapsed!"

Henry shot up and ran out to the courtyard. There was Ossi, lying on the ground, his face drained of all blood, his forehead covered in sweat, frothing at the mouth. Henry shook him. "Ossi! Ossi! What is it?"

Only a rattle came from Ossi's throat.

"Get the syringe and coramine!" screamed Henry. Ossi's pulse was hardly perceptible. More and more froth was coming from his mouth, then a loud wheeze. The coramine was injected intravenously, with no effect.

"There's no pulse!" cried Dino. "He's not breathing! Artificial respiration!"

"Ossi for God's sake...Ossi?" Henry shouted at him desperate for some response.

People began to appear and concerned whispers turned into panic as more and more onlookers arrived to witness the dreadful scene of Ossi lying in the dust, skin pale as milk, black hair soaked in sweat and bright red blood gurgling from his mouth.

Henry and Dino began to compress his chest and extend his arms above his head in rhythmic motions, calling at him, shouting at him to hang on, and barking at the crowd to give him some air. Their shouts became sobs as they exhorted him to come back to them, not to die, their voices hoarse, hysterical. Ossi was dying and they could do nothing.

They continued artificial respiration in despair while a swelling crowd stared, horrified. Slowly the terrible reality began to dawn; still they continued their efforts not daring to stop for that would mean the unthinkable. But after ten minutes they had to face the reality: that fine, talented, handsome, vibrant, young man was indeed dead. It had all happened so quickly. Ossi, who only an hour before had been the hero of the match, was dead. It was inconceivable and utterly heart-breaking.

Dr Gottlieb, an experienced middle-aged internist from Prague, came to the courtyard.

"Had he ever suffered from any heart disease?" he enquired of the distraught friends sitting on the ground, around Ossi's dust-covered still body, wiping their eyes in total disbelief.

"Some degree of valvular heart disease, following rheumatic fever," said Dino, through his tears.

Dr Gottlieb shook his head.

"He must have suffered a massive pulmonary embolism. He should have known better than to play football with such a heart."

Other doctors arrived. Dr Frankel from Vienna asked more questions. Some specialists disagreed with the diagnosis and spoke of coronary thrombosis, acute cardiac failure and so on.

All this talk, what use is it? thought Henry. *What difference does it make what he died of? He is dead, isn't he? Barely twenty-seven years old.*

Dino crouched down by the lifeless Ossi his eyes streaming with tears, his chest heaving with heart breaking sobs. Henry stood speechless, shattered, shaken to the core, dazed and unable to grasp the reality of what had just taken place, before his very eyes. Henry couldn't cry. He never had been able to, not even when his beloved Mundek died.

"That blow to the chest must have mobilised an embolus," persisted Dr Gottlieb. "And that final run of his must have clinched the issue. It was the *coup de grâce.*"

The news of Ossi's death swept through the camp like wildfire; more and more people swarmed into the courtyard. Ossi was still lying on the ground, his black eyes staring into space, his face ashen. Henry closed his eyelids. Young Scholz, who was very attached to Ossi, wept convulsively. He was devastated. Heartbroken.

"Such a kind, generous and handsome young man," he sobbed, "and he had to die in this lousy concentration camp!"

Henry was lost for words. He just put an arm round young Scholz's shoulders. Batyushka Borstyn stood pale and silent, wiping away a tear. Wolf and Lubicz both cried unashamedly. The crowd of onlookers comforted one another, shaking their heads, muttering their sorrow for the loss of the heroic Dr Gerber who had never said a bad word to or about anyone.

"Why don't you lift him and place him somewhere decent?" came a shrill voice.

The ring of people split to let her pass. Sonia, still in the same festive attire she had worn at the football match, went up to Ossi's body and knelt beside him. She took his hand, brushed his hair from his forehead and then she got up. Her eyes were red, her face ashen and her hands trembled as she tried to steady herself.

"We cannot leave him lying here like a dog in the gutter," she said firmly.

Henry's first reaction at the sight of her was one of anger, bordering on hate. *If it had not been for you,* he thought, *Ossi would still be alive. He only played in that match to please you!*

Something of Henry's thoughts and feelings must have shown in his eyes for when she met them Sonia seemed to shudder, and lowered her own immediately. *The bloody bitch!* thought Henry. *She made a fool of him.*

People wished to pay their last respects. "Such a fine young man;" "a real gentleman;" "A good doctor and so young;" "Handsome like a film star." And so it went on.

Dino and Henry lifted Ossi's slender body and carried it to his bed. Later that evening it was moved into Sabatini's hut.

"We are to blame," said Dino. "We should have known better. We should never have allowed him to play."

Henry was quiet. He looked uncomfortable with the thought.

"It's no good blaming ourselves. True, we had heard of his rheumatic fever. Some valvular leakage was also vaguely mentioned, but it never amounted to much. He led a normal life."

"Did he?" asked Dino. "Don't you remember how breathless he got after very light exertion, or a quick run?"

Now, with hindsight, it was easy to put two and two together. Henry remembered how out of breath Ossi had been after that run from Sonia's hut, and many other pointers. *Yes! I ought to have seen. I ought to have used my clinical judgement. But how does one prevent an adult, a doctor, from leading his own life?*

But Dino went on in the same self-accusatory vein.

"There is no getting away from it. We should have taken greater care of him. After all, we are both qualified physicians!"

"All right Dino!" he protested. I will accept my share of guilt; but where does that get us? Will it bring Ossi back?"

It was suggested that Ossi's parents ought to be informed. Only a week ago this might have been possible. But now, with the German advance, how was anyone to know where his parents were hiding? Besides, they must have enough troubles of their own in their present predicament. What good would it do to add to their burden?

Henry did not sleep that night and it is doubtful whether anybody else in the *camerata* did.

"First little *Tikvah* and then Dr Gerber," lamented Wolf. "There is not much blessing on our heads just now."

According to Jewish law, originating in the subtropical climate of ancient Israel, Ossi's corpse had to be buried the following day. A simple, rough-hewn coffin was handed over by the camp authorities. Only a limited number of close friends were supposed to attend the funeral but the authorities were generous on this occasion and permitted a huge procession to follow the coffin bearers to the cemetery.

Hearts were sad, but the sun shone brightly on that June morning.

"It's almost a sin to be buried on such a beautiful day," murmured Szafran, wiping tears from his eyes.

Moishele Perlman's face was grave and worn. His spaniel eyes looked even sadder than usual, revealing the deep-rooted melancholy of this man, who hid his feelings under the mask of a clown.

Dino, Henry and Ossi had been to the cemetery before, when Mr Meiersohn's body was laid there to rest. On that occasion Ossi was walking. Now, he had to be carried.

How strange life is, reflected Henry. *Who would have thought that Dr Ossi Gerber, the suave, sophisticated Ossi, brought up in Poland's 'Little Paris', the same Ossi who'd studied in Montpellier, Florence and Genoa and who loved the haunts of the French Riviera, would end his life's short journey in a remote, nondescript town in Calabria?*

The gravedigger had done his work. Like Meiersohn's resting place, it was close by the wall. Another burial of an outcast. The moment had come to lower the coffin. There was no Rabbi to say the prescribed prayers, but Mr Librowicz recited 'El maleh Rachamin', 'Merciful God'. The weeping and sobbing increased until Henry, who was usually shy of public exhibitions, felt compelled to speak.

> *"Dear friend, you're home. We none of us know where we will end. Your troubles are over. The ancient Greeks believed that those whom the gods love, die young. I do not know whether the gods loved you, but all of us here certainly did. Farewell, dear friend. Bon voyage."*

A hand clasped his wrist. It was Sonia's. His first impulse was to draw away, but he overcame it. She looked broken, yet her bearing was solemn and dignified. Mourners threw a handful of earth onto the coffin; there were no flowers in accordance with the Hebrew tradition. Mourning and flowers do not go well together in the Jewish way of thinking. Jews do not embellish grief. They submit to its undiluted impact, and so the mound looked desolate and bare. It was heart-breaking to think of Ossi, entombed in the summer of his life, without even a stone to mark the resting place of his mortal remains. *Sic transit gloria mundi.*

It was time to go back to the camp. The agents began to show signs of impatience. "It's getting late, *andiamo!*" One last look at the grave, and they left.

Chapter 26

Life goes on

The tragedy of pain is not so much the way it hurts, but the way it passes. Even the most atrocious grief and heartache fades until it almost ceases. True, pain leaves scars, but these are usually buried in a secret shrine, only to burst into consciousness occasionally and the rest of the time, with a little effort, they don't intrude.

So gradually life in Ferramonti returned to normal, if such a description can apply to the existence in a concentration camp. Henry resumed his work in the pine wood, glad for the distraction from thoughts of Ossi's tragic death. He looked forward to the daily routine, the tinkling of the bell and the exchange of news and merchandise with Maria; the semblance of freedom it offered.

One day Maria presented herself wearing an unusual costume, a bright blue and gold skirt with strange-looking ornate trinkets and bracelets.

"You look so nice today, Maria! But what are all these strange ornaments you are wearing?"

Maria chuckled. "You know, I am not really Italian. Many of us in Calabria came over from Albania. Our ancestors ran away from the Turks about five hundred years ago. But we still follow their traditions."

Henry was surprised. "I did not know you were a 'foreigner' too, Maria. But why are you wearing your national costume today?"

"It's an Albanian holiday. A celebration; something to do with our hero Skandaberg."

Strange, this innate craving to cling to one's ancestral roots, thought Henry, *to preserve one's identity, however worn and faded it becomes.*

"Where is your home, Maria?"

She pointed at some heights beyond the Crati. "Over there in the hills."

"Quite a distance from here, isn't it?"

"It's far enough, but I have to make a living. My husband's in the army. All I have is Ciuccio. I'd be lost without my donkey." She turned and patted her shaggy little friend, putting her arms about his neck with affection.

"Do you have any children?"

"No, not yet" she replied, coyly.

Henry liked Maria. She always had been fair in her dealings with the internees and was content with a small profit, just to keep her going. It was the common bond of 'underdogship' that endeared her to the internees, and them likewise to her.

For a week or so after Ossi's death, Sonia did not come to Henry's *camerata*. He had seen her in the distance but did his best to avoid her. Now for the first time she was waiting for him on his return from work.

"I hope you don't mind my being here, but I need some provisions." Though her face bore traces of the recent emotional impact, she was as impeccably dressed as ever and this had an irritating effect on Henry. His eyes narrowed.

"What do you need?" he asked dourly.

"Anything you can spare."

Henry busied himself rummaging in his rucksack, avoiding looking her in the face.

"Henry."

"Yes?"

"You are avoiding me. Why?"

"What makes you think so?"

"You saw me the other day but pretended not to."

Henry did not reply. He was not going to be drawn into an argument; he was not in the mood.

"I must have upset you in some way, but I don't know how; I only feel it must have something to do with Ossi."

Henry cut her short.

"Sonia, I am tired from work and not in the mood for analysis. Just take those eggs and mortadella. We can settle the account another time. I have a bad headache."

Sonia looked downcast. His harsh way of shutting her up left her silent and hurt. Seeing the expression on her face, Henry felt a little sorry for his brusque manner.

"We can talk some other time. Perhaps tomorrow."

So she collected her victuals and left.

Henry stretched himself out on his palliasse as he always did after work. He felt disgruntled and dissatisfied with himself. Something in him prevented him from examining his own feelings. It seemed as if an invisible barrier, self-erected, had arisen to impede his thoughts from deeper penetration.

A heated discussion was going on in the *camerata*.

"I am afraid our Ruskis are not doing too well," said Szafran. "The Nazis... *der Schlag soll sie treffen* ... are reported to be on their way to Smolensk and threatening Kiev in the South."

"Let them threaten!" broke in Borstyn. "Nobody dies from threats!"

Henry was reluctant to get involved in their discussions, but observed nevertheless, "Mr Borstyn, did you really expect the Germans to advance so fast?"

Batyushka Borstyn came over to sit beside Henry's bed.

"Supposing they have advanced a hundred, three hundred kilometres, so what does that matter? Russia extends from the Pripet marshes to Vladivostok! Many, many thousands of miles! I'm not alarmed in the slightest."

Let's hope he is right, mused Henry, and went out to have a thorough wash after the day's work. While he held his head under the tap, Dvorak slapped him on the shoulder.

"Heard the latest? Two internees are missing."

"Who told you?"

"One of the *chappers*."

"Who is missing?"

"They're not sure yet, but it seems as if it's Sokolov and that Italian Jew, Benedicenti, from Torino."

Soon after this news broke, all *capi camerata* were summoned to the *comandante*'s office. Henry did not relish the idea of meeting Signor Rizzi again, though he did not entirely dislike him.

On arriving at the 'White House' they were ushered into Signor Rizzi's office almost immediately. There was not much room for all the *capi,* so they had to squeeze in as well as they could. Signor Rizzi sat at his desk surveying them in silence. With studied deliberation, his eyes scanned each member of the delegation.

"I am sure you know why I have sent for you."

No one replied, so he went on. "We Italians have a long tradition of chivalry. We treat our prisoners humanely. Anyone disagree?"

Again no one spoke.

"We have let you run your own affairs without too much interference, but apparently this was not appreciated by some of you." Picking up his riding crop, he swung it round with circular movements of his wrist, then suddenly he hit the desk with it. "So what the hell do you think will happen? We'll have to tighten up security and make life more unpleasant for everyone!"

"With due respect, Signor Rizzi, why punish us all because of the irresponsible behaviour of two stupid men?" This was Dr Bernheim speaking.

Signor Rizzi listened attentively, but he screwed up his forehead and his lips lifted in a sardonic smile.

"So I suppose I ought to give you all a bonus for not running away. Nonsense! Some people only learn the hard way!"

Having said this, the comandante seemed lost in thought; or was he only taking his time, to keep the *capi* on tenterhooks? He straightened himself up and his expression changed almost to a degree of benevolence.

"Things are going well for us. The Soviets are *kaput*! Soon the war may be all over. So I don't want to make a big issue of this stupid escape of two misguided fools. They'll be caught anyway."

He picked up a pencil and started pounding his desk with it, unable to dispense with his bit of showmanship.

"Some restrictions will have to be enforced. Escapes will give this camp a bad reputation. So, after sunset no one is to leave his *camerata*, except to go to the latrines. Further, it will be the duty of each *capo camerata* to check the number of occupants and to report immediately if anyone is missing. Understood?"

He looked at them, one by one. "I'm letting you off lightly this time, but don't imagine I shall be as lenient in future!"

The interview was over.

Everyone felt relieved. It was not too bad after all. Considering the Axis powers were riding on the crest of a wave Henry would have expected much more flamboyance from the comandante, unless in spite of his swagger he was playing safe.

Next morning on their way to work, there was a noticeable change in the agents. Previously their march had been free and easy, but this time the order *"In fila di tre!"* was given.... "in threes!"

However, as soon as the group was past the camp sentry, discipline slackened again; the agents were as casual as ever. The internees had simply to remain in sight during their work sessions; the guards enjoyed their *Chianti* and lounged about as usual.

After work, Henry found Sonia back in the *camerata*, chatting to Borstyn. She greeted Henry with a tentative smile overlaying a basic apprehension.

"Have you brought me anything?"

"Some butter and a small piece of bacon."

Sonia seemed ill at ease in the *camerata*, so Henry suggested they went outside to settle their account. Once this was done there was an embarrassed silence. Sonia took her courage in both hands. "You promised you'd talk things over with me."

"So what is there to talk over?"

"Plenty," said Sonia firmly.

"Such as what?"

"Why you have such a grudge against me that you avoid me."

No good beating about the bush. She had asked a direct question, which required a direct answer. "I don't want to upset you, but since you insist, I must be frank. I believe Ossi would still be alive but for you."

She gasped in shock, her hand to her mouth. "Why, for God's sake?" she asked in an anguished whisper.

"Ossi would never have dreamed of playing in that match but for you. He wanted to impress you, and with his heart condition ..."

Sonia interrupted him. "But how could I know? I never knew there was anything wrong with his heart. Did you?"

She had touched upon a delicate spot, for here was the crux of the matter.

"Yes I did."

"And what did you do about it? Did you try to stop him?" Henry lowered his head. "No, I didn't. But I did not realise how seriously his heart was affected. It never showed much….." His voice trailed off.

Sonia's face hardened, a flicker of reproach crept into her eyes.

"You did know his heart was affected. Nevertheless you didn't think there was much wrong with him? You are a physician. I am not. I didn't even know about his heart disease. So how can that make me guilty?"

What she said was all too true; her logic was quite irrefutable. However, as is so often the case when a man is pushed into a corner by the weight of an argument, Henry abandoned reason and took refuge in an emotional outburst.

"I know all that!" he replied angrily, "but Ossi's whole personality and behaviour had changed because of you. He became soft and silly, like a dressed-up monkey!"

Sonia remained silent, waiting for Henry's anger to peter out. Deep down, Henry was well aware that his rage and fury were irrational; after all, Ossi was at liberty to act and behave as he wanted to, but he was not going to admit it. Not even to himself.

"So what is it you're accusing me of? That Ossi had taken a liking to me? That I should have tried to prevent it by giving him the cold shoulder? Did his liking me kill him? Or was it his heart disease?"

Again Henry erupted. "You should have left him alone!"

His voice was full of bitterness, but as he uttered it, he realised the sheer stupidity of his remark. Sonia had not forced Ossi to fall in love with her. He was a grown man. Still, Henry was determined to stand his ground.

"I think enough has been said today. Let's leave it at that."

He left her stranded where she was. He did not bother to shake hands.

As he was about to enter his *camerata*, Henry's gloom was lifted as he saw Moishele chasing something in the courtyard.

Above his head he wielded a stick, bringing it down periodically to hit something on the ground. No one was ever surprised by Moishele's antics. He often pretended to do something unusual to get people's attention, then he'd laugh in their faces because he had fooled them. This time, however, it seemed as if he was up to something in earnest.

"What are you up to, Moishele?" asked Henry, glad for the distraction from his encounter with Sonia.

"Chasing lizards," Moishele replied, breathlessly continuing his chase.

"Lizards? Are you mad? What do you need lizards for?"

Moishele looked at him, surprised. "What do I need lizards for, he asks? Why, for my eagle, or buzzard, or hawk — or whatever he is."

Again it was impossible to tell whether Moishele was joking.

"Since when have you had an eagle?" enquired Henry, suspicious of some trick afoot.

Moishele shook his head from side to side, as if abandoning a hopeless case.

"That shows how much you know about camp life. Don't you know I got it from the cemetery? He must have fallen out of his nest in the wall; or else he tried his wings and came a cropper."

Even now Henry was not convinced the story was true.

"Why didn't you show it to me before?"

Moishele was losing all patience.

"Why didn't I show it to him before? Hear that? When do we have the honour of seeing you at all? At seven in the morning, when every self-respecting Jew dreams of *borsht* or Jerusalem or simply snores his head off, he chooses to go out with the *goyim* to chop wood in the forest. Then he comes back about six, more dead than alive, starving and just in time for *appello!*"

He suddenly darted away, chasing the poor little reptile into a corner, where he finished it off with a blow of his stick.

"Got you, you brute." He picked up the lizard and held it dangling by its tail.

Henry was nauseated by the half-squashed reptile.

"You are the brute! Why did you have to take a fledgling?"

"It was on the ground! Almost fully grown. Besides, it had two piercing black eyes and a sharp eagle's face, just like Dr Gerber's."

Henry said no more. *Strange,* he mused, *how from a place of death, Moishele has managed to bring back something alive.*

Chapter 27

Forgiveness

Next day, when Henry came back from work, Sonia was not waiting for him, nor the day after. Instead of feeling relieved he was irritated. Her words at their last encounter still reverberated in his mind, despite his attempts to suppress them.

Having nothing better to do, he went over for a look at Moishele's bird. He found Moishele in the midst of a poker game, but as soon as he saw Henry, his clown face broke into a broad grin. When Moishele smiled his whole face joined in with every one of its many folds and wrinkles.

"Hello! Nice to see you for a change. Tired of labouring? Come and join in some intelligent work."

"No thank you. I've come to see your bird."

Moishele was pleased. "Welcome to the zoo," and pointing to his gaming pals he added, "this is the asses section. Now I'll take you to the birds and show you my eagle."

They went into Moishele's courtyard and there to Henry's surprise was a well-constructed aviary, made of wooden sticks and wire netting.

"Not bad," said Henry, who with pigeons and canaries had learnt many aspects of aviculture.

"Not bad," he repeated, recalling with a little twinge of his heart, the flight cages Mundek had constructed for the young canaries.

"Eagle my foot!" he said eventually, inspecting the bird at closer range. "Not even a hawk. Most likely a buzzard or an owl of some sort." The bird was perching on a branch inserted inside the cage. "But you've done a very neat job, Moishele."

"Thank you for the compliment. Shall I feed him for you?" He opened a tin can and took out a dead lizard. "He really likes them fresh — the brute — when they are still twitching; but he's adapted to prison diet, like the rest of us." Moishele pushed the lizard's head through the wire mesh and the bird grabbed it immediately and gulped it down.

"Well, what do you think of him? A real *nosher*. The trouble is I cannot keep up with him. All I do is chase lizards."

"How did you know what to feed him?"

"We've got a vet in our camerata. He's told me they eat mice, insects and snails."

Henry laughed. "So why do you feed him on lizards?"

Moishele made an impatient gesture as if to indicate he was getting tired of the slow-motion brain of his interlocutor.

"Where the hell do I find mice here? They'd have died of hunger on our starvation diet. And snails like moisture. Have you seen any snails in this Sahara? The only creatures that prosper are lizards. That's why. *Capito*?"

Henry had to laugh at Moishele's logic and practical sense. "Do you ever vary his diet?"

"I give him insects if I can find them. Besides, Mrs Heller sometimes brings me a few scraps of meat."

"Is that so? By the way, how is she?" Henry asked casually, "I have not seen her lately."

"Sonia? She's been sick in bed for the last two days." He stopped abruptly. Moishele had built-in tact. Despite his loud mouth and mocking ways he knew where to draw the line; but he soon recovered his poise.

"Would you like to come with me to see her? I'm sure that would cheer her up."

Henry hesitated. "I don't really know."

"What's there to know? Why make an issue of it? Come on!"

As an old friend of the Heller family, Moishele unceremoniously went in and out of Sonia's hut. They found her in her dressing gown. She did not look well at all, but seeing the two of them, her face lit up. "Oh! How nice of you to come."

Henry felt uneasy. "I was told you were ill in bed," he said apologetically, as if to justify his visit.

"I've only just got up to cook some food for the children." In spite of her illness the room was clean and as orderly as the cramped space would allow. "Won't you sit down?" she gestured to the only chair.

Moishele scratched his head. "Look Sonia, you know I don't stand on ceremony, but soon there will be *appello* and first I must catch some crocodiles for my vulture. Tell you what. You stay a bit, doctor, and keep her company and if there is time, I'll come back. All right?" Moishele went and there was an embarrassed silence. Henry glanced at her sideways. She did not look her usual self.

"I think I owe you an apology." She did not reply, so he went on. "Perhaps I haven't been quite fair to you. I have done a good deal of thinking recently. You asked whether it was Ossi liking you or his heart disease that killed him. No doubt it was his heart ... perhaps you shouldn't have encouraged him ..."

"I didn't!" Sonia broke in.

"Anyway, to some extent I may have used you as a scapegoat for my own guilt feelings." She made no comment, but sat closer to him. "You are right, of course. Both Dino and I ought to have known better. But you know the proverb: there are none as blind as those who will not see."

This time Sonia broke her silence.

"There is no point in blaming yourself either. Blind or not blind, had you realised how ill he really was, Dino and you would certainly have stopped him, or at least tried to."

Henry looked wretched as he went over the events of Ossi's death, so Sonia tried to divert his attention. "Would you like something to drink?"

She felt intuitively what was going on inside him for despite all her reasoning and logic she blamed herself too. Surely, like most women, she was flattered by Ossi's attentions, but she had not encouraged them. They were all in the wrong. Since Henry had not replied, Sonia renewed her question. "Can I offer you a drink?"

"No thank you. I'd better go, the appello..."

"That blessed *appello*! If it didn't exist, it would have to be invented, like the Jews."

Henry was intrigued, but this was no time for quarrels and as she put out her hand he bent and kissed it this time, perhaps because she looked ill and pathetic without her fancy makeup and he did feel a little sorry for her.

Chapter 28

Below the Belt

The work in the forest carried on and Henry wondered how many more bundles that glade would yield. It was the same routine day in, day out, but being out of the camp gave a fleeting sense of freedom which never lost its appeal.

"One day," said Maria, "when the war is over and my husband is back from the army, you must come to visit us."

It was as well he had the opportunity to accept her invitation that day, for when he got back to camp he was greeted with the disquieting news of two further escapes. Probably the failure to recapture the first pair had encouraged others. Henry expected the *capi camerata* to be sent for again but Signor Rizzi did not even bother. Instead he issued orders which were passed by the agents and also posted up in front of the *questura*, the camp police station

- It is forbidden to leave the *camerata* after the last roll call
- The number of guards will be doubled, with orders to shoot on sight anyone outside his *camerata* after sunset
- All voluntary work outside the camp to cease forthwith
- All privileges, football matches, bathing in the canal to be withdrawn
- Further restrictions will be imposed in the case of any insubordination

It sounded bad. One particular order affected Henry vitally. He would no longer be allowed to work in the wood. This was quite serious, dependent as he was on that little extra money and the supplies of provisions. Still he was lucky to have enjoyed his privilege for so long, so he would just have to accept this change of fortunes philosophically although he wondered how he would manage.

Since his last visit to Sonia he had not seen her for some time, but he was not going to call on her on his own. Not in this camp, where gossip was most people's sole means of escapism. He was determined to keep out of her way, though he couldn't work out why. The latest camp orders, however, prompted Sonia to pay him a visit.

"I have just read these new orders. I do feel so sorry for you."

"We are all in the same boat."

"I know, but you did love your outdoor work and you needed the money."

"Never mind, I'll survive."

Then, unbidden, Sonia sat herself beside his bed.

"You will tell me if you need anything, won't you?"

Henry smiled vaguely.

She took out a packet and offered him a cigarette. "I've had a big parcel from Milan."

Henry accepted. It tasted marvellous. He looked at the brand. "Xanthia! I used to smoke them too—once. They are really Egyptian. I am surprised you can still get them today."

She laughed ruefully. "If you can pay the price, you can get anything…war or not."

"By the way, how will you manage, now that I no longer work outside?"

Sonia disposed of that with a contemptuous wave. "No problem there. There is a saying: a donkey laden with gold can surmount the highest walls of any fortress. Money will surely climb the barbed wire of Ferramonti."

Henry did not like that remark. In the present circumstances it sounded cynical and vulgar. He thought of the hundreds of other internees who were destitute, but he kept his thoughts to himself. Sonia fished in her bag for a bar of chocolate, broke a piece for herself and offered the rest to Henry.

"No, thank you. I don't eat chocolate." This was a blatant lie, as the sudden flicker in his eyes betrayed.

"You liar! Why won't you have it?"

Henry groped for a satisfactory answer. "I don't know, but somehow I'd feel mean and…"

"Nonsense!" she broke in. "Because there are so many folk starving in this camp have I to starve too? More than half of humanity exists at starvation level. Look at India, China. Does that mean I ought to choke each time I eat something?"

Her argument had the ring of logic but unfortunately — or fortunately — men do not live by logic alone.

"I'm not boasting," she resumed, "but at least half of my parcels go straight to my friends and neighbours."

This was true. Sonia was noted for her generosity. So he let himself be persuaded into accepting the chocolate though still reluctantly. For a while there was an uneasy silence.

"You are still very much on the defensive. Why, Henry?"

He looked at her, pretending surprise. "I thought we had cleared that up when we last talked things over."

"Not quite." She paused, lowering her head and her voice. "When we first spoke about this dreadful tragedy you said in your fury, 'You should have left him alone.' What precisely did you mean?"

Henry hesitated with his answer. "Frankly, I can't remember saying that, and if I did I don't know now what it meant."

But Sonia was not to be so easily brushed off and pressed him further.

"Let's get out of here" he said suddenly, getting up to leave, aware their conversation was attracting attention.

"Well?" she continued once they were outside and out of earshot.

"Why go on about it? I spoke in anger when one is inclined to hit below the belt."

Sonia smiled, a kind of 'knowing' smile.

"Never mind Henry, go on."

"What I meant," he said eventually, "was that your relationship was unsettling him, as well as exhausting him physically."

Sonia's eyes were shining and oddly triumphant.

"How did our relationship exhaust him physically? You thought I'd seduced him?"

Henry halted and so did she. He looked her squarely in the face.

"I have tried to avoid it, but if you will have it, then yes! I thought the physical demands of your relationship were draining him."

A bemused expression flitted across her face.

"Has it ever occurred to you with all your fine talk of psychology, analysis, etc. that you could be just plain jealous?"

To say Henry was shocked would be a gross understatement. He was confused and startled, all the more as he suddenly realised that what she said had penetrated the farthest recesses of his mind, causing something to click into place. Had Sonia taken a prodigious shortcut through all the intricate maze of his emotions, like Alexander cutting the Gordian knot?

"Let me tell you this, you great psychologist: a man who is as aggressive and offensive towards a woman as you have been from the start is only proclaiming his interest in her. Women know this instinctively without a diploma in psychology."

Henry was gradually recovering his poise. "I really don't know what to say to you. You baffle me!" But though he was putting on a cool front he was deeply unsettled.

"If it's any consolation to you," resumed Sonia, "I'm jealous too, of that woman in the camp you didn't wish to get involved with."

A strange sensation crept over Henry, a sensation as physical as an electric current, throbbing down his spine. But his lips broke into a smile as he shook his head.

"You amaze me, Sonia. You have a very vivid imagination."

Sonia smiled back. "No good pretending, Henry. This simple lesson is free of charge. But as you seem to have a slow conduction rate and take such a hell of a time to grasp things I'm leaving you now to digest it all."

Henry was left in a state of turmoil and utter confusion. With Sonia's last words still reverberating in his mind, he entered his *camerata*, where he was faced with another aspect of crude reality.

"Bad news *capo*," Szafran informed him. "Smolensk has fallen. And look at these headlines: Half a million Russians surrounded in Kiev."

This was even more catastrophic than the fall of Smolensk for even Russia with all its millions of people could not easily afford such huge losses in men and equipment. During the Napoleonic war, despite some fierce battles, Kotuzov managed to disengage most of his troops by retreating deeper inland. But Hitler's forces seemed bent on preventing this, cutting the lines of retreat with pincer movements. Under such circumstances it was just possible that history, for once, might not repeat itself. It was no good deluding oneself, the situation was grim. A heavy depression came over him. It was almost a physical experience of heaviness, a dead weight on his shoulders and a crushing oppressiveness in his chest. Things had been going gradually downhill of late: Ossi's tragic death, little *Tikvah* dying in captivity, his working permission revoked, the German invaders' triumph. And what about his hope of leaving the concentration camp on board a ship? That glimmer of hope had died together with Ossi's mortal remains. It would remain, what it had most likely been from the start, a fantastic dream of two hungry souls crying out for freedom.

That night he was unable to get to sleep. He tried counting sheep, he tried regulating his breathing, changing positions, but all in vain. Though the news from Russia was serious enough, he had to admit to himself that it was Sonia's unexpected revelation which had upset him more than the war bulletins. *Such is human nature,* he mused; *although man flatters himself he is rational, Homo Sapiens is basically an emotional entity, at the mercy of dark and contradictory impulses.* Must he acknowledge Sonia's allegations? Was he involved with her? Nonsense! How could he be? With such an ostentatious exhibitionist who throws money about? Besides, apart from anything else, she had been Ossi's woman. His body was still warm in the grave. The whole idea was preposterous!

"An abomination," he said aloud, pronouncing each syllable staccato.

And yet, he reflected, *man has always been attracted to and fascinated by abominations. That's why he needed the Ten Commandments and so many taboos. Oh! This blistering mattress, how could anyone get to sleep on it, even with a mind as serene as a cloudless sky?*

Some saying or motto was struggling to surface. He tried to recall the exact words because he felt they had a bearing on his predicament, but try as he may he couldn't. Was it conceiv-

able that with all her imperfections, her eccentric and ostentatious behaviour, he could really have such feelings for her?
No, it would be madness! Ah! That was it! He remembered all
of a sudden a quip made by Nietzsche: 'There is much madness in love, but there is also much reason in madness'.

Strangely enough, after he'd recalled these words he felt almost at peace, as if he had found justification for his *malaise*;
but soon after he smiled. Why look for such lofty, high-flown
words? Why not the simpler quip of his fellow students:
'When the little man is up, down slides the brain into the
arse's trap!' Soon after, he fell asleep.

Chapter 29

Sonia spins

Henry woke in the morning much fresher than he'd ever expected and caught himself even whistling, something he had not done for ages. Sleep is a very mysterious phenomenon. All kinds of complexities and paradoxes can solve themselves in Morpheus's arms. He had to admit that he was looking forward to meeting Sonia again. Though he could not fully accept her implications, he no longer repudiated them completely out of hand. Next time he was going to make sure that there was plain speaking. Moreover he was not going to look her up. If she wanted to see him, she knew where to find him; although it would be different if he ran into her by chance. Most likely at this early hour she would be looking for vegetables at the stores. Individual shoppers had to go early to beat the bulk buyers. No harm in just strolling over to the *piazza*.

In fact Henry found most of the kitchen chefs and buyers already assembled there, Linzer among them. As usual, he was engaged in animated conversation and gesticulation, but spotting Henry — his *protégé* — he immediately shifted all his attention to him.

"What are you doing here? Bored now, with no work?"

Henry shook his head. "Just strolling around."

Linzer was not that easily deceived. He had his finger on the camp's pulse, as well as his ear to the ground. Very little escaped him. Somehow Henry's unexpected appearance in front of the stores at such an early hour made him suspicious.

"Are you looking for something special? Or somebody?" he asked, watching him closely.

"I told you," replied Henry rather crossly, "just idling about."

Linzer changed the subject. "Well, have you seen our lost sheep yet? They are in a dreadful condition, unshaven, black and blue …"

"What are you talking about?" Henry broke in impatiently.

Linzer looked genuinely surprised. "So you don't know yet? They have caught our two migratory birds—the first lot that went—and brought them back last night."

"How do you know?"

"Never mind. They're under lock and key now."

"Where did they catch them?"

"Just north of Naples. Near Capua. Sokolov's face is swollen like a balloon, his lips are split and he has two lovely shiners. It was that agent from Turin—that one who used to give us the creeps—who caught him."

A queue was forming in front of the provision stores. Those with children had priority. Linzer seemed to spot someone in the queue which caused him immediately to throw Henry a quick, searching glance.

"Why, good morning, Mrs Heller. Doing your shopping?"

He was cute and had a shrewd knowledge of human frailties. Henry remained cool, pretending the encounter was nothing to him.

"Good morning, Mr Linzer" said Sonia. "Anything worth having in the stores?"

"There are some cucumbers and melons. Quite good and cheap."

"And how is Doctor Raupner?" Sonia asked as casually as she could. Henry merely bowed silently in reply. Sonia's turn came and after filling her bag, she gave them a friendly nod and was about to go when Linzer, with a faint smile, addressed Henry.

"Hey you, with the old world Viennese charm, how about carrying the lady's bag?"

Damn him, thought Henry, *there's no fooling him.*

"Allow me," he said, taking her bag.

"How are you really, Henry?" she asked as soon as they were out of earshot.

"Not too bad. A little tired."

"Didn't you sleep well?"

"The situation on the Russian front is pretty worrying," he replied, caught somewhat off guard.

"Is that the only reason you didn't sleep well?"

Henry was annoyed; losing his patience he halted abruptly.

"Stop it. I don't like these silly games!"

She met his gaze with a twinkle in her eyes.

"Then what sort of game do you like, Henry?" she asked, suppressing a chuckle.

For a fleeting moment Sonia's frivolity seemed to disarm him, but quickly a flare of temper testified to his mounting tension.

He turned to leave, visibly agitated and disarmed by her bluntness.

She seized his wrist. "No, don't go! I hardly slept a wink all night." Her whole attitude and expression had suddenly changed; she wasn't playing any longer. So they went on in silence, digesting what was already said and hesitating to say what still remained unspoken.

Henry was the first to give in to the need to clear the air.

"What I can't understand is, how you can transfer your affections from one man to another, just like that."

"I didn't need to transfer them. I liked Ossi, I liked him very much. He was kind and gentle. I was flattered. He was more like a friend."

Henry scowled. "I find that hard to believe, you were always together."

"What else could I do? You were always away labouring in those blessed woods. But I always came over as soon as you were back from work."

"You wanted your provisions."

"You are a fool! Certainly I wanted my provisions. That's why I came the first time. But later it was you I wanted to see."

"He always looked at you with adoring eyes."

"Did you ever see me making eyes at him? If I meant more to him, I could not help that."

"I saw you holding hands!"

Here she burst out laughing. "Holding hands? Is that such a sign of great passion?"

Henry was not convinced. "But you have been Ossi's, have you not?" he blurted out.

Sonia grinned. "Ah! That is the crux of the matter! Your masculine pride! If you mean making love, I never did. He was a fine, sensitive man and a real gentleman but not really my type." She let her voice linger in the air as she threw a glance at him. "Who knows, had it lasted longer, it might have come to that. No one can tell." She started to giggle. "Besides, there was no opportunity."

Henry didn't like either her tone or the implication of her remark. "I can't make you out. You contradict yourself so much."

Sonia smiled. "The trouble with you is you have no sense of humour. You attach too much importance to words. You take everything literally. Things have to be either black or white. Life isn't like that."

They had arrived at her quarters. "Would you like to come in? I'll make coffee."

"Thank you but I'd rather not."

"Well, as you like." She took her shopping basket, and closed the door behind her.

Chapter 30

Complications

As soon as Sonia had closed the door behind her he regretted not having accepted her invitation. *It's better this way,* he told himself. No need to rush headlong into something he might feel sorry for soon after. So far their relationship had progressed at a snail's pace. One might say they were tip-toeing towards each other. Without doubt, physically she was most attractive and desirable. But little wonder —after a year in a concentration camp he was as sex-starved as a dog on heat—and those swaying hips and voluminous breasts were so provocative!

What irritated him was the way she assumed so much; as if he was already helplessly caught. Besides there were still too many contradictions and inconsistencies in what she said. On the other hand, supposing she did tell lies—what did it matter, if he only desired her physically? Why attach so much importance to whether she and Ossi had been lovers? Was it only masculine pride, as she hinted?

This fruitless dissection was getting him nowhere. Was he merely a spawning salmon helplessly caught in the net? *A propos* salmon, he vividly recalled Dr Bernheim's remarks during one of their analytical sessions. "Sexual behaviour remains a mystery. Take the strange example of the salmon. After several years at sea that salmon has to go back to the very same river from which he came. He must penetrate deep upstream into the river's womb, like a phallus penetrating the vagina. On his way he has to fight against the current, jump over obstacles, weirs and waterfalls, and only at the source of the river can the sex act and spawning begin. Why this obstacle-ridden ceremonial? Why that particular river?"

Henry reflected upon Dr Bernheim's words which now seemed to have wider implications. Why should one particular woman hold attractions for us which other women, equally endowed with physical beauties, do not? Why do we have to exert ourselves, climb upstream, face inner conflicts, social ostracism and a lot of tribulations if another woman could provide the same physical satisfaction? There must be more to it than meets the eye. Immersed in thought, he went back to *camerata* 3. The habitual humdrum activities in the barrack had a sobering effect. Spitz, a bucket of water between his legs, was busily cleaning hats. Little Wolf was repairing his broom, while Borstyn and Laufman discussed politics.

"Well, how did it go?"

Henry recognised Linzer's voice immediately and turned round to face him.

"How did what go?"

"I mean how are things developing?" asked Linzer with a smirk on his face.

Henry's brows contracted.

"Come to the point. What is it you want to know?"

Linzer smiled. "No need to pretend with me. You know very well what I mean."

"Whatever you're after, the answer is mind your own business." Though Henry sounded aggressive he wasn't really that deeply upset.

"I don't want to be nosy," said Linzer, "but I hope you're not getting yourself entangled in any," he paused searching for *le mot juste*, "complications." This was the patron speaking to his *protégé*.

"I told you once and I repeat it: mind your own business."

"All right then. Please yourself!"

Henry was annoyed with Linzer for having restarted those ruminations from which he had escaped only a few minutes before. But Linzer was right of course, he was teetering on the brink of complications. It only needed one step forward to set the ball rolling, to provoke an avalanche. Should he back out because of fear of complications? Well, then he might just as well live under a glass bell for life was full of complications. To dodge them out of cowardice meant depriving oneself of the very salt of existence.

Borstyn and Laufman were still at it, defending their political convictions. As a journalist, Laufman was well informed of pre-war political machinations behind the scenes. Usually tight-lipped, he could warm up when anyone trod on the corns of his political hobbyhorse.

"Russia has sown the wind and is now reaping the tempest! In 1939 their non-aggression pact with Hitler seemed very astute. A masterstroke on the world political chessboard. Let Germany and the Allies tear each other to pieces and when both are bled dry Russia would reap the harvest. But France's catastrophic collapse changed the situation. The Russian grandmasters' move backfired and it is Russia that is bleeding now."

Borstyn, the Russian Jew, who had survived pogroms and the communist revolution that made him an *émigré*, still had a soft spot for his birth country.

"Mr Laufman, with due respect for your journalistic erudition, I think it's unrealistic to expect morality in politics. Politicians have to do what is best for their country, unburdened by sentimentality or ethics."

Henry had heard enough. His microcosm had problems enough of its own. If he couldn't even master his own tiny world what good would it do to get involved in the bigger one outside? Later that night Henry hardly closed an eye. It was the second night in succession of wrestling. *What am I wrestling with?* he asked himself. *Windmills? Like Don Quixote?* What was it that perturbed him most? It was no good spending hours on his analysis with Dr Bernheim if he proved incapable of shedding a glimmer of light on his predicament. He resolved to take a grip on himself and look at the situation impartially, objectively, as if he were the therapist guiding his patient.

Question number one: *What is so special about Sonia, apart from her physical charms?* Answer: *She was not only the woman of my best friend, but also the woman of my dead best friend. So what?* Henry reflected, *last night I cried out ABOMINATION! So there must be a taboo.* He now remembered Dr Bernheim's remark that behind all taboos lay fear, fear of retribution from gods, demons and ghosts. *Am I afraid of offending Ossi's ghost?* How could that be, since he did not believe in ghosts? Ossi was dead, wasn't he? So how could he care?

Henry realised that self-analysis was a most arduous task, because it is subjective. One is inclined to rationalise because one wishes to believe what one wants to be true. This was getting him nowhere. Then suddenly a thought flashed through his mind. He remembered Dr Bernheim's remark about modern man having lost the key to his archaic past. Though he did not believe in ghosts intellectually this was surely a flashback to primeval experience, from that ancient buried layer to which he had lost the key. Now for the first time he really understood Bernheim's theoretical assertions that modern man, unknown to himself, is still very deeply rooted in his remote past.

So Henry argued with himself: what was the use of reasoned argument if one is driven by instincts, emotions, nebulous impulses and beliefs going back to the infancy of mankind? Of one thing he was sure: he was not going to let Sonia push him into anything.

Chapter 31

The Die is Cast

For three long days neither of them went to see the other; Henry continued to argue with himself. By the fourth day he thought he knew what he wanted and what he was facing. He tidied himself up and resolutely set off. On the way he saw her children playing nearby. Good! The coast was clear. His heart was beating faster and his knees were trembling by the time he knocked at her door. Sonia, a dressing gown loose on her shoulders, opened it. For a split second, which prolonged itself unendurably, she stood motionless in the doorway, searching his eyes, while mingled expressions of wonder, surprise and joy flitted across her face. Then she moved quietly aside to let him in. Directly the door had closed behind them, Henry took her hard by the wrist and, deliberate of movement, drew her close. Their eyes bore into each other. Then she smiled.

"So you have come."

"Yes, I came. You knew I would!" and with a violent jerk he pulled her right into his arms.

Their lips met hungrily, and for a few seconds they clawed at each other, their bodies clamped together. She glanced at the door and quickly pulled away.

Henry leant his back against the door pulling her to him. "Now no one can get in," he murmured as he buried his head in her neck, holding her close again. When his hands caressed her through her robe she winced and pulled away.

"No! Not there!" she exclaimed sharply. But then to his delight Sonia permitted all other explorations without any resistance. Yet as soon as his wandering hand found her breasts again she drew back. "No, I don't want that! Not there!"

Henry was baffled. "You are a strange one," he said smiling wryly.

Sonia freed herself from his clasp. "That's enough for today."

Someone was trying the door, so Henry moved and it flew wide open at a hearty push. "Mamma, I'm hungry. When are we going to eat?"

"Soon darling, I'll call you." She said it as naturally as she could with cheeks aflame and hair all dishevelled. Sonia closed the door and tried to regain her composure.

There was a heavy silence between them.

"Well, it's nearly time for *appello*," Henry remarked casually.

"Shan't I see you again today?" She gave a little cry of disappointment.

Henry shook his head. "You know we aren't allowed out of barracks now after the last roll call."

She stroked his hair, kissing him passionately as if the months of waiting had finally opened up a dam of desire.

He turned on his heel and smilingly left her.

Alea iacta est, he thought. The die is cast. It had taken ages to make a move but it had taken only seconds to break the barrier down completely and open up the floodgates.

As he went back to his quarters his heart was thudding madly, partly because of his inner turmoil, partly because of sexual frustration. *Now I'm left with my neck scrubbed clean, and all for nothing.*

This had been a standing joke at home. As a little boy he had reluctantly submitted to a scrubbing and general beautification to impress a rich aunt from America. In the end she did not turn up and little Henry had complained he'd had his neck scrubbed for nothing. That was just how he felt now and he smiled wistfully.

Not surprisingly he had yet another restless night, tossing and turning on his miserable mattress. His aroused sensuality kept him awake but there was yet another reason why he could not sleep: hunger pains in his stomach. He missed that little extra food he used to earn with his labour in the woods. Somehow he got through the night and was the first in the breakfast queue. Never mind the quality of that horrible witch's brew they called coffee, he had to put something warm in his stomach. *Love doesn't go well with an empty belly,* he reflected. Perhaps he would have to sell something and so he began rummaging in his suitcase looking for something he could exchange for food, deciding eventually to sacrifice a shirt. Pity he wouldn't be seeing Maria for she would have given him a fair deal. Maybe Pasquale could help; he had a heart of gold, but the sentry on duty told him there had been a reshuffle and Pasquale would come on at night. Henry was disappointed for hunger had begun to bite deep in his guts. Well, perhaps Moishele could help.

Pasquale's sentry box was quite close to Sonia's hut and he was very tempted to call on her, but now felt he had to avoid compromising her. Ossi was still fresh in all their minds.

Moishele was busy feeding his 'eagle'.

"How nice to see you."

Henry handed over his shirt. Moishele looked embarrassed. "As bad as that?"

Henry nodded.

"I suppose you are hungry?"

Henry nodded again.

"Look, I have a little olive oil and a piece of bread. Take this meantime and we'll settle when I've sold your shirt." He went inside and fetched a jam jar half filled with olive oil as well as a sizeable piece of bread. Henry sat down on a bench and dipped the bread in the olive oil, a tiny bite at a time, to savour every morsel as if the most exquisite delicacies were being offered to his palate. His body had been forced to rely exclusively on the starvation diet and his depleted body avidly absorbed the high calorific fluid.

Moishele, who had tactfully kept away busying himself with his bird, now came to sit beside him. "How are you going to cope in the future?"

Henry shrugged his shoulders. "I'll have to sell gradually what I have for food as long as it lasts. We doctors have only our 'honour'. You can't get fat on that."

That little snack had only roused Henry appetite and when he went back to his *camerata* he was again first in the queue for the midday meal.

"Oi! *Capo*! What's the hurry?" asked Lubicz, but he must have sensed something unusual in Henry's behaviour for he dipped his ladle twice, filling Henry's bowl to the brim. Dr

Wunderstein, the miser, who was behind him, was ready to
protest, but after an initial effort, "Thhhhat is not ffffair," he
was beaten by his stammer and the shove from the next man
behind him. That Scrooge could have lived like a king, but preferred to keep his bundles of thousand lire notes tucked away
under his mattress.

Late in the afternoon Henry made up his mind to go to Sonia. He felt that enough deference had been paid to public
opinion.

"Why didn't you come sooner?"

"I was thinking of you, Sonia. The gossip ... and..."

She snapped back brusquely. "You needn't worry on my account." Then she sat down beside him and took his hand. "I
want you to know that I do not care about gossip."

Henry was intrigued and a little uneasy. "I hate to remind
you, but you are married."

"So what?"

"Well, what about your husband?"

"He should be here!" she snapped back emphatically.

There was a brief, uncomfortable silence.

"I do not understand," said Henry. "Some time ago, when I
raised the subject, you didn't seem to resent his absence. You
said this way he was able to provide for you."

"What else could I say? I didn't know you very well then."

"So you are upset about his being away?"

"Of course I am!" she yelled back. "His place is here with
his family."

"Then what about his bread-winning role, his providing for
you all?"

"We'd have to manage like all the others. Besides, he has
plenty saved. He's having a good time in Milan."

Henry grinned. "Does that mean you want a lover to pay
him back?"

"Oh don't be so stupid!" she exclaimed angrily.

Henry smiled. "Don't get worked up. It's none of my business."

Sensing that despite his easy manner, Henry was piqued
and his masculine *amour propre* injured, Sonia stroked his
cheek gently. "But it should matter, you fool!"

"Perhaps you don't mind the gossip because you hope it may reach him in Milan?"

She got up, sounding really cross now. "You have a devious talent for seeing things that are not there!"

Henry got up too. "Let's not waste time quarrelling," he said, reaching out for her.

She smiled and put her arms around him. Again they kissed, mauling each other savagely, and then he ripped off her brassière. She suddenly seemed to stiffen and tore herself away from him.

"I suppose it had to come! So take a good look at them!"

Henry stared at her bare breasts. They were badly scarred all over. Sonia had tears in her eyes. "That butcher did it! That butcher in Milan!"

Henry did not know what to say. He waited. Silent.

"It was after my baby son died. I got milk fever, mastitis. That butcher ...the surgeon ....lanced them so badly I developed abscesses in both breasts. He just kept on cutting and cutting. I had such beautiful breasts!"

She blurted all this out in a flood of tears. Henry stroked her hair. "What does it matter, Sonia?"

She pushed him away. "Do you mean you like this sight? It doesn't put you off?"

"It certainly does not" said Henry, and he meant it.

"Do you know what it does to a woman?"

Henry smiled. "I don't, but I can see what it does to you, because you are so vain ..."

She began to retaliate angrily then suddenly she changed her tone and expression.

"Do you remember your discussion, when you asked why I dress up? A clever jeweller hides his defective gems under elaborate filigree. I hide my imperfections under elaborate garments."

Henry patted her hand. "I think you are dramatizing the whole thing."

"Think so if you like, but you are not a woman."

Strangely enough Sonia's scarred breasts had brought her closer to him. Perhaps because it was the first time he'd felt sorry for her. He wiped her tears and held her hands in silence.

"Would you like to have supper with me and the children?" she asked, as an afterthought.

"I can't. I have to be back before roll call. *Capi* have to check numbers before *appello*."

He would have stopped had he really wanted to, but being destitute again since his loss of work he had grown ultra-sensitive about charity. A proper meal would have been most welcome, but his pride prevented him.

"I do wish you would stay."

"I can't," repeated Henry, and after a moment's reflection — or inspiration—he added, "But I shall come tonight."

Strange how these words had sprung from his lips without any conscious volition. Sonia's face lit up and her eyes shone excitedly. "When did you decide this?"

"Just now," he replied, smiling.

Suddenly she seemed frightened. "But the sentries are supposed to shoot anyone moving in the dark."

"No they won't. Not in Italy."

"But if they did, if …"

"If my grandmother were hung upside down, she'd be a money box. If, if…"

"No need to be so rude. I'm really worried!" She was both delighted and scared. "Promise you will be careful."

Henry ignored this platitude.

"Tonight the stars look down benignly. What worried me most was the gossip."

"So what of it?"

"Tonight Pasquale, my friend, stands guard quite close to here. He wouldn't care even if he did catch me. Well, see you tonight then. At midnight."

Back at his *camerata* he felt his stomach rumbling and joined the queue. Barely had he sat down to consume the watery concoction in his bowl when Deborah, a small casserole in her hands, entered the *camerata*. "Mamma said to bring you this."

Henry felt most uncomfortable, particularly with young Scholz, who happened to be next to him, casting an enquiring

eye on Henry and the casserole. A wonderful aroma rose from
the steaming earthenware container. "Thank you Deborah!
You are a good girl. But you must take it back to your mother.
You can see I am eating my supper already."

Little Deborah stood still, not knowing what to do. "Now
off you go. It's nearly time for roll call." He directed her gently
towards the door.

The child ran off, but Scholz continued to scrutinise him in
silence. Henry could feel the reproach in his eyes. Young
Scholz had been very attached to Ossi. *Why the hell had she to do
this?* To have to refuse that appetising dish was tantalising
enough; to endure Scholz's reproachful look was much harder.
Perhaps he was really more concerned about his own reputation, he mused, than hers.

Appello came and went; the days were getting shorter and it
was dark in the *camerata*. He lit a candle, stretched himself out
on his palliasse and tried to read, but he was unable to absorb
anything. Time seemed to be dragging its feet; it was a hell of a
wait until midnight. There was a lot of noise and talk in the
camerata. Talk, talk, always the same discussions: the war, the
strategy, politics, dirty stories, and gradually, imperceptibly,
exhausted from three sleepless nights, he dozed off.

He woke suddenly with a start, almost in panic. Had he
overslept? The lights were out and it was quiet in the *camerata*
except for the snoring. Henry got up slowly, took his sandals
off and tip-toed barefoot out of the *camerata*. The sky was overcast and he frantically tried to read the time for certain on his
wristwatch. It was either ten past eleven or five minutes to
two. Whatever the time, he'd have to make a dash for it — or
rather a crawl — for it was safer to drag himself on all fours. He
didn't want to take any unnecessary chances. So he crawled on
his belly like a snake past the oak tree and across the football
pitch, keeping a middle course, as far as possible from the sentry boxes on both sides. His progress was slow and his hands
and knees soon became bruised and torn. Complete silence
shrouded the night, apart from the occasional hoot of an owl
and the beat of his heart which pounded against his ribs from
excitement as well as from fear, for one could never be certain
what the guard would do. Now he could distinguish the sil-

houette of a sentry and he lay low for a while, breathing heavily. If he could see the sentry there was no reason why the man should not see him.

The heavy clouds broke for an instant and in the hazy flicker of the stars Henry could read the time correctly. It was half past eleven. This meant that it had taken him twenty minutes to cover a distance which normally took two minutes at a leisurely pace.

Unexpectedly something hit his face, scratching it. He had to take a grip on himself not to let out a cry. He felt and heard the rush of air and then he dimly made out the wings of a bat. Dragging his body along he suddenly had to smile as he recalled a very fitting Italian proverb: *'Tira piu un pelo di fica che cento buoi,'* in other words, 'One hair from a cunt pulls harder than a hundred oxen.'

The faint outline of the family compounds became visible. Only a hundred yards or so separated him from Sonia's little hut now. There were lights on in some of the family dwellings and he could even hear voices and singing coming from one of them. Now that he was in Pasquale's territory he grew bolder and covered the distance in no time. Reaching the door, he stopped. Better not knock as it might wake the children. The door creaked and he gently pushed it just enough to let his body through, then he wriggled inside. His heart was beating violently in sweet anticipation. Slowly and gently he crawled towards Sonia's bed and pushed his trembling hand under the blanket. The bed was cold and empty. What could this mean? What was she up to? True, he had said, 'See you at midnight,' but this was not meant to be taken literally. Besides, where was she gallivanting at this time of night?

He was furiously disappointed and completely turned off.

'Devil take her!' he cursed and sat himself on the edge of her bed, sulking. But before too long, his sense of humour returned and he decided he'd surprise her. He crawled under her bed, ready to pounce when she came back. A strong smell of hay from her mattress had a pleasurable soothing effect.

There were sounds and voices outside. Yes! That was Sonia talking to a man whose voice sounded vaguely familiar. The footsteps halted at Sonia's door, but the conversation continued. *What the hell is she up to now? The 'green-eyed monster' took over. So it seems I'm not the only one. Probably she is coming from him, the Messalina!* The door creaked. Were they coming in?

"Thank you Mr Berenson. It was a nice party."

Ah! Now Henry recognised Berenson's voice, the dental mechanic, a bachelor with a family hut of his own for use as a dental surgery; supposed to be a womaniser too.

"I hope we shall see you again at the next party. Goodnight Sonia."

Sonia crept in and shut the door. It was impossible in the dark to discern what she was doing, so Henry had to strain his ears to guess. Right at the door she stopped and Henry heard a muffled thud from casting off her shoes. Her barefoot steps were barely audible. Next Henry heard her brushing her teeth. There followed a sound of something soft hitting the floor, which must have been her skirt, and then the rustle of silk. Sonia's footsteps came over to the bed and although she might cry out Henry could not resist suddenly grabbing her ankle. But she did not utter a sound; instead she just bent down and grabbed a handful of his hair. Henry came out from his hiding place and got to his feet. He put an arm round her waist and drew her towards him. Her body felt hot and yet she was shivering. His body hungered for hers and the thin silk, through which he could feel every curve of her body, heightened his excitement and desire. They kissed passionately, their lips fused, their tongues entwined. He brushed aside her shoulder-straps and her negligée slipped to the floor. She stood naked, trembling with desire.

"Let's put a blanket on the floor," he whispered.

Concrete floors do not creak, so now they could let themselves go. Starved as he was after all these long months, he still managed to control his desire, to prolong their love-play and the exhilarating erotic pleasure. Hours went by in a sequence of embraces, some ardently lascivious, some languid. They could not speak, words were superfluous. Only occasionally did they whisper into each other's ear. In the end, exhausted and drained, they fell asleep in each other's arms.

Henry dozed with one eye open, for he had to get back before daybreak, both for the children's sake as well as his own.

While he lay beside her, a strange sadness came over him: *post coitum omne animale triste*. He recalled Dr Bernheim's words: 'a man and a woman engrossed even in the most primitive acts of copulation are like a couple of marionettes, mere puppets, deriving their impetus from some string-pulling, mysterious external force.'

But there was no time for philosophising. Sonia was still fast asleep when he let his fingers glide over the voluptuous curve of her hips. "I must go now," he whispered.

"Mmm," she whispered back and cuddled closer.

Henry freed himself from her clasp and groped carefully for his shorts and shirt. Then he bent down again, kissed her eyes and stroked her hair.

"You must get back into bed now." Then he left.

The chilly air raised goose pimples all over his skin and when, after a long and tedious crawl, he reached his own bed in the *camerata*, he fell heavily on it and slept like a log. It must have been ages since he slept so soundly and when he finally emerged the world seemed a nicer place.

Chapter 32

Relationships

Henry's high spirits were not to last long, however. When he began to sober up and mull over the last night's events his euphoria gradually evaporated. He started brooding. There were too many questions begging an answer. How was it that despite recent strict orders, she had been out of her living quarters till almost midnight? What sort of party had she attended? How well did she know Mr Berenson?

Almost imperceptibly at first and then abruptly, his peace of mind vanished, replaced by doubts and anger. Gossip or no gossip, after the morning's roll call he was going to see her and clear matters up.

On his way he worked himself up into a temper and by the time he knocked at her door his anger had escalated to fury. So it was astonishing and sobering to find Sonia with furrowed brow and an enraged expression.

"You are a fine one!" she greeted him as soon as he entered.

Unprepared for such a reception, Henry was taken off balance, but after a moment's reflection he concluded: *Aha! Attack is the best form of defence*. But Sonia did not relent. "He pretends he is not hungry! He sends my stew back! And yet he sells his shirt to get food." She was genuinely upset and indignant. "Big guy! Shares a bed with a woman but treats her like a stranger!"

"Who told you about the shirt?"

"Never mind! It doesn't matter."

"It must have been Moishele! When I see him I'll wring his neck!"

"You won't do any such thing. He is your friend and he means well."

Henry calmed down. Moishele wasn't a gossip. His intentions were good. "Anyway, I can't see why it should concern you if I do sell a shirt, nor why you should make an issue of it."

"Why it should concern me?" she snapped back. "You make love to me and yet think so little of me you won't even accept a little food. Can't you see how insulting and humiliating it is?"

"You've got the wrong end of the stick, Sonia. You really have."

She made a disgusted face and spat at him like a cat. "What kind of woman do you take me for, if it's easier for you to sell your shirt than accept from me a simple token of friendship?"

"You're distorting the whole thing. I do not like gifts from women. It makes me feel like a kept man. That's all."

This time he really roused her to boiling point.

"First of all I am not 'women' and secondly, do I look like an old spinster, a hunchback, a fat old widow who has to buy a lover?"

Henry could not help laughing. "If it comes to that, I ought to be paying you, not the other way round."

This little joke took the heat out of their argument and Sonia smiled. "It may still come to that. If the war lasts long enough. But jokes apart, you lack delicacy. I hate to say it, but I'm sure Ossi would never have acted like that. It's just your stupid pride."

Henry did not like that reference to Ossi, but did not retort. Instead he changed course to another facet of the problem. "It's not only pride. I also have to respect the feelings of others. They all looked sideways at me in the *camerata* when Deborah brought that casserole. To them our relationship is an insult to Ossi's memory."

At first Sonia did not reply, but then she raised her head defiantly and looked him squarely in the face. "If you are a man you'll acknowledge me openly and not act as if you are ashamed of me. I don't give a damn for what they think. Ossi was never more than a dear friend to me. If they read more into it, that's their business."

Henry was getting a little weary of this conversation and his weariness soon changed to annoyance when he suddenly remembered the purpose of his early visit. "Look, I came this morning especially to clear a few things. Instead you got in first and put me off."

Sonia raised her eyebrows and looked at him quizzically.

"I want to know," Henry continued, "why the camp rules do not apply to you."

Her eyebrows shot up even higher. "I don't know what you mean."

Henry looked at her fixedly. "We are not supposed to leave our quarters after last *appello*. But you were out."

Sonia, realising what he was driving at, suppressed a smile. "These rules have very little meaning for families. No one is going to run away leaving children behind. The *chappers* know that."

Henry could see the strength of her argument. "All right, but what were you doing until midnight."

"I went to a party."

Henry tried hard to contain his anger. "You went to a party, knowing I was coming at midnight?" He was almost yelling at her by now.

But Sonia kept her cool. "Sit down Henry. This party was arranged last week." She paused. "I do not want to brag, but you force me into it. I wanted to give my neighbours a treat, something to eat, so I called it a 'party'. Some of them are as touchy, stupid and stubborn as you about accepting anything."

"In that case, why was the party not held in your place?"

"Because of the children, of course! They have to sleep. All the families have children, so we held the party at Berenson's surgery. He is a bachelor."

"How long have you known Berenson?"

Sonia held her hand out at knee-height. "From when I was so high. He's much older than he looks and was a friend of my family in Frankfurt. Satisfied? You are surely not jealous of him?"

Henry made a contemptuous gesture of disdain but did not reply.

Most—all—of her explanations made sense, but it hurt to acknowledge this reality. Perhaps he had made an ass of himself. He sat silent, too proud to apologise.

Sonia came to his aid. "Let's forget this stupid inquisition, Henry. It is a shame to start bickering after such a wonderful night."

He could not but agree so he held out his arms and they kissed and made their peace.

And so it continued. Days became weeks and in time their relationship stabilised as their encounters, furtive and rare at first, came out into the open. There were many sarcastic remarks, jibes and bitchy comments, especially from the women. Henry realised it was a hollow pretence to say we do not care about other people's opinion, for in truth we do, very much. Under the guidance of Dr Bernheim, Henry had become trained to look for the roots of feelings and concluded that it was foolish to deny the herd instinct, for a rejection by the herd signified loss of protection, isolation and danger.

Gradually the innuendos subsided, especially as they seemed to have no effect on the two people involved. Gossip thrives on secretive behaviour and is doomed in the light of day. People accepted the situation for what it was: an affair between a married woman and a bachelor. No more, no less. Nothing new or exciting about that. Thus the unsavoury connotations at first attached to their relationship, faded away, with only two exceptions. One was young Scholz, who in his youthful, idealistic belief in friendship and loyalty could never stomach his capo's behaviour. The other was Dino, who for perhaps similar reasons, could not reconcile himself to Henry's relationship with Sonia. In the end he moved to another *camerata*. The Triumvirate had died with Ossi and belonged in the past. Henry was sad, but was equally aware that everything in this world had its price, which had to be paid in one form or another. He accepted this, though he still felt uneasy if he chanced to meet Scholz's reproachful eye when a savoury dish was brought into him by one of the children. For Sonia had won in the end. She said she could not possibly be expected to eat while he was starving.

"It would choke me," she said. And he couldn't really blame her, for he would have felt the same, had their roles been reversed.

Chapter 33

Time to Go

They were now approaching the autumn of 1941 and swarms of migratory birds began to appear in the cloudy skies. These travelling birds held a special fascination for Henry because their unimpeded flight in limitless space fired his imagination and his yearning for freedom. Some flocks were composed of numerous tiny navigators, so many as to obscure the sky; they created endless variations of formations, altitudes and sounds. One day, watching the flight of a flock of very large birds, he was intrigued by its unusual formation and size. He was unable to identify the species.

"Those are storks," observed a calm voice behind him.

Henry turned to face the speaker. It was Yadranka, 'the girl with the flaxen hair'.

"We have lots of them in Yugoslavia. They fly south at this time of the year."

"Yadranka! How are you? It's been a while!"

"Not through any fault of mine," she replied coolly. "Your feet seem to carry you in different directions nowadays."

Touché, thought Henry, and changed the subject. "How is the school doing?"

"Thank you, the school is doing fine."

There was a barrier between them. She seemed resentful and though she was still very young, there was sufficient feminine subtlety, and cattiness, in her to get at Henry obliquely.

"Do you still miss your friend? I mean the one who died, not so long ago," she asked pointedly.

Henry did not reply right away. She had unerringly found the sorest spot of all. He looked at her searchingly and sadly, wondering at the same time whether he had been wise in smothering rather than cultivating a relationship which had seemed quite promising at one time.

"Yes, I do still miss him," he replied eventually.

She looked at him scornfully. "I'm glad to hear that," and having planted her dart, she was off.

266 Ferramonti—Salvation behind the barbed wire

She must be hurt, thought Henry. Nothing much had happened between them and yet there had been a refreshing spontaneity and naturalness during their few encounters. Could it be that he had exchanged gold for brass, he asked himself, a married woman for an unsophisticated, open young soul? It couldn't be helped now.

Henry tried to assess his feelings for Sonia. She most certainly was an attractive woman, somewhat brash and full of herself. Though she could be a little crude sometimes she was also frank, proud, outspoken and generous. As for trusting her that was a different matter; complete trust is diminished with an adulteress. After all, if she can deceive her husband, so she can you! Henry was also aware that this infatuation with Sonia had arisen from weakness. Love ought to arise from strength. Only then is it inspiring and uplifting. With Sonia, he was often plagued by bad conscience, by doubts, scruples and the feeling of hateful surreptitiousness.

As for his nocturnal visits, he kept them down to a minimum in order not to push his luck. As *capo camerata* his conduct would be doubly condemned if he were caught. Besides, the nights grew colder and the long crawl became an ever-growing ordeal. On those occasions when he managed to drag himself over at night they celebrated veritable erotic feasts, but these sometimes left him with an unpleasant taste, because of the mute—yet accusing—presence of children, deceived as they slept. 'Macbeth doth murder sleep.' But it was no use shedding crocodile tears over it.

On the Russian front things looked gloomier than ever. Leningrad was encircled except for a tiny corridor on Lake Ladoga. The way towards the Crimea in the south seemed open, and most terrifying of all was the unhampered push of the Nazi hordes towards Moscow.

Batyushka Borstyn, despite his heroic attempts to look confident and cheerful, could not hide his innermost fears and he side-stepped discussions. No doubt the future of Europe rested on Soviet Russia's shoulders; paradoxically, it was for the Soviet Union—an eastern dictatorship—to save western democracy from destruction. Now that the chips were down it was again 'Holy Russia' not the Soviet Union that had to be saved for in their desperate bid to rouse the masses, an appeal to mystic patriotism and not merely to the revolutionary spirit was made.

Autumn brought gales, storms and unusually low temperatures for Calabria. Most of the internees were confined to barracks by the torrential rains. The stone-dry ground was by now saturated. At first there were a few puddles, which gradually grew in size as the downpour continued. In the end all the pools began to coalesce, forming one large pond, which led Moishele to nickname the camp 'Ferramonti by the lake'. Having nothing better to do, he drew a poster, showing a woman reclining under a palm tree by the lake, and large blood-sucking Anopheles mosquitoes resting on each breast and knee. The poster had an alluring caption:

Come to Ferramonti by the lake

Slimmers' diet you'll take

Bloodletting while you sleep

Your safety and your keep

Concerns us. So we may

Watch your step, night and day.

Moishele nailed the poster up in front of his camerata, but it drew the wrath of Tommasini on his head. He tore it down, cursing the *'Maledetti Ebrei'* and their stupid jokes.

Despite the bad weather, the building of new barracks was resumed. This was difficult to understand, but the internees had given up hoping to draw any conclusions from the haphazard stop-go methods of the 'Macaroni Eaters', as little Wolf called them. Soon, however, the reason for these hastily-built constructions became obvious, when large numbers of Greeks and Yugoslav—both Jews and Gentiles—began to arrive. The new influx brought a welcome diversion, valuable information and variety into the camp's stagnation. Among the Gentiles there were several powerfully built specimens, born and bred in the freedom-loving mountains of Yugoslavia.

These freedom-fighters' hatred for the German invader equalled—and sometimes surpassed—the loathing of Ferramonti's Jewish population for their common enemy. But they viewed the war with different eyes and were more light-hearted, for whichever way it ended, they had a homeland to go back to.

The very nature and circumstances of Henry's relationship with Sonia made it unavoidable that it should have frequents ups and down. In the beginning they were both very touchy and distrustful but gradually, when the rough edges had been smoothed out, they learned to make allowances for each other's susceptibilities and idiosyncrasies. Henry never liked Sonia's occasional comparisons of himself with Ossi, and also her disregard of public opinion. Sonia for her part hated to be considered merely a vainglorious exponent of fashion. She often felt underrated, protesting that there was more to her than just a pretty face. Most of all she got cross about Henry's stubborn refusal to accept but the most rudimentary material assistance from her. "It seems as if you were choking at each bite you accept from me."

Eventually they'd reached a state of equilibrium—a kind of armistice—when they began truly to enjoy each other's company, not only in bed, and they even made plans for the future.

And then one afternoon, Henry chanced to meet Reimer, the red-haired yekke. Reimer looked quizzically at him and asked, "Have you read the list yet?"

"What list?"

Reimer hesitated. "So you haven't heard," and could not help adding sarcastically, "otherwise occupied I bet."

"Cut it out," said Henry. "What are you trying to say?"

Reimer looked him squarely in the face. "A number of us internees are being moved to different camps."

This was a bombshell! Henry looked bewildered. "Is my name amongst them?"

Reimer's expression was no longer sarcastic when he nodded. "Yes, your name is on the list and so is Mrs Heller's, but the women are going to a different place."

There was no malice, no gloating over the news, in his voice. Henry stood there, thunderstruck.

"Does it say where we are going? Or when?"

Reimer shook his head.

"What about you? Are you being transferred?"

"No, not me," replied Reimer, as if he resented the fact, and went his way leaving Henry in a state of perplexed confusion.

Strange how life can be, he reflected. Only a few months ago he would have been happy, overjoyed, to go anywhere away from this godforsaken, stinking hole. Such a move would have acted like a blood transfusion, revitalising his atrophied zest for life; besides, things couldn't be much worse elsewhere. Now the situation was very different: there was Sonia. His first impulse was to run to break the news to Sonia, but it was not good alarming her unnecessarily, for the sake of her children. He began to speculate. *Why are only some people being transferred? What is the criterion? Is this transfer a reward or punishment?* Henry experienced an overwhelming need to get some clarification. He resolved to seek out Signor Rizzi right away.

The old woman servant must have read in his face the urgency of his visit for she went straight inside to get the *comandante's* consent for an audience. The *comandante's* desk was cluttered with folios and documents.

"Oh, it's you," he said, quite informally.

Signor Rizzi listened to Henry's questions, half smiling. "So, you don't like the idea of being transferred?" It was impossible to judge from the inflection of his voice whether he was joking or mocking.

Henry struggled to find the right words. "All I would like to know … I mean, is this a move for the better or is it some kind of punishment?"

The *comandante* laughed. "You must have a guilty conscience if you're expecting to be punished."

"Oh no, Signor Comandante, I have not…."

"Listen!" the comandante interrupted him. "We need room. All these Greeks, Yugoslavs and God knows what have to be placed somewhere. Some people must be moved. My instructions come from Rome. I know nothing. I only follow orders."

"But surely," protested Henry, "the Ministry's instructions must be based on your reports."

Signor Rizzi looked Henry over in silence, fixing him with a penetrating stare and ignoring Henry's last remark. "It seems you are not pleased about this move. Why? Is anything holding you here?"

Henry wasn't sure whether Signor Rizzi was playing cat and mouse with him or whether he really did not know.

"I have my friends. Old comrades."

"Is that all?"

From the way he put his question, there was no mistaking it; there was a mocking, though not malicious, expression in his eyes. The old fox did know. After all he had his henchmen to keep him informed. "Anyway," Signor Rizzi continued, "the war will be over soon. Russia is *kaput*! Don't you think so?"

Henry remembered that the comandante had used the same expression '*kaput*' some three months ago when the German offensive in Russia had started. On the other hand his optimism was by no means unfounded, since German forces were reported to be fighting in the outskirts of Moscow.

"Signor Rizzi, since the beginning, people have been telling me that it will soon be over and yet the war continues."

"Then let's hope this time it's true."

With these words and a grin, the comandante rose and dismissed Henry.

As on several previous occasions, Henry left the comandante's office not much wiser than before. In the position he held, Rizzi had to be ambiguous. True, he and Sonia were not the only ones to be transferred but the *comandante* must have had his reasons in every case. It was just possible he looked on their relationship as a potential source of trouble which might adversely affect the camp's morale and discipline. Obviously no one could tell if that was true; one could only surmise.

He went straight to Sonia and found her in tears. As soon as she saw him she flew to him and threw her arms about him. She was in a state of near hysteria. "What is going to happen to us? What will I do with the children?"

He tried to calm her down. "Come, come! It's very sad and distressing but it's not the end of the world, besides it couldn't be much worse than here."

"Can't it?" She only cried more bitterly. "And what about us? Does that not worry you at all?"

"Of course it does! But what can we do? After all, they are not sending us to Siberia. We can't be so far apart."

Sonia continued to weep. "How can you take it so calmly?"

"What choice have we got? When the war is over we shall meet again."

But even as he uttered these words Henry knew that their episode was over. Since Mundek's death, he had learned to cope with grief and loss, probably because part of his innermost soul had remained numb ever since. At all events, they were not to be separated immediately. A merciful weaning time was given to them to get used to the idea.

Apart from this distressing experience, which had come like a thunder bolt, there was the anguish about the impending fall of Moscow. An aura of tragic doom emanated from a silent Batyushka Borstyn. He was a shadow of his former confident self. But then — after a week's fighting in Moscow's suburbs — the war bulletins introduced two words with increasing frequency: 'Heavy snowfalls!' and Borstyn's furrowed brows began to straighten out again.

An ancient Hebrew sage once said, 'Live your days as if each were your last'. These words were spoken in a different moral context but Sonia and Henry unwittingly followed that principle, savouring each of the remaining days for they knew they lived on borrowed time. In fact this respite lasted only a few weeks. Henry was the first to go.

END OF BOOK ONE

Book Two

October 1941—May 1942

Chapter 1

Destination unknown

They left Ferramonti in October 1941 on a dismal day, overcast, wet and windy. From a sky heavy with clouds there fell a silent, fine drizzle, intensifying the general gloom. The grim weather chimed with the melancholy of the internees departing for an unknown destination, and with the bad news gleaned from the camp newspapers and others, that Kiev had fallen to the Nazis. Apart from those internees already sickened with anxiety over their families in Poland, the unspoken fear now gripped the others. The Russian Bear was teetering.

The army truck, overloaded with men and luggage, laboured along its bumpy way. It had no cover so all were gradually drenched. Henry looked up at the sky where a flock of large birds, necks outstretched, were flying in well-ordered formation, beating their wings in synchrony. These were neither storks, wild geese nor swans, for they were exceptionally large and uttered some strange, harsh cries.

After a moment's reflection Henry exclaimed, "Cranes! Look at that flock of cranes!"

"Cranes?" asked Baumgart. "The cranes of Ibycus?"

Henry did not get it at first, though Baumgart's words had a familiar ring. Then it dawned on him: Schiller's poem *'Die Kraniche des Ibycus'* describing the Greek poet's murder and his vindication through the utterances of cranes.

Let's hope these cranes are not a bad omen, Henry muttered to himself.

"I'm getting soaked," wailed Baumgart. He was a very pleasant and cultured man, an architect, with whom Henry would gladly have chatted in other circumstances, but just now he felt reluctant to be drawn into conversation. He looked around, counting the men in the truck. There were twenty-six of them. Apart from Baumgart, whom Henry knew well, there was Finzi, the Egyptian Jew, Dr Rauch, a pharmacist and a pompous middle-aged ass; then Gurewicz, the bass-baritone, a lovable rogue with a colourful character. The rest of his travelling companions he only knew by sight.

Strange the sadness of leaving Ferramonti! True, most of his gloom stemmed from being torn away from Sonia, but that was not all. He would miss Moishele, Wolf, Mario, Batyushka Borstyn, Linzer, Scholz and the rest of the motley crew with whom he had shared the cramped and basic living conditions of the last 15 months. Oddly enough he would not miss Dr Bernheim. Maybe he had outgrown him or perhaps he harboured a grudge against him for exposing Henry's character flaws during the training analysis. The workings of the human mind are indeed often a mystery.

But friends apart, there was also something about Ferramonti itself — a kind of *spiritus loci* — that he would miss, despite the dreariness. That something was the special Ferramontese aura arising from its random assortment of suffering, hopeful and defiant humanity.

"Get ready! *Scendete!*" yelled the guard as the truck slowed down. They had arrived at Mongrassano railway station, which was deserted and desolate.

"I wonder where they're taking us?" Baumgart pondered.

Dr Rauch, cock-sure and self-opinionated, had already made up his mind on that subject. He wrinkled his forehead portentously. "No doubt somewhere near Naples, probably Campobasso."

Henry was tempted to ask why he was so sure of their destination but resisted getting involved in an argument. The two militiamen who were to guard them pushed them towards the far end of the platform, though it was hard to understand why they had to drag their luggage all that way. A shrill whistle announced the approach of the train. The wagons appeared to be packed with soldiers, peasants and bundles of all kinds. At first it seemed as if the train were going to pass them by but when it eventually halted the last carriage, completely empty, was almost facing them; so the militiamen knew what they were doing after all.

To their relief it was not a sealed wagon. In fact it was surprising how informally their transport was handled. Was it again the southern '*Menefreghismo*', or exuberant confidence in victory after the Nazi triumph in Kiev, which explained their laxity?

Those acquainted with each other chose the same compartment. Henry, looking out of the window, felt an oppressive weariness creeping over his heart. As the train moved on, the Crati Valley came into view. So they were travelling north.

"You see" said Rauch, pleased with himself, "We are going up towards Naples."

Now they were passing Tarsia and the cemetery where Ossi and Meiersohn lay buried. A deep sigh involuntarily escaped him.

"Sorry to leave Ferramonti?" asked Baumgart, more an observation than a question.

"It's strange, but I am."

"You might be right at that. The ills we know are better than those we do not. God knows where they are taking us."

Finzi, in his habitual charming eastern manner, tried to reassure them. "I'm certain it won't be so bad. At least we'll get away from these malaria swamps."

No one bothered to contradict him, not even Rauch, who always knew better. They kept silent, engrossed in their own thoughts and anxieties. Things could indeed be so much worse.

After so many months of isolation from the maelstrom of life it was fascinating to watch the jostling crowds in the stations as they journeyed north: *carabinieri*, peasants, intermingled with militia in fascist uniforms, railway officials, soldiers, a hoarse voice, rising above the din, repeated incessantly, "*La Stampa, Corriere della Sera, Ossovatore Romano.*" The news vendors were doing well. There was always a thirst for news from the front especially when things were going well for the Axis powers.

The train moved on. The minutes ticked by, everyone deep in their thoughts, their unexpressed fears about their attendant fate as daylight began to fade. Henry pressed his forehead against the cold window pane feeling the steady swaying rhythm of the locomotive. He had a throbbing headache. The rain and mists which obscured the desolate landscape increased his sadness. Finzi was the first to get up and open his suitcase. He took out a pair of slippers and neatly packed small box containing bread and cheese.

Gurewicz sniffed the air. "Hey you!" he called out. "I hope your feet don't smell as strong as your Gorgonzola!"

"Gorgonzola?" replied Finzi. "You must be joking. Where would I get Gorgonzola in a concentration camp?"

Finzi was a kindly man who always tried to please, and though one could not call him servile, there was an occasional hint of oriental submissiveness bordering on servility. He was a big man, lantern-jawed, with an olive complexion and out-size hands and feet. *Acromegalic*, thought Henry, ever the doctor, as he looked at him. After changing into his slippers, he began to eat, his prodigious mandibles chomping forcibly and slowly.

"You do like your comfort, Finzi," said Gurewicz mockingly to which Finzi only replied with a smile and a nod as he went on chewing.

"I bet you lived like a great *pasha* in Cairo, with strings of belly-dancers and such," continued Gurewicz.

"Oh yes! A Jewish *pasha*," Finzi laughed scornfully. "I was in hotel work back then…hard work, and anything but a *pasha*'s life."

It was obvious that Gurewicz was bored and so he had to find someone to needle. This was one of his favourite pastimes and he excelled at it.

"Well, they do say you were a proper ladies' man, sneaking into bed with all those rich old American spinsters."

Finzi stopped chewing and bared his huge white teeth in a broad grin. "Yes, I did sometimes. But not the old ones. Mine were all young and fresh."

Dr Rauch, who was sitting next to Finzi, looked down his nose making it clear he did not approve of this kind of conversation. But Gurewicz was not inclined to take any notice of Rauch's displeasure. In fact, Rauch's disapproving demeanour only whetted his appetite.

"People say Egyptian Jews have a cock the length of a Hungarian salami sausage."

"I've never measured mine," replied Finzi tartly. Though his tone remained civil enough, one could sense he did not like take the turn the conversation had taken.

"Somebody told me that Egyptian Jews make their living as gigolos to middle-aged matrons."

Finzi stopped eating, and looked Gurewicz in the eye. "You seem to think you know a lot about Egyptian Jews. How did you make your living in Rome?"

The conversation was threatening to get out of hand, bordering on the offensive, so Baumgart put an end to it. "That's enough now, Gurewicz, why don't you just mind your own business?"

It was brazen for Gurewicz to start talking about moral conduct, his own way of life was only too well known. Although 3 years younger than Henry, he was almost bald and had a sizeable paunch despite Ferramonti cuisine; he was also very tall and made an imposing figure. But he had one truly great asset: his voice, a magnificent bass-baritone. It was mostly on account of this voice that so many of his idiosyncrasies, bordering on rudeness and general infringements of good taste, were overlooked. He'd studied singing in Rome and like many students was always short of cash, but according to rumour, he had few scruples about increasing his income by tricks of one sort of another. He was amoral rather than immoral, therefore his conduct never seemed to trouble him. Gurewicz felt he was entitled to his due from society, because of his voice and his contribution to opera and *bel canto*. He was a notorious scrounger, with the nickname of 'King of the Shnorrers' but one could not help half-liking him probably because of his great dedication to his muse. He was a rascal and proud of it.

The *'shlepper'* train progressed at a snail's pace, stopping at every isolated village. Henry leaned back and closed his eyes as if sleeping. He wondered what Sonia was doing. Pity he had not been able to bid her farewell in a manner befitting parting lovers. The last hours before his departure had been so turbulent and chaotic that he had not had the time nor the opportunity to seek her out. Later in the *piazza*, before they got into the truck, in front of all those people, he'd had to refrain from any excessive show of emotion. All he could do was to say goodbye and shake hands as he had done with many others, including Yadranka, who had come unexpectedly to wish him *bon voyage*. In his present melancholy frame of mind it seemed to him that life consisted of a never-ending sequence of farewells.

Baumgart lit his pipe and the pleasant aroma tempted Henry. He had learned to roll his own cigarettes quite deftly being unable to afford the manufactured kind. Baumgart had no need to economise. His wife was German, Aryan, and was allowed to stay and work in Rome. Compared with the others, Baumgart was well provided for. He was an urbane, intelligent man, of stocky build, with a craggy face and very prominent, bushy eyebrows.

"Would you like to try the pipe?" he asked, watching Henry's efforts at rolling himself a cigarette in the cramped confines of his seat.

"No thank you. I've got used to this exotic blend of tobacco."

Baumgart smiled. "What's so unusual about it?"

"It's made up according to Moishele's recipe: one third tobacco, one third dried dandelion, one third dried mint or what have you."

Rauch was clearing his throat and beginning to fidget uneasily. "If you must smoke you'd better go out in the corridor."

There was nothing unreasonable or offensive in his request except for the way he said it. Dr Rauch could never utter a word without making it sound like the Ten Commandments. A pompous, conceited individual blinkered by self-righteousness, he went through life unable to see beyond the end of his nose. There wasn't a spark of humour in him and his countenance was as rigid as a waxwork.

"I do apologise, Dr Rauch," said Baumgart, getting up, "I didn't know you disliked the smell of tobacco." He was too civil and polite to argue, and though Henry felt inclined to object to Rauch's high and mighty ways, he nevertheless followed Baumgart into the corridor.

"Well, thank God it's not a locked compartment, otherwise we'd never hear the end of it."

"They don't bother locking us up anymore," observed Baumgart. "What with the Nazis at the gates of Moscow, why should they worry about us?"

They smoked in silence for a while.

"How did you come to be in Ferramonti?"

"I worked in Rome with the Ministry of Housing, town and country planning and that sort of thing. My wife is Aryan and has connections. Well, one day they came and said they felt very sorry and all that but really they had no choice. Strictly speaking, they said, my wife and daughter ought to be interned as well. Mixed marriages, the Nazis frown on them you know, anyway, in view of special circumstances they'd allow my wife and daughter to stay in Rome."

He drew on the pipe, exhaling the bluish smoke in huge puffs as the train rattled its way. "Obviously I would have liked to have my family with me but I don't begrudge them their freedom. I must also confess I do enjoy the extra comforts they can send me." That last sentence he muttered almost apologetically.

Re-entering their compartment, they found a loud and animated conversation going on. Dr Rauch was holding the floor, pontificating as usual about what marvels he'd been performing in Milan before his internment. "I have a huge laboratory with all the most up-to-date equipment." Turning to Henry he added, "We used to do a lot for doctors, microscopical and biochemical work, blood counts and so on." He sat stiffly erect and his voice resounded with inflated self-admiration.

"Did they also send you piss and shit for examination?" asked Gurewicz, who had an instinctive antipathy to Rauch. An expression of disgust and contempt pervaded the latter's face.

"If you mean did we perform analyses of urine and faeces, yes we did."

Gurewicz, tenacious like a bulldog, was not easily shaken off. "I'm told they had to send the piss and shit to your laboratory in golden containers. Is that true?"

Rauch did not bother to reply, instead he looked at him with an expression full of hatred and offended majesty. Unfortunately, Rauch's inability to take a joke, crude or otherwise, acted upon Gurewicz like a red rag to a bull. He could not resist the temptation to put banana skins under Rauch's humourless pomposity. A mean glitter came into his eyes; he was about to let fly a heavy broadside.

"Dr Rauch, if your laboratory was so wonderful how is it that no one has ever heard of your miserable hole? To hear you talk, one would have thought half of Milan depended on your services. I think you are a story-teller and a buffoon!"

Rauch's wax-like mask became even more waxen; but to prove that life was still pulsating beneath it, two throbbing veins stood out on his temples. "You loud-mouthed, cheating scoundrel! You apology for a human being!" he yelled, beside himself. "If you don't shut that filthy mouth of yours, I'll knock your teeth down your throat."

Well, well, there was more life in the old dog that one had suspected. For a fleeting moment Henry felt some sympathy, even a liking for him. "For God's sake, Gurewicz!" shouted Henry, torn between anger and amusement. "We are all sick of your crude insinuations. If you can't control that tongue of yours then shut up."

Gurewicz, glad to have provoked the high and mighty Rauch to a degrading show of temper, wore a satisfied grin on his face, his mission accomplished.

They had travelled almost six hours, so Naples could not be too far off. Perhaps Rauch was right after all. The train was slowing down but it was impossible to tell whether this damned slowcoach was approaching a station or merely suffering a passing hiccup. One of their 'protectors' knocked at the compartment door.

"*Preparatevi!* Get ready! We are getting off in a few minutes."

The asthmatic whistle of the engine heralded their approach to a station and with screeching brakes, the train came to a halt. Their carriage being the last one, stopped at the far end of the platform.

"Salerno!" Dr Rauch was triumphant. "What did I tell you? Salerno is only a stone's throw from Naples."

Picking up their cases and following the crowd, the internees were ready to make for the station exit but they were stopped in their tracks.

"Wait here! *Fermatevi!*"

There followed a brief consultation between the two militiamen and one of them made his way towards the centre of the station. The remaining guard, left on his own with twenty-six internees, must have felt uneasy, for he kept his hand constantly on his holster. Throughout the journey the guards had treated their charges in the most distant and impersonal manner. There was no protective cover at the far end of the platform so they all got drenched from the rain, which was now pelting down heavily.

Finzi, on tiptoes and craning his neck, suddenly announced, "He's coming back. There's another man with him."

The peaked red cap proclaimed the other man as the *Capo Stazione*. He seemed annoyed and was gesticulating wildly.

"*Porca miseria!* This is all I needed on top of all this muddle." The stationmaster looked cursorily at the group of internees and then turned his back on them. "Special carriage! Where would I get any special carriages?"

The militiaman showed him a document. "It's from the Ministry."

This time the stationmaster turned round and looked closer at the internees. "They seem quite decent people, *gente per bene*. Why a separate carriage?"

"*Ordine del Ministero*," repeated the guard, and that was that.

The *Capo Stazione* shook his head. "I'll have to telephone around and see what I can do" and with that then strode off purposefully.

It was still pouring; their train was not supposed to arrive for three long hours. Henry sat on his suitcase, his old travelling companion, all battered and worn. Now that it was soggy from rain, the cover was softening and bulging in places but he did not care. If it burst under his weight, well so be it. There was no treasure left in it anyway. The whole concept of treasure had become meaningless in the face of hunger, loss of family and liberty.

As he sat there drenched and cold, his mind went back to that glorious summer's day when they had first assembled at the *Questura* in Genoa. On that occasion he had also been perched on his suitcase, as was Ossi Gerber. *Poor Ossi! Rotting away in the rain. Why should they have to sit in the rain, apart from others, like a colony of lepers?*

No matter how hard he tried he could not shake off his melancholy broodings. There are days where everything seems draped in black. This certainly was one of them. A general atmosphere of gloom descended on the group and no one spoke a word. They felt like pariahs, excommunicated from the rest of humanity, like cattle in the field, left out to graze and soak in the rain. The station was empty except for a few officials going in and out of their offices.

A train was approaching and stopped. The deserted platform suddenly became animated and pulsating with life. Newspaper vendors emerged from nowhere and so did pushcarts loaded with fiascos of *vino* and *gassose*. People began to pour out of the train. Soldiers and yet more soldiers, mostly Italian with a small group of Germans, who could be distinguished at a glance for they were taller, smarter, stiffer and walked with the arrogant self-assurance of the would-be *Herrenvolk*. *"Corriere della Sera"* — *"Il Popolo"* —cried the news vendors— *"Ultime Notizie."* Whether the ambitions of the Axis powers or the humiliations of the allies, the press got its daily bread. They had never had it so good as they made a roaring trade out of human carnage.

And then came a catchy tune, from the German soldiers as they marched past.

'Vor der Kaserne vor dem grossen Tor' ending with the refrain *'Wie einst Lily Marlen'*, a contagious tune with its flowing cadences, haunting and easily summoned, both by friend and foe. Unlike the rest of the soldiers, this particular group wore tropical kit. They seemed more energetic, more arrogant too than the rest, as they sang aloud, shoving through the crowds, sweeping aside everything and everybody that stood in their way.

"It's the *Afrika Korps*," said Baumgart nervously.

As the crowd swept through the exits, the station fell silent again. The stationmaster reappeared, gesticulating.

"E' fatto! I have sorted it!" He beckoned them to follow, but the guards shook their heads.

"They can't sit in the waiting room: *non e' permesso."*

"There's another place," explained the stationmaster.

He led them to a large hall, a kind of deposit for all kinds of goods in transit. The place was ill lit, smelly with rat droppings and in great disorder, but after the wind and rain on the exposed platform it was sheer bliss. There were no seats or benches anywhere, so they squatted on their luggage. The big warehouse-depot held a variety of goods, vats of oil and wine, baskets of fruit and vegetables piled one on top of the other, reaching almost to the ceiling. Two faces pressed against the depot's window panes. A moment later two German soldiers, a sergeant and a corporal, entered. They scrutinised the place and shook their heads in disbelief.

"Is this a waiting room? *Ein Wartezimmer*?" asked the sergeant with an inflexion of disgust.

"*Non capisco*," replied the Italian guard.

Carried away on the spur of the moment Baumgart said in pure German, "*Nein das is kein Wartezimmer*."

The sergeant's eyes widened in astonishment. "*Sie sprechen Deutsch*? Are you German? What are you doing here?"

Baumgart hesitated, regretting his imprudence. He did not wish to disclose their identity but having started the conversation he could not draw back.

"Wir sind Internierte."

"I don't understand. *Ich verstehe nicht*. German internees? Why?"

The corporal nudged him with his elbow. "Can't you see? These are Jews! *Dreckige Juden*!"

Without giving them a further glance both turned on their heels and walked out.

Rauch was beside himself. "You should have kept your mouth shut! Just think what they might have done to us!"

Baumgart agreed. "It was utterly stupid of me."

The two militiamen regarded them sympathetically. They did not fully understand, but guessed what had taken place. Very few Italians harboured any friendly feelings for the Teutonic race, to which they referred as *Testa Dura* and *Teste di Cazzo* or similar unflattering epithets.

Henry felt sick at heart and disgusted with the crude arrogance of these German soldiers. He was anxious to get to their destination, whatever the place might be. Signor Rizzi, for all his bark, was not too hard a taskmaster. Italians seldom are. Whoever their new master was, surely he'd not match the brute arrogance of these *Herrenvolk soldiers.*

Their train was nearly due. Slowly the deserted station began to liven up as it gradually filled with civilians and soldiers. When the train arrived the internees had great difficulty in making their way through the crowd, which by now almost jammed the platform solid. Their strange procession with a guard at each end met with suspicious glances and they were glad when they finally got to the uncovered end of the platform. The train was already full to bursting, and how all those waiting people could ever be squeezed in was hard to imagine. The crowd had already spilled over to the far end, blocking the internees' efforts to board their carriage.

"*Questo compartimento e' riservato!*" yelled one of the militiamen as he hauled off some of the would-be passengers.

"But it is empty! *Vuoto!*" protested the intruders angrily.

"It is reserved, I tell you. By order of the Ministry!" shouted the guard.

At that moment, the same two German soldiers emerged from the jostling crowd. "*Komm Hans*" the sergeant called out. "This carriage is empty."

He tried to open the carriage door, but the two militiamen placed themselves in front of it. "*E' riservato per ordine del Ministero!*"

The sergeant's eyes narrowed and his face set grimly. "Out of my way!" With one mighty swipe he pushed one of the guards aside. In a reflex movement the latter's hand flew to his holster and so did the German's.

But the crowd's attitude changed suddenly. The same hostile crowd that just moments before had been protesting and shoving against the militiamen now made a quick *volte-face* to side with their compatriots.

"Leave him alone, *imbecille!*" they yelled, closing menacingly on the Germans, looking determined and really ugly. Henry was amazed at their boldness. Allies or not, it was that deep-rooted, secular contempt and defiance of the Italians against the Teutonic barbarians, dating from Roman times, that came to the fore. Nor did they appreciate being ordered and pushed around in their own country.

"That is a transport of Jews! *Ein Judentransport!*" the sergeant screamed, and although the Italians, at that time, were not exactly in love with Jews, their dislike of Germans vastly outweighed any artificially imported anti-Semitism. Most of them felt their alliance with Germany was like a temporary pact between a mackerel and a shark: it could never end well.

But the Germans didn't give in so easily. "In *Deutschland*, we transport Jews in cattle trucks! Or else we shoot the lot!" the sergeant yelled at the top of his voice. However his comrade, the corporal, realising they were outnumbered and that the crowd's passions were riding high, put a restraining hand on the sergeant's shoulder.

"*Komm* Fritz! Leave these damned Italians with their filthy Jews!" and he dragged him away.

Henry was shaking with fury. His body was trembling with outrage and disgust that human beings could so abandon common decency. But it was Gurewicz, who in a rare moment of moral indignation cried out, "These arrogant bastards! One day they'll choke in their own shit!"

The crowd split, leaving a corridor for the internees to board the train. Seized by an upsurge of patriotism, these people felt proud of their militiamen, for having stood up to their overbearing allies. Exhausted, physically and emotionally, the internees slumped into their seats. None of them felt like talking or eating; they were too tired and demoralised. Listening to the monotonous rhythm of the wheels, they took refuge in sleep, the great consoler and quencher of pain.

But that blissful escape was not to last long, for they were awakened in the cold middle of the night, when it was pitch dark and told to get out. Dazed and frozen they stumbled out of the train, still numbed from their broken sleep. This station was Teramo. Outside a truck was waiting.

"Did you get some sleep then?" asked one of the guards, once they were seated. This was the first time their guards had shown any interest in them. Sharing that revolting incident must have brought prisoner and jailer closer to each other. And in fact now they proved quite communicative.

"This is the province of Abruzzi and Molise. Mountain country!"

"And where are we going?" enquired Finzi.

There was no point in making a mystery of it now. "Notaresco, a little town in the Abruzzi, about twenty kilometres from here."

Gurewicz could not miss the opportunity to get at Rauch. "Well, Mr Know-all? This isn't Naples as you predicted."

Rauch ignored the jibe, feigning sleep.

Despite the darkness a strange luminosity pervaded the landscape. Something high and white was glistening in the distance. It caught Henry's eye.

"That is Monte Maiella," said the guard, "and Gran Sasso, the highest peak in the Appenines is not far from here."

The ice was broken; the guards warmed up as they took turns describing the Abruzzi.

"These mountains are a favourite hunting ground for the rich. Plenty of venison and especially wild boars. Many wolves, even bears, live here in the wilder parts."

Fraternising with prisoners was forbidden but now at journey's end they could relax.

"They make magnificent sausages here, smoked ham from pigs and boars. In Roman times, this was the country of the Marsi, renowned as magicians and sorcerers. Today there are famous snake charmers here — the *Serpari*."

The dawn was breaking and the white of the glacier became suffused with delicate pink and crimson. The truck began to descend on a serpentine road. They could now see the town from afar. Like all Italian communities, its buildings blended harmoniously with its surroundings, of which it seemed a natural extension. The stone-built houses and cottages leaned against each other, supported here and there by pillars and arches. The streets were narrow, so that the houses seemed to topple over each other in a semblance of natural rock formation.

The truck stopped in front of the larger stone buildings where the internees were told to alight. Henry wondered why they had to get out in the middle of the town. There was nothing resembling a concentration camp in sight; no barbed wire anywhere. Perhaps that large stone building was a prison of some sort.

Chapter 2

Caffè and Casino

It was still very early in the morning and there was no one about. The little town, bathed in the rosy light of the rising sun, seemed fast asleep. The prevailing stillness communicated itself to the internees who unloaded their luggage quietly as if afraid to disturb the peace. Suddenly the heavy door of the large building was flung open and out came several men, large grins on their faces and gesticulating wildly.

"Finally! You're here at last! About time too!"

Obviously they were expected, for the men had come out to welcome them despite the early hour.

As Henry was scrutinising the faces of his new comrades, he gave a start as he recognised under the faint morning light, an old pal, a school-friend from Vienna and later a fellow student at Genoa University.

"Albert!" he cried half in disbelief. "Albert! My God! Is it really you?

Albert Goldfarb, straining to see where the call had come from, was suddenly transfixed. His mouth dropped open and his eyes seemed to pop out from their sockets. "Henry! You old rascal!" He ran over to greet his old school chum, a huge grin on his face.

They embraced and shook hands vigorously. "Where have you been?" asked Albert.

"In the concentration camp at Ferramonti. In Calabria."

"Oh no!" said Albert in a hushed voice. "I've heard of that dreadful place."

Henry smiled. "It's not exactly the Garden of Eden, but you know, you can get used to anything."

Albert grabbed Henry's arm and led him through the gate. He was excited and more than happy to have an old friend with him.

"Where is the camp?" asked Henry.

Albert shook his head. "There isn't one."

Henry's face expressed his astonishment. "So where are we to stay then?"

"Here!" He gestured to the large imposing stone building behind them with a smile.

"Is this a prison of some kind?"

"No! We just live here. We're allowed to move about in the town. It's not like prison at all! This is what they call *confino libero* Henry. Freedom but with limits!"

Henry stopped dead. He could scarcely believe what he was hearing. What was the catch? "You mean there are no restrictions at all?"

"There are some. We are not supposed to leave the town boundaries and have to be back in by sunset. But no one takes the regulations too literally. The people here are very friendly."

Henry listened open-mouthed. Here he was in the middle of the night in a small hilltop town, hundreds of miles from Tarsia, face to face with a long-lost school friend greeting him as if they were at some holiday camp.

It seemed too good to be true, and compared with Ferramonti this was paradise! Already Henry could feel the cool fresh early morning air, so different from the humidity and red dust of Ferramonti. It took some time before Henry dared to believe what Albert was telling him. Their present quarters, a town hall, had been temporarily converted into a hostel for the internees. It had three floors with wide rectangular corridors going into various rooms.

"Isn't there a guard in the building?"

"No, but they keep an eye on us unobtrusively."

Albert led him into a hall, which served as a common room, but Henry was not bothered about seeing the interior of the building. He was dying to see outside, to walk through the narrow streets without restraint or restrictions.

"Albert, show me the town."

"What is the rush? It's early. The shops are closed. Besides there will be coffee soon."

"Never mind that 'coffee'. I've had a belly-full of it in the last fifteen months."

So they went out into the streets, almost deserted at that hour, but to Henry that didn't matter. He inhaled hungrily as he enjoyed the feel of the solid cobblestones under his feet after the dust and sand of Ferramonti. The narrow streets, bathed in scarlet, picturesquely intersected by supporting stone arches, were a painter's delight so touching in their simplicity. "Albert! I can't tell you what it feels like. It's so long since I walked free like this." Henry felt choked with emotion. "I feel almost human again."

They came up to the piazzetta, the small town square, and the throbbing heart of each rural community. Several women were busying themselves putting up market stalls and an elderly man was sweeping the pavement under a small arcade in front of his little coffee bar. There were two little tables placed under the arcade.

"Ah!" exclaimed Henry. "The Caffè Borsa in Genoa's *Piazza de Ferrari!*"

Albert laughed aloud for he too was one of the gang of students who used to spend many an hour in happier times under the Caffè Borsa's arcades in *Via XX Settembre,* watching the girls go by and often undressing — metaphorically speaking — those who'd caught their imagination. How far remote were those unburdened days of light-hearted youth!

"If I can afford it I shall always be down here," said Henry with a deep sigh of pleasure.

They went back to their quarters and the common room, where the usual *'ersatz Kaffee'* was served.

A middle-aged man with greying hair and a friendly smile came to sit beside Henry.

"I hear you are a doctor." Henry nodded. "My name is Sobel. They've made me *capo* here, against my will. Not because of my outstanding brain but on account of my age." He had a pleasant way of chuckling after each sentence, reminiscent of that other grand old man, Altman. "We have a room," he continued, "that's a kind of first aid post, and if you like you could have a bed put in there."

"That would be fine. Thank you…"

"No need to thank me," Sobel interrupted. "The least we can do for our doctor is to give him the privilege of privacy."

This was a further unexpected bounty because of all the ills in Ferramonti, Henry had found the permanent lack of privacy the hardest to bear. Strange, he thought, how fickle life can be. There were doctors by the dozen in Ferramonti, yet here, apart from a doctor Alter, the surgeon, and Albert, who was not fully qualified, there was only himself.

"Just the same, thank you again," said Henry, noticing with a side-glance the green of envy in Dr Rauch's eyes.

"And I shall supply what is needed from my laboratory in Milan," added Rauch. He could not miss this opportunity for self-promotion and had to salvage some prestige.

Albert took Henry to the storeroom, where they selected an iron bed and a mattress. Henry burst out laughing. "A mattress! A real mattress! You should have seen the sack of straw I had in Ferramonti. Each night I cursed it. Each night I resolved to fill it properly next day, but I never did. I almost feel sorry now for having left it incomplete."

When they carried the bed into his room he found that it contained a proper table and chair; none of those wobbly contraptions of Ferramonti. Why, his room even had a balcony! "All this is incredible, Albert!" Henry murmured almost to himself in disbelief as he leaned over the balcony rail, admiring the rooftops wrapped in the soft light of daybreak. Despite his elation he shed a few tears, so overcome to be once more treated as a person, not a prisoner.

"Come come, my friend!" Albert patted him gently on the shoulder, realising the emotional toll that Ferramonti's privations had taken on his chum.

Henry composed himself by conjuring up the supreme pleasure his new environment could offer. "Albert, let's go down to that coffee house in the *piazzetta*..." He stopped in the middle of his exalted enthusiasm. "But the trouble is, I am skint. Not a lira in my pocket. Can you help me out?"

Though usually reluctant to ask favours, Henry had no qualms about borrowing from an old pal. Borrowing amongst students is such a common occupational hazard no one ever thinks twice about relieving a friend of a few lire. To Henry's surprise, Albert took out a wallet containing several banknotes. "Not to worry, my friend!"

Henry was flabbergasted. "Where did you get all that money from?"

"There is opportunity to earn a bit in town, unofficially of course. Most young men are in the army, so there's a shortage of hands. I give lessons in German. Besides, there is always the roulette."

"The what? Roulette? What do you mean?"

"You'll see," replied Albert calmly. "Meantime, let's go."

Henry ran down the steps, his heart beating with joyous anticipation. To sit in a coffee bar seemed at that moment the peak of human experience. Only the day before, his soul was filled with the most gloomy and sinister forebodings. Today his heart ached for joy, and all because of an ordinary house, a room of his own, a table, a mattress and a coffee bar. It took them only a few minutes to reach the *piazzetta*, where Henry made straight for the bar.

The same old man, who had been sweeping the floor earlier on, came to serve them.

"A friend of yours? *Un amico*?" he asked.

"*Si, un amico. Un medico*," replied Albert.

The old man's demeanour, which had been friendly, became deferential. "*Un dottore*," he mumbled as he hurried back to the bar to prepare the *espresso*.

Henry stretched himself, and clasping his hands behind his neck he rocked himself, beaming happily all the while. The sun, the blessed Italian sun was shining, illuminating that marketplace with a radiance of its own.

"It's lovely, Albert. It's so glorious I can't find the words." Again his eyes misted over.

Albert relished every minute of his friend's contentment. A girl with a serious, timid face and big black eyes brought the coffee. She looked closely at Henry, intrigued by this stranger, but didn't say anything.

"Who was that girl?" Henry asked, never one to miss an attractive female.

"She's the youngest daughter of that old man. Her name is Graziella."

"A nice girl. A fine, sensitive face," remarked Henry.

The market stalls were now in full swing, crammed with fruit and vegetables, pottery, kitchenware and all sorts of *bric-à-brac*. Henry watched intently, listening to the bargaining and trying to follow that strange cadence of the Abruzzese dialect.

Albert excused himself and walked off. Henry didn't mind sitting on his own for a while. The same girl came back and took the empty cups away. She gave him a searching look and Henry thought she was hankering to talk to him but didn't dare.

Albert came back. "Here you are, my friend," he said, holding out a packet of cigarettes. Henry was touched. "I think I've forgotten what a real cigarette tastes like."

He lit one straightaway. Rocking gently in his chair and exhaling clouds of smoke, Henry felt at peace with the world. Graziella busied herself at the neighbouring table.

"You know the girl," said Henry with a nod in her direction, "she gave me such a peculiar look while you were away."

"That's because you are a doctor. Her father told me she has tuberculosis. She may be frightened of you."

The two old friends, glad to have met again, sat under the arcade, exchanging old memories and discussing friends and foes. They had known each other from the age of twelve and had plenty to tell each other. Time flew by. They talked and talked, they smiled and they laughed, clapping each other on the shoulder as they remembered each funny or juicy episode.

"Do you remember Gandelman?"

"No," replied Albert. "He must have come to Genoa before my time."

"Well," resumed Henry, "he was a Rumanian Jew. He was smallish, fresh from the provincial backwaters of Rumania. Someone must have given him my address for he came straight to me from the station with his luggage and all. He wanted to stay the night, hoping to find lodgings the following day. There was no room, so he asked if he could sleep in the bathtub. My landlady did not object, but could hardly control her laughter. Next morning he knocked at my door to borrow a shaving brush and soap. He had his own razor. Soon after I went into the bathroom and found him with his face literally covered in blood. I looked at him, aghast. 'You are bleeding all over!' He was unperturbed. 'I always do,' he replied and, unconcerned, he continued shaving. Apparently this awful bloodletting he considered as a normal by-product of shaving. He then asked for my towel. Naturally with all that blood from his face, I was not exactly thrilled by the idea, but told him reluctantly to take it. I was already nearing the end of my patience and so when a minute later he asked to borrow my toothbrush, as if that were the most natural thing to do, I got hold of him by the scruff of his neck and threw him out! What a nut case!"

They laughed till they cried.

"I haven't laughed like this in ages," gasped Henry, catching his breath.

They had been sitting there for almost two hours. It was time to go back, have a wash and unpack. Lunch was served in the common room, with people taking turns to wait on others. The quality of food compared favourably with the Ferramontese concoctions, because more money was available from the sporadic or regular earnings of various members of the community. The basic allowance of five lire was the same as in Ferramonti.

Conditioned to the Ferramonti *siesta*, and still feeling the effects of the journey, Henry looked forward to an hour's sleep. He longed to stretch himself out on a proper bed and mattress. Almost immediately he fell asleep and when he awoke the winter sun was setting. Henry stayed in bed a little longer, savouring the long-forgotten luxury of being alone, and reflecting on the imponderables of life. When he got up he switched on the light and smiled happily at the additional bonus of electric illumination.

There was a knock on the door and Albert came in.

"I was here an hour ago, but you were fast asleep, snoring your head off."

Albert lent Henry a helping hand in tidying up the room and organizing the medicine bottles, liniments and bandages, setting some of them out on shelves and stowing others away in drawers. The room now looked habitable, even cosy. A loud vibrating noise made Henry start. It was the sound of a gong. "What is that?" he asked, "*Appello*?"

"No! It's the usual signal for the evening meal."

Henry laughed. "In Ferramonti we had three roll calls a day. It almost drove me round the bend."

Most internees were already sitting at their tables and Mr
Sobel, the *capo*, came over again to Henry. He seemed to have
smartened himself up to the extent of wearing a black jacket
and tie. Henry wondered why he had bothered, unless he
wanted to impress the newcomers with the dignity of his office. Just then Mr Sobel rose.

"I hope the doctor and his friends will be our guests of honour tonight." He seemed to wink a little at Albert, who winked
back, smiling. Henry was a little bewildered, but his astonishment escalated to perplexity when after the meal Sobel rose
again, announcing solemnly, *"Mesdames and Messieurs, faites
vos jeux."*

Henry was astounded. What was the meaning of that
croupier's cry with which Henry had been so familiar in his
gambling days? In no time the long table in the centre of the
room was cleared of dishes and covered with a green cloth
overprinted with numbers in black and red. A small roulette
sprang up from nowhere and so did two gaming rakes and
fiches.

"Mesdames et Messieurs, faites vos jeux!" repeated Sobel,
smiling.

Henry didn't believe his ears and eyes. Of all things, roulette was certainly the last he'd expected when setting out for
his unknown destination.

"Give me some *fiches* for five lire," said someone.

"Give me ten," said another.

Henry was dumbfounded. His eyes shone, but he had no
money.

Albert could read his thoughts. "People don't have to pay
for the fiches right away. Mr Sobel notes their debts in a little
book. They pay when they have earned some money. But the
bank pays on demand."

"Rather one-sided, isn't it?"

"Don't worry your head over it. Sobel knows what he is doing. He is a passionate gambler himself and makes a few extra
lire. He holds the bank. Have you ever known the bank to lose
in the long run?"

Apparently Sobel was a wealthy man, or rather, rich by
comparison, like the one-eyed king among the blind.

"Faites vos jeux!"

In a flash Henry recalled the nights of excitement and anguish when, cut off from his family, no passport and prohibited from working, he'd tried his luck at the casinos of Venice and San Remo. He remembered the thrill of his big wins, the despair of heavy losses, the stupid rituals and superstitions that forced him to enter the gaming rooms by certain routes only, the nonsensical selection of numbers derived from his train seats, from tickets and similar absurdities.

"Faites vos jeux!"

Henry plucked up his courage. "Mr Sobel, may I have *fiches* for five lire? But I must warn you I haven't a single coin in my pocket."

"Take as much as you like, doctor. You'll give me the money when you can."

The game was in full swing now, with some people winning and some losing.

"Well, *Herr Doktor*, aren't you going to play?" asked Sobel, and proceeded to call out, "*Rien ne va plus.*"

There it was, the signal Henry could never resist, for when the wheel was spinning was precisely the moment when Henry liked to place his bets. He was a 'serial player'. The last number being 15, a somewhat distant relation of the zero sector. Henry placed his *fiches* on three numbers of that series: 26, 32, and 3.

"*Trente-deux, rouge, pair et passe!*" Sobel announced.

Henry's heart missed a beat. He'd got a *'plaine'*. He began to experience that quickened pulse of old and repeated his bet. He won again. And then again! This was his night, he felt, when nothing could go wrong. He felt it in his very bones! His excitement grew out of all proportion, his eyes sparkled, he felt light-headed and momentarily forgot where he was, confusing Notaresco with the chandelier-lit salon of San Remo. Albert did not like the look of this. He suspected that Henry, having previously been infected with the gambling bug was in danger. Originally he'd played to keep his head above water but he'd gradually fallen prey to the nerve-tingling lure of the blind ivory ball and now was about to fall into the trap again.

"I think you've won enough," said Albert.

Sobel, however, although on the losing side, seemed to be enjoying Henry's luck. It must have been the enjoyment of a *voyeur*.

"Let him play. This is his night."

In the end Henry had won twenty seven lire. He paid Sobel the five lire back and was left with twenty two lire in his pocket. In truth this was a paltry sum, a trifle, but penniless as he had been, this pittance seemed to him a fortune, an unexpected gift from heaven. It meant that he could sit at the coffee bar every day for more than three weeks. It meant that for a limited period he could look into shops knowing he could actually buy something if he chose. This had been the most wonderful day, one to cherish for many years to come.

Chapter 3

Settling in

Next day, Henry began to take an interest in his new companions. Among them was a young man by the name of Schöntal, whom Albert introduced with the words, "This is our chess genius."

Schöntal was a tall, round-shouldered individual, who seldom looked one in the face, but when one chanced to meet his eyes there was a burning intensity in them. He rarely spoke, always looked tired and kept to himself; clearly a total introvert. On hearing of Henry's interest in chess he offered to play him and demolished him with his brilliance.

He had come to Italy from Vienna as a refugee, and had spent some time in Genoa under the most precarious conditions. There was something weary and tormented about this unassuming young man, one of life's casualties, despite his victories in chess.

Apart from Schöntal, there was yet another 'genius' amongst them, a Hungarian Jew by the name of Krohn. He was a contract bridge genius, but unlike Schöntal, who played chess for chess sake, *ars gratia artis*, Krohn made his living from bridge. He was in a class of his own, head and shoulders above the average bridge player. Normally Krohn wouldn't have bothered with this unimaginative bunch of dilettantes but here they were fair game for him, small fry, whom he could pillage to his heart's content. Krohn needed the money.

After a laborious and adventurous journey, on foot, on horseback and as a stowaway, he had arrived in Italy completely destitute. He was an ardent communist and had no scruples about 'fleecing the rich', except that there were no rich among them. A little man with a lively weasel face, Krohn had a pair of deep-set penetrating eyes which were constantly on the move. His memory was phenomenal, photographic, enabling him to register every card that had been played. Once the game was over, he kept away from the others. One sensed that he had only contempt for the rest of the internees.

After the excitement of the first few days, when the impact of the new surroundings and way of life had worn off a little,

Henry began to settle down and fall into a pleasant routine. Soon after breakfast, he would go out—alone or with Albert—and walk through the narrow cobbled streets, window shopping and exploring the area. Just to walk in freedom gave him a feeling of deep satisfaction. Then he would sit down at the coffee bar to read a newspaper. To be able to do so publicly was another privilege. He recalled how out-of-date newspapers discarded by Parrini's construction workers in Ferramonti would be seized furtively and consumed in the *camerata* down to the last word to glean news of the war or of life in the outside world. No, he took nothing for granted as he sipped his espresso in the Caffè Imperiale under the arch in the cobbled *piazzetta*.

Sometimes he would listen to the old man's tales about the snake charmers, about the 'good old days' when sausages and ham were plentiful and cheap. Occasionally he would exchange a few words with Graziella, who seemed by degrees to be losing her apprehension and reticence.

In the afternoons he would play chess with Schöntal, read a book, tinker with his medicines and drugs, write letters to his pals in Ferramonti, or play bridge. Once a week, after the evening meal, the customary roulette session was held but never again had the imagination or the luck of that first night revisited him. He was afraid of losing what little he had, placed only smallish bets and managed to break even most times.

And so his first month in Notaresco passed, as Henry enjoyed the freedom, the fine crisp air, and the friendly tolerance of the locals, who treated him with a degree of respect, despite being an internee. As the only fully qualified doctor in town, this conferred some status. Since the 1938 racial laws, Jews were forbidden employment so Henry was, here in the little town of Notaresco, finally achieving some recognition for all those years of study.

To his surprise Henry discovered yet another young man to whom the appellation 'genius' might be applied, with some reservations. His name was Lapidus, though he was nicknamed 'Strings'. This young man was a guitarist of extraordinary talent, inseparable from his instrument, which he had carried all

the way from Hamburg. Lapidus was only nineteen years old,
a small chap with curly hair, a flat frog nose and a pair of legs
so bandy he 'couldn't stop a pig in a passage' as the proverb
goes. His gift lay not only in the mastery of his instrument, but
also in a prodigious talent for composition and improvisation.
Often a small group of music lovers would assemble in
Henry's room to listen to Lapidus's virtuosity. He would usually start with conventional themes, Granados or Albeniz, to
warm up, but soon he would give free rein to his imagination
and improvise original and exquisite music of his own. Sometimes he would play non-stop until far into the night, mesmer-
ising his audience. Lapidus called these improvisations
'Notarescana'.

In the second week of December 1941 the sleepy little town
of Notaresco woke to the shocking news that the Japanese had
launched a surprise attack which had all but destroyed the US
naval fleet at Pearl Harbour in the Pacific. The USA had been
dragging its heels about entering the war in Europe up to this
point but now there was no holding them back: the USA declared war with Japan. Just three days later, two British battle-
ships, the Prince of Wales and the Repulse, were sunk by the
Japanese who had also taken Guam and had begun to infilt-
rate Malaysia. The internees could talk of little else and as
usual there was much speculation as to how this might affect
them. Some had no doubt that the USA had the potential to
pull round. The big question was whether they would be
given enough breathing space to get their war machine in full
swing or would they be bled to death before they had time to
recover from their wounds? This promised to be a very
gloomy Christmas for the Allies and for all whose hopes and
fates rested on them but for the little town of Notaresco, nest-
ling in the shelter of the snowy peaks of the Monte Maiello,
Pearl Harbour and all it represented became yet another factor
in the great chess-game in which they were nothing but onlookers.

Nonetheless, Christmas was drawing near. Unlike the
northern practice of decorating little fir trees, palm branches
were used here instead. After all, Jesus was born in the land of
the palm. Cribs with the Holy Family—known as 'presepio'—

made their appearance in windows and shops, with the most lavish and spectacular one placed in the *piazzetta*. The figures were carved in wood as is customary in mountain regions, and testified to the skill of Italian peasant art.

There was also a procession during which the Madonna was carried through the streets. She wore her Sunday best and on her silk robes, draped in graceful folds, banknotes were pinned. This was the customary local way of collecting money for the church and the poor.

The market stalls bustled with feverish activity as the Christmas festivities approached. They were decorated with garlands and coloured paper chains; they overflowed with displays of gold and silver stars, glittering paper, tinsel, blue and red glass balls and delicate silvery filaments. In spite of rationing, the rustic population managed to produce some extras: little nut cakes, honey buns and *brioche*, lots of ice cream and plenty of fruit. Customs, in difficult and uncertain times, assume even greater significance for they confer a sense of security in their habitual rhythms.

Henry sat at the coffee bar, watching the festive preparations, while the old man gave his running commentary.

"Ah!" he sighed, "Christmas is supposed to be the season of goodwill. But the world has gone mad. *Tutti matti!*"

Henry seldom replied. He got used to the old man's chatter, which he regarded as a sort of background music.

"Look at those miserable stalls! They used to sell pheasants, ducks, geese, turkeys, hares, smoked ham and all the best produce of the Abruzzi." He sighed again. "This is no longer a season of joy. My youngest son is in Tripoli — a soldier — and my daughter Graziella, she's sick."

Henry, who had been lending only half an ear to the old man's monologue, suddenly switched his full attention to his discourse.

"Graziella is ill, you say? What is the matter with her?"

"The doctors say she has tuberculosis."

"How long has she been ill?"

"Since she came back from the convent nearly two years ago."

Henry had studied TB in the department of Professor Maragliano in Genoa and had some knowledge of the subject.

"How did the illness start?"

"She was losing her appetite and weight. Then she started coughing. Once or twice she spat blood." He stopped to wipe his eyes. Then he went on. "They took a picture of her lungs and later they sent her to a sanatorium."

At that moment Graziella came to the table. The old man had the sense to drop their conversation but he put his arm around her shoulder.

"She is a good girl, my Graziella. If only she would eat!" and he slapped her on the back. "She only picks at her food like a bird!"

In his adolescence, Henry had entertained romantic notions about pulmonary tuberculosis. His first awareness of that dreadful disease originated from the '*Lady of the Camellias*', a tale used later by Verdi in '*Traviata*' followed by the tragic consumptive Mimi in '*Bohème*', all of which added to his fragmentary knowledge of the illness. He had also learned that this scourge had taken its toll on so many great men, like Mozart and Chopin. And yet their tragic death in the summer of their life did not quite eradicate the romance which in his adolescent mind surrounded that disease. Only on taking up the study of medicine did these romantic notions evaporate as he began to see tuberculosis for what it was: a curse and a killer.

He made up his mind to help Graziella if she'd let him. For the moment Henry decided not to pursue the matter, but leave it for an occasion when he could have a few words with her when her father was not about.

One day a huge box bearing the Milan postmark and the name of a laboratory was delivered to Rauch. It contained surgical spirit, catgut, cotton wool, surgical needles, bandages and other items of a similar kind.

"What is all this for?" was Gurewicz's comment. "Anyone would think we were opening a hospital." He was intent on spoiling Dr Rauch's great hour as the benefactor of the internees. "Surgical needles and catgut," Gurewicz continued, "who the hell is going to operate?"

"I am," declared Dr Alter, the surgeon.

"You?" Gurewicz exclaimed, full of contempt. "Don't make me laugh!"

Gurewicz was no respecter of age or social standing. Dr Alter was a Polish Jew in his fifties. He was fat, with a bloated face and heavily sagging bags under his eyes. Rumour hinted that he was not averse to drink when he could get it. He always talked about the surgical feats he had performed in Krakow but somehow no one seemed impressed. Gurewicz had touched a raw nerve.

"So, I make you laugh, do I? Wait till you get appendicitis, you arrogant puppy. It will be my turn to laugh then."

Dr Alter proclaimed that he had been second assistant to a Dr Wiesental in Krakow, which name apparently must have carried some weight, for he repeated the name *ad nauseam.*

On sunny days Henry liked to sit on his balcony. The street sloped and usually there was a little rivulet of water flowing down the middle of the road. Henry would admire the slanting roofs opposite with the heavy stones on top, presumably to prevent them from taking off during gales.

Opposite Henry's balcony lived a buxom young woman who liked to sing all day; she appeared to be alone, at least as far as Henry noticed. She had an endless repertoire of songs and seemed to never tire of singing them at the top of her voice. Though her blaring recitals got on his nerves, Henry eventually came to accept her vocal acrobatics as one would adjust to the nuisance of a neighbour's non-stop radio, or the noise of a waterfall.

One day Baumgart was excited when he joined the bridge party as his wife and daughter had been given permission to visit him during the Christmas holidays.

"I have not seen them since my internment in Ferramonti. I am over the moon."

No one commented. There was a hush. He quickly realised his *faux pas* since none of the others had seen their families either.

"How stupid of me," he apologised, "I was carried away."

Henry sought to reassure him. "We don't begrudge your bit of good luck and we are all looking forward to meeting your family."

Baumgart was all churned up. His mind was anywhere except on bridge. Krohn, whom he was partnering, showed signs of mounting tension and irritability. All he cared for was to get on with the game to make some money.

"I do wish you'd concentrate a little, Mr Baumgart."

Baumgart apologised, but Gurewicz, crude and tactless as ever, opened his loud mouth.

"Don't take any notice of him, Mr Baumgart. He's only jealous."

"Jealous? Jealous of what?" asked Krohn calmly.

"Well, who'd come to visit you, you little twerp?"

Krohn, his eyebrows contracted, regarded him fiercely but didn't say anything.

It was only three days to Christmas. Although this was not a traditional holiday time for the internees, taking part in the host nation's festive seasons had always been the norm for the Wandering Jew and the internees took pleasure in the excitement and festivity they saw around them in the little town and its people. The coffee bar was being adorned with seasonal decorations and Henry gave a helping hand, fastening pretty coloured chains to the ceiling. Then he sat down as usual, ordering an espresso. But to his surprise Graziella put down a huge piece of cake as well.

"No Graziella," Henry protested, "I cannot afford this."

"It's on the house. My father said so," she replied.

As the old man had gone out into the market, Henry seized this chance to have a chat with Graziella.

"How are you keeping? I have been told you have not been too well lately."

Graziella blushed. She did not like to talk about her illness and carried on clearing the next table, avoiding Henry's eyes.

"Not too bad," she replied eventually.

"Have you lost any weight recently?"

"Only a bit."

"Any fever?"

"Just now and then."

She was embarrassed, feeling some kind of stigma attached to her illness. Henry did not want to press her, but after a while he asked casually, "Do you still get some treatment?"

"I used to get injections of calcium."

"Don't you get them now?"

"Our doctor has been called up. I have to get my injections in Chieti or Teramo, and that is too far."

"Would you like me to give you the injections?"

Again a deep blush crimsoned her face and neck. "I don't know. I wouldn't want to be a bother."

"No bother to me, Graziella. I am a doctor, you know."

She did not reply right away.

"I shall have to ask my father."

Henry left it at that. With such a delicate personality it was better not to rush things.

Soon, it was Christmas Eve and Baumgart's strained anticipation of his family reunion communicated itself to all the others. Symbolically, Baumgart's wife and daughter became everyone's wife, daughter, mother or lover, and eagerly expected by everyone.

Eventually the long-expected autobus from Teramo arrived. On alighting from it the first words that Mrs Baumgart uttered were, "Richard, Hong Kong has fallen!"

Somehow these words were an anti-climax for everyone. Not because of the fall of Hong Kong—to hell with Hong Kong—but because in their imagination each of them had romanticised that first encounter after so long a separation, embellishing it with a range of colour from his own palette.

"Oh Papa!" exclaimed his daughter, and fell on her father's neck. Baumgart embraced and kissed them both. "Oh! Darlings! How lovely to see you again!" His voice was choked and he could hardly keep his tears back.

He then turned to his pals, who were standing back discreetly.

"Let me introduce you to my wife and daughter."

They all shook hands, after which the others departed, leaving the Baumgart family to enjoy their reunion undisturbed. Mrs Baumgart, in her early forties, was tall, blonde and sturdy and had cold blue eyes. In contrast, her daughter had nothing of her mother's Nordic looks. She resembled her father, having his brown hair, and smaller stature and gentler look about her. Baumgart had arranged lodgings for the two women in an inn close to the internee's quarters. Judging by their apparel and luggage, they were not short of money. Most of the time Baumgart spent with his family, but for comradeship's sake he came occasionally for a meal with his pals.

On Boxing Day he invited some friends over to the inn, Sobel, Albert and Henry among them. Mrs Baumgart had good dress sense, though she looked rather austere and formal in her dark blue evening attire. She received the internees coolly, but her daughter, Anna-Lise, gave them all a very warm and friendly welcome.

In Mrs Bertha Baumgart's opinion, the Axis powers, aided by their mighty ally, Japan, had already won the war. Out of politeness, for understandably she could not help having patriotic feelings, despite her marriage to a Jew, no one contradicted her. She went on saying how it was Germany that had to bear the brunt of the war, and time and again had to rescue the Italians in their ill-conceived, and worse executed, campaigns.

"We would have been better off without them," she said in an unguarded moment, making it quite clear where her hopes and sympathies lay.

"*Blood is thicker than water*," Henry thought, trying his hardest to make allowances for Bertha Baumgart's partisanship. Richard Baumgart blushed to the roots of his hair and despite his lively chatter, he seemed on tenterhooks.

Sobel, who by now had drunk almost half a bottle of Orvieto Abbocato, was in good form, chuckling and enjoying himself.

"And how do you like it in Rome, Mrs Baumgart?" he asked jovially.

She gave him an odd look, as if resenting his familiarity, but replied, "The usual Italian muddle, lack of organisation and order."

"Have you any news about the Jewish situation in Germany?"

Her expression hardened. Clearly she did not like this question.

"It's getting worse. Mass deportations to concentration camps. Even for mixed marriages and their offspring."

"What do you mean precisely?" asked Sobel.

"Unless the Aryan spouse is willing to divorce the Jewish partner, both parents and children are sent to concentration camps—or worse."

She screwed up her eyes and wrinkled her forehead. "Even in Rome life gets more difficult every day. They're getting less tolerant of German nationals' mixed marriages, even abroad."

An icy silence fell suddenly at the ominous implication of these words but Sobel came to the rescue.

"We must hope for the best. The Devil is never as black as he is painted."

Throwing a side-glance at Baumgart, Henry was shocked at the utter transformation of his countenance. He looked sad and pale, almost defeated.

It was Anne-Lise's turn to come tactfully to the rescue.

"This is supposed to be a merry season, mother! So, for now, let's put such gloomy thoughts aside." She put her arms around her father and kissed him on the cheek.

However, the dark shadow which had imperceptibly descended on them all was not to be dispelled that easily. The internees stayed for a while in an atmosphere of forced hilarity, largely engendered by Baumgart's generous offerings of wine. They even seemed to enjoy themselves when the fumes of *vino* began to take effect, but when they stepped into the cold winter's night, they promptly sobered up.

Albert nudged Henry. "I would not give much for Baumgart's marriage." Henry made no comment. He felt sad and very sorry for Baumgart, whose high expectations of joy threatened to turn into a nightmare. Sobel sighed, and muttered something sotto voce which sounded like, "Such is life."

Two days later the Baumgart women went back to Rome.

Chapter 4

Medical Matters

now fell, carpeting the little town over the next few days, reminding Henry of happier times as a child in Vienna, where Christmas was celebrated in style. And so, the internees decided on a little celebration of their own to mark New Year's Eve. They made some garlands to brighten the place up then worked out a programme of entertainment to satisfy the diverse tastes and talents of their audience. Finzi, the Egyptian, would perform some Arab impressions, Gurewicz volunteered to sing operatic arias, while Krohn, the bridge professional, agreed, somewhat reluctantly, to entertain with card tricks. Lapidus was entrusted with creating a festive atmosphere by playing improvisations of 'Notarescana'. And to crown the occasion, a special roulette session would be held after the entertainment to see in the New Year.

Cheap local wine was bought to enhance the festive mood and a few local delicacies, chestnuts and *sfogliatelle*, little sweet pastries, somehow found their way onto the internees' dinner plates. As it turned out, Gurewicz's operatic arias earned the greatest applause. His was a truly magnificent voice; his delivery totally professional.

Lapidus's 'Notarescana' unfortunately suffered from frequent interruptions by the audience, who were feeling the effects of the cheap wine. They had been drinking steadily all evening and some had reached the point of no return. Sobel's eyes were sparkling, Krohn, heartily complimented for his sleight of hand, seemed more animated than usual, and even Schöntal became bolder and actually looked people in the eye. Stuffy Rauch lost some of his starch and his mask-like countenance displayed a silly grin, quite unusual for this self-important ass.

And so in the prevailing hilarity and horseplay, a good deal of Lapidus's 'Notarescana' was drowned by the noise. But the one most affected by the wine was Dr Alter. He had drunk more than his share so his bloated face and eye bags were even puffier than usual. Several times during Lapidus's delicate *pi-*

anissimos, he started singing Polish songs at the top of his voice, distorting the sounds with his sagging jaws.

"Shut up you clown!" yelled Gurewicz, but Dr Alter continued to make a nuisance of himself, particularly offensive to a professional singer's musical ear.

Sobel in his normal suave way did his best to calm him down. "Maybe you'd better lie down, Dr Alter. You'll feel better."

But Dr Alter objected. "What's wrong with being merry?" he blabbered as he continued to fill the room with his vocal contortions.

"The fat swine has been drinking too much again!" cried Gurewicz, which coming from him, overweight as he was, struck everyone as highly amusing.

But Henry was not amused. He resented Gurewicz's insulting vulgarity, especially towards a colleague. "Just hold your tongue! You're addressing a professional man after all!"

Gurewicz responded with a contemptuous laugh. "Professional man, my foot! Professional boozer perhaps, and so bad at that, he can't even hold it."

At this insult, Dr Alter staggered to his feet, waving his fist in Gurewicz's face. "You! You!" he jabbered, "Just mind what you say to a surgeon of note!"

Again Gurewicz burst out laughing. "A surgeon? I wouldn't let you cut my corns!"

Dr Alter made a grab at Gurewicz, but unsteady on his feet, he slipped and fell to the floor after which he became as docile as a lamb, when Sobel led him out of the room. Gurewicz had the true killer-instinct of a pike, choosing his victims mostly from the injured and maimed. As soon as he sensed a human weakness or defect in anyone he had to pounce on it.

With Dr Alter out of the way, Lapidus went on undisturbed with his *impromptus*, plucking gently at the guitar as well as the audience's heartstrings. Baumgart's eyes were wet. He had been weeping.

Henry was not drunk, but in that friendly, communicative condition produced by a slight tipsiness. He was in an expansive mood and had to fight back the temptation to disclose something to Albert he had kept quiet about for years. It was a harmless student prank, but Henry was afraid of offending Albert if he told him the truth.

It happened about seven years back, in those halcyon days of light-hearted student life, soon after Albert had arrived in Genoa. Before long, the fraternity of foreign students took him under its wing, describing all the attractions and warning him of the dangers of Genoa, in particular the criminals, brothels and pimps in the port area. To give him a first-hand illustration, they went down there with him one night but it so happened that all was quiet and peaceful.

"Where are all those hoodlums and pimps you spoke of? Where's all the brawling and killing?" he'd asked, looking down his nose, unimpressed.

The other students took it badly. How dare he belittle 'their' Genoa's wicked nightlife? They decided to teach him a lesson and contacted a student by the name of Fenster, an accomplished actor. Together they hatched a plan, to meet on a certain day and hour in an agreed part of the old port. To lend further piquancy to their enterprise they also resolved to meet at the Caffè Borsa after the job was done.

On the pre-arranged day Henry and three other students set out with Albert to the old town, ostensibly to visit some places of ill repute in the port. Henry directed their steps towards the chosen spot, a *cul-de-sac* in a derelict quarter. It had been raining, so there was nothing unusual in the tall man standing under a street lamp, sheltering under an umbrella. The collar of his raincoat was turned up, the brim of his hat turned down, concealing his face completely. As they came closer, the tall man began to swear and approached them with the swaying gait of the inebriate. Suddenly he pounced on Albert, caught him by the throat and started hitting him with his umbrella, screaming and cursing while he worked him over. The rest of the students took flight while Fenster continued to beat the daylights out of Albert.

Henry and his pals took refuge in a doorway, stifling their giggles. Eventually they heard Albert's distressed voice calling out to them and they re-appeared. Albert was shaken, frightened and bruised; his left eye would become a veritable shiner. He was furious as he accused his pals of cowardice.

They apologised as well as they could, confessing that they too had been terrified. In the end Albert accepted their apologies, calmed down and agreed to join them in the Caffè Borsa.

The best part was still to come, for after a few minutes that same Fenster, minus hat and umbrella, 'happened' to pass in front of their table, when Henry invited him casually to sit down, and introduced him to Albert.

"I hear you are a freshman. Do you like Genoa?"

There was a kind of perverse merriment in the air. Albert smiled mysteriously, exchanging knowing glances with his comrades.

"I liked it all right, until tonight."

"Why? What happened tonight?" enquired Fenster as innocently as he could, and Albert poured his heart out.

"He was a madman! A madman with staring crazy eyes."

Fenster feigned great interest and sympathy.

"But would you recognise him, if you ever saw him again?" he asked, while the rest of them held their breath and bit their lips to suppress their mirth.

"I certainly would!" replied Albert. "How could I ever forget his face?!"

This was the silly prank they had played on Albert and to this day he was unaware of it. Henry had to struggle with his better judgement not to blurt out the true story to Albert, for the alcohol circulating in his blood was threatening to loosen his tongue. But he controlled his urge for confidences.

"'Perhaps I will tell him one day," he muttered to himself, "but not tonight." It would have been a shame to disturb the happy frivolity of the New Year's Eve celebration.

With the Christmas and 1942 New Year celebrations over, life resumed its normal rhythm. As soon as Henry went back to his regular morning coffee, the old man approached him immediately.

"I have been waiting for you, *dottore*. Graziella told me. I would be most grateful to pay for any treatment."

"It will cost you nothing." Henry cut him short. Luckily there was a large stock of calcium gluconate, a common enough preparation, among the medicaments at his disposal, though Henry had little faith in its therapeutic value. He had seen too many die, despite intensive calcium therapy. The only treatment was rest, rich diet, fresh air and calcium therapy, which amounted to precious little. One day, he was convinced, research would find the answer to this scourge of humanity. Meanwhile he would do what little he could. Though Henry refused any fee he gladly accepted the hospitality of the bar. Henceforth no charges would be made for coffee or anything else he chose. This in itself was sufficiently rewarding. Henry had come to like this timid and sensitive person and if her illness was in its early stages he could possibly help her.

Graziella was still very nervous, blushing whenever he spoke to her, but as time went on she came out of her shell little by little and learned to look him in the face without colouring to the roots of her hair. Her temperature oscillated. At times it was normal, at times sub-febrile. He wished to examine her.

"Go ahead," said the old man, "she is in your hands. May God bless you."

I *may well need his blessings*, thought Henry, listening to Graziella's chest. Both apices seemed to be affected, the left more than the right. An X-ray would have been a great help, but as an internee his hands were tied. He talked it over with Sobel.

"It is very kind of you to take so much trouble, but I must warn you, you may get into trouble yourself."

"How is that?"

"They may accuse you of practising."

"It's not a criminal offence! Doctors do practise medicine!"

"I know, but you're an internee." Sobel scratched his head, wondering how to get out of the impasse. "Perhaps it would be best to see Signor Gaspari, the *Capo Polizia*."

So they went to his office. The *Capo Polizia* was a little, inoffensive looking man, whose face was adorned, indeed dominated, by a huge black moustache. He listened to Henry in silence, nodding intermittently to indicate he understood what it was all about.

"You understand," he said at length, "an internee is not supposed to fraternise with the population, much less to treat people." Henry did not reply. Signor Gaspari seemed ill at ease.

"I really ought to report this, but I know you only want to help. Anyway, what do you want me to do?"

"May I have your permission to go with the patient to the hospital in Chieti to see her medical records, arrange an X-ray?"

"Out of the question!" interrupted Signor Gaspari, shaking his head. "No internees are allowed out of the town. These are my orders."

"In that case, may I give a letter to the hospital doctor?"

"No you can't. You are not supposed to have any official dealings with any institution whatsoever! You are an internee."

Henry felt discouraged, humiliated and helpless. Though Signor Gaspari had been very civil he had nevertheless rubbed it in, reminding him repeatedly of his real status as a mere Jewish internee, not a practising physician.

The *Capo Polizia* felt uncomfortable. Kind and weak by nature, he had never liked the responsibilities his position imposed on him. He would have liked to help, but didn't know how.

"I'll tell you what I will do. I will get the hospital records, X-rays, etc., and show them to you, here in my office. Officially I know nothing at all about the whole business."

By and large, Henry was pleased with that solution and thanked Signor Gaspari for his kindness.

Chapter 5

Doctor and Patient

Time in Notaresco, on the whole, went by very pleasantly and smoothly, often approaching the state of '*dolce far niente*'. Only occasionally did anyone require medical attention and except for Graziella's regular intravenous injections Henry had very little to do professionally while chess, bridge and Lapidus' guitar provided pleasant diversions. The only disturbing, or rather frightening, facts of life came from the war bulletins, extolling the unstoppable Japanese forces, swarming all over the East like rapacious locusts.

One morning, while sitting on his balcony, Henry suddenly became aware that spring was around the corner. Contrary to northern latitudes, spring in Italy is mostly uneventful, for the transition from winter is barely perceptible. Snow falls rarely, except in higher altitudes and the plethora of evergreens diminishes the impact of nature's seasonal awakening.

It was on one of those lovely mornings when the sun sparkled on the cobbles that Henry, while taking a stroll, was approached by an agitated group of his comrades.

"Doctor! We have been looking for you!"

"What's wrong?"

"The woman opposite. The one who sings! She has cut her hand so badly, Dr Alter can't stop the bleeding."

Henry made haste, and while running upstairs to her apartment, could hear the woman before he could see her, for she screeched like a pig being slaughtered.

"*Mamma mia! Santa Madonna!*"

On entering the room, Henry found her in a state of hysteria; nor was she the only one for Dr Alter was at least as agitated. He was rushing aimlessly around the room, ostensibly looking for something. The woman's hand and forearm was swaddled in an enormous cocoon of cotton wool and bandages soaked with blood, which was dripping onto the floor. Signora Maria Cerletti was yelling, crying and groaning by turns, invoking her own mother and Jesus Christ's.

Catching Dr Alter in mid-circuit, Henry demanded what it was he was seeking so urgently.

"These needles are too small! I can't thread the catgut through the eye! There are no others and you'll have to hurry before she loses more blood."

Dr Alter went to the window and tried again in the brighter light. His hands were shaking badly. Meanwhile Henry, after removing the bandages, inspected the wound and examined the mobility of her fingers.

"Luckily it's just a question of stitching up the hand," he said after his examination.

Dr Alter was still fidgeting with the needle. Small wonder — agitation and alcoholic tremor are not exactly a surgeon's best friends!

"Permit me," said Henry and threaded the needle for him, whereupon Dr Alter hastened to proceed with the suture.

"Don't you think we'd better clip the needle to a needle-holder?" asked Henry as tactfully as he could. Dr Alter looked distressed. Henry clipped the needle for him; but as soon as the needle touched Maria's skin she let out a dreadful yell followed by a piercing shriek, which reverberated throughout the entire building. Panic-stricken and helpless, Dr Alter looked at Henry and made as if to hand over the needle to him. But Henry shook his head.

"Don't let her screams bother you! I'm sure you'll stitch her up much better than I could ever do."

At the same time Henry slapped Maria's face, the classic way to bring hysterics to their senses. This simple measure had the desired effect. Maria confined her outbursts to invoking the saints, to which no one objected. Clumsily, with tremulous hands, Dr Alter completed the suture and when this was done he gave Henry a warm look. Nothing was said but, from that day, Alter never mentioned his assistantship with Dr Wiesenthal, which in itself was a great relief to all.

At Schöntal's suggestion, Henry agreed to take lessons in the theory of chess and was astonished by the wealth of thought and literature that had gone into that game over centuries. They discussed opening strategy and tactics and reconstructed some brilliant games of the grandmasters. In time they got to know each other better, so occasionally they discussed topics unrelated to chess. Sometimes Henry had the impression that Schöntal wished to tell him something, but lacked the courage to do so. Then one day, after a game, Schöntal seemed to dither.

"Herr Doctor" he said at last, "Albert mentioned that you're interested in psychology." Henry nodded.

"He also said you underwent psycho-analysis recently."

"That's right. It was a Training Analysis and not completed. It's necessary if you want to work in the field of analysis."

Schöntal was getting increasingly nervous and worked up. Henry came to his aid.

"Well, did you want to ask me about it?"

This was the little push Schöntal needed to pluck up his courage with both hands.

"I wonder...what I mean...," he could not find the right words and then he spurted out, "Would you mind analysing me?"

"It would be a pleasure. Besides, I could repay you this way for the lessons in the noble game of chess."

Schöntal's face lit up. "That would be very kind" he said, greatly relieved.

Henry smiled. "But I must warn you! I'm only a beginner."

"Oh! I have every confidence in you," he added enthusiastically, which is how Schöntal's analysis began.

Henry was glad to have an opportunity to try out his newly acquired skill on someone who was crying out for help, for the greater a person's genuine craving for relief, the greater the prospects of benefiting from analysis. Henry was aware of his limited theoretical knowledge as well as his total lack of practical experience, but reasoned that everybody had to make a start sometime. One thing he promised himself: *primum no nocere*, (first, do no harm). After the first unavoidable skirmishes, known as 'resistance', in which the patient unwittingly erects defences to confound the analyst, things began to unfold by degrees.

Schöntal had lost his father when eleven years old. Mother was the sole breadwinner, who'd struggled hard to make ends meet for himself and his younger sister, Klara. Consequently, things were pretty grim at home. There was a shortage of everything. The family had to give up their comfortable apartment and move to a smaller flat in the poorer district of Vienna. It was cramped, so Schöntal had to share the same bedroom as his sister. Mother was too busy to take proper care of the children. She was out at work most of the day, and when she got back, she was too tired to clean up the house, or repair the children's garments. New clothes were out of the question and so the children's appearance began to suffer. First it was only untidy, but then it became unkempt and plain dirty. His teachers at school made deprecatory remarks and the children soon followed suit, adding their own epithets: 'Smelly Jew! Dirty Jew!' and so on.

David Schöntal became very self-conscious, insecure and beset by feelings of inferiority. His performance at school deteriorated. He also had to stay at home frequently, when his sister was ill, as there was no one else to look after her. This again had a disturbing effect on his studies. Gradually he began to have ambivalent feelings towards his little sister. On the one hand he loved her, because she was the only being close to him; on the other hand, he developed hostile and aggressive feelings towards her, because she kept him away from school.

There were but few toys to play with and the children had to invent their own games. One day his little sister suggested, "Let's play dogs!" Without understanding the implications she had seen dogs copulating and it had struck her as funny.

"First I ride on you, then you ride on me."

That is how it all began. David began to experience sexual excitement from this childish game which over time led to the invention of more complicated sexual games and as they shared the same bedroom, they extended their 'game' during the night. With increasing sexual awareness, they began to realise what their game was really all about and gradually conflicts and guilt feelings began to build up. This state of affairs had persisted for years, until Schöntal's escape to Italy.

Chapter 6

Graziella

One day the old man greeted Henry with great excitement.

"You must have set things moving, Dottore! Graziella is going today to Chieti to have another picture taken ... a what-you-call-it, an X-ray."

This was good news. As for Graziella, she seemed strangely agitated. She was and she was not pleased, torn between hope and fear of what that X-ray might reveal. She had dressed up for the occasion and looked very pretty.

"*Grazie dottore*, for all the trouble ..."

Amazing, Henry thought, what the raising of her morale had done to her carriage. That habitual round-shouldered, almost hunchbacked posture had vanished and she held herself erect for the first time. Henry was aware that no matter what the illness, the patient's morale and zest for life were the most important therapeutic factors. Instilling hope and confidence is probably the greatest skill of the physician.

"You look very nice, Graziella. I wish you would always stand up straight like that. Your lungs can expand better which is very helpful in your condition."

Graziella blushed.

"I will try, *Signor Dottore*."

Two days later Henry called over to see the *Capo Polizia* who gave him a voluminous case sheet and a large folder containing Graziella's old and recent X-rays.

"You must look through the records here. They can't be taken out of office!"

Henry sat himself in a corner to examine the extensive notes, which also covered her period in the sanatorium. All examinations of sputa showed acid fast tubercle bacilli. The onset of her illness had been rather acute. Her old X-rays confirmed that both *apices* of her lungs were affected. Henry hastened to examine her recent X-rays and focussed his attention on a roundish shadow under her left collar bone. Then he read the X-ray report:

'Infiltration of both apices. Left more than right. A small cavity in the left sub-clavicular region ...' He didn't bother to read the rest. Clearly the consumption was progressing.

Poor Graziella, he muttered to himself, *just left to the mercy of calcium gluconate*; he felt terribly sorry for her, for there was something pathetic about Graziella. She was unobtrusive, timid and shy and if no energetic steps were taken, she would inevitably die, quietly and without protest, like the last flicker of a candle. Certain individuals are not endowed with elbows, fangs or claws. They are nature's pre-destined sacrificial lambs. Graziella was one of them. She needed protection and more important even, to be inspired with the desire to live. To fall in love is surely one of the strongest incentives for survival. Unfortunately Henry could not be the one. He could, however, give her affection and attention, for she was certainly a sweet young girl. This might mobilise some dormant life force in her.

His first reaction was to recommend her return to a sanatorium, but on reflection he decided that such a step would do more harm than good. It would only augment her feeling of doom; besides, separation from her old father, to whom she was deeply attached, would also adversely affect her health. Last and not least, she would also miss him. So it was best to leave things as they were, gradually introducing a sterner regime of extra care.

One day, as Henry sat on the balcony, Maria Cerletti, the vocalist, called out to him *"Le rondini son tornate."*

Henry looked up and true enough, the swallows had returned. He nodded and smiled back to Maria, who since her accident had become very friendly.

Well, it was really not so surprising the swallows were back, as it was the beginning of March. Five months had passed since Henry's arrival in Notaresco. There were no significant changes in their pattern of life, except for their game of bridge, which they now played in a small wood-panelled room redolent of pine, where they were out of reach of molesting *kibitzes*. This room was in the inn where Baumgart's family had stayed and the arrangement worked to the benefit of both the innkeeper and the internees, who would sometimes order an espresso, a glass of wine or the like.

Krohn was as money-grabbing as ever, a fact which prompted Sobel to remark that despite his communist convictions, he was more of a capitalist than all the rest of them. The little bridge genius reacted merely with an ironic smile, without bothering to reply. But, they surmised, he must have accumulated a small fortune, considering his regular winnings and his reluctance to part with any money.

Baumgart seemed subdued of late, though there was no overt cause for it. Sometimes he sat brooding, avoiding company.

"Cheer up!" said Sobel one day. "Soon it will be Easter and your family will be coming to visit you again."

Baumgart did not reply; his face grew sadder.

"No, they won't be coming at Easter," he said eventually, trying to appear as unconcerned as possible. But he was visibly labouring under some stress and in the end, unable to contain the pressure any longer he said, "My wife won't be coming this Easter ... or any other. She is divorcing me."

"Why on earth? asked Sobel, sounding shocked but underneath not so surprised.

"She cannot stand the pressure and blackmail any longer. The German authorities threaten her with deportation to Germany or worse."

"I feel terribly sorry for you ... and also for your wife," Sobel said, almost in a whisper. Henry also had had an inkling of this outcome, but he was shocked nevertheless.

Baumgart wiped away a tear, which had silently crept from his eye.

"She says she is doing it for our daughter's sake. I really can't blame her. But just the same ..."

He had to keep a tight grip on himself not to burst into tears. There was nothing anyone could say.

Meanwhile, Schöntal's analysis was progressing slowly, hesitantly and against his own subconscious resistance. Gradually the following facts came to light. He had not been feeling well for years, suffering from headaches, tension and anxiety. He also blushed for no obvious reason and could not look people in the eye. Occasionally he went into paroxysms of panic, without there being any overt reason for it. All these disturbances had become even more intense since he left Vienna. Arriving in Genoa destitute, he'd had the good fortune to be accepted into the household of a Jewish widow on the recommendation of the Genoese relief society for refugees. However, though compassionate and fair, the woman had designs of her own. Schöntal, despite his considerable loss of weight, was still an attractive young man, especially to a woman widowed for three years, who had secret longings for the embrace of a comforting masculine arm. She fed him, pampered him, brushed and cleaned his only suit and tactfully arranged for him to earn a little money besides. Impatiently she waited for some tangible response and when this failed to materialise, she put it down to the wretchedness and reticence of a refugee. So, one night she decided to take matters into her own hands and boldly got into his bed. But Schöntal could not perform.

"And that is worrying me, Herr Doktor. Why have I become impotent?"

Henry remained silent, though he knew the answer for he had discovered that the art of listening was far more subtle and productive than speech. If given sufficient time, Schöntal would find his own answers, which was far better than explanations.

It was a lucky coincidence that gave Henry an opportunity to treat two patients with different requirements simultaneously, for Graziella's need for help was even more pressing than Schöntal's. Though in her case treatment was mostly physical in nature, it required a good deal of the psychological approach to achieve the desired end. It was imperative to gain Graziella's confidence. His feelings for her were affectionate, compassionate and protective, not unlike the feelings one has for a sister; but things were different with her. Whenever he had to examine her chest, she became very nervous. Henry, had to tread very carefully. No matter how professionally and soberly he proceeded during examinations, her increased pulse and breathing rate, the flushing of her face, bore witness to the surge of her emotions.

"If you want to get well, you must do as I tell you."

"*Si, dottore*, I will."

"You must start eating properly, plenty of milk and eggs."

"Eggs are rationed, Signor Dottore."

"That's no problem in a little town like this. And every afternoon I want you to rest in bed for two hours."

Graziella looked alarmed. "But I couldn't possibly. Who will serve in the bar?"

"Something can be arranged. I'll talk to your father."

"But ..."

"No buts!" interrupted Henry, smiling, and Graziella's face glowed with happiness. She looked at Henry with adoring eyes, welling with gratitude.

Henry had to tell the old man of Graziella's delicate balance of health.

"I will do all I can, *dottore*. There is no need for her to serve in the bar. I can manage." Then he sat himself beside Henry and asked almost in a whisper, "Is she going to live?"

Henry was not prepared for this kind of question, believing the old man to be blissfully unaware of the seriousness of her condition. Evidently this was not so.

"We will have to do all we can," Henry replied evasively. The old man understood and did not press any further. He laid a hand on Henry's shoulder.

"Soon it will be Easter, *dottore*. Will you do us the honour to come to our dinner? *Il pranzo di Pasqua?*"

"Certainly. I would love to."

Chapter 7

The Songbirds

Outside the Notarescan micro-cosmos, the war continued unabated. The tactics of the three Axis partners could be likened to a relay race with Italy a non-starter. With Hitler's army bogged down in front of Moscow, Nippon stepped up the pace with fireworks of their own, capturing Singapore. That formidable fortress with its reputation of impregnability was captured from the rear, since all Singapore's defences were directed towards a naval attack. This stunning Japanese success had a demoralising effect on the Allies and consequently on the internees.

"You wait!" said Finzi, trying to lift himself up by his own braces. "Once the American eagle unfolds its wings, it will swoop down on the Japanese fleet and tear it apart."

"Amen!" said Sobel, unconvinced.

"You must admit," continued Finzi, "that the prospects look better than two years ago, when all seemed lost. Things can only improve."

"Amen," repeated Sobel, and this time he sounded more cheerful.

Most internees had found a way of improving their financial situations by giving lessons or doing some manual work. The only person who did not make the slightest effort to earn some money was Gurewicz. Nevertheless he seemed to be doing well enough. He smoked expensive cigarettes, so as not to irritate his vocal chords, ate well and had plenty of spare change. It was an enigma, how he managed to do so well. True, he was in debt to most of the internees, but once bitten they had all stopped lending him anymore. The mystery of Gurewicz's prosperity remained unsolved, until one day Capo Sobel was called to see the Capo Polizia. There he was told that an internee, "A bald man, tall and fat," had run up debts with most of the local shops. The Capo Polizia wanted the internees to settle these debts to avoid a scandal, which would only damage their reputation. It was not difficult to guess who the culprit was. Henry had never seen Sobel in a rage, but this

unusually good-humoured, friendly man was certainly fuming with anger now.

"You are a confidence trickster and a disgrace. I would not
give two hoots if you only involved yourself, but you sling
mud over us all!"

Sobel's face went so red, and the veins on his temples
swelled to such a degree that Henry feared he might have a
stroke.

"Now calm yourself, Mr Sobel. We'll make a collection
among ourselves to pay what this irresponsible fool owes the
shopkeepers."

Throughout these tirades Gurewicz sat grinning defiantly
and then remembering some slogans he had picked up from
his Roman friends of doubtful reputation, he took an unusual
line of defence.

"All ownership is theft! I only take back what others have
stolen. It is called redistribution of wealth."

Krohn, on hearing this, produced one of his most sarcastic
smiles; he did not seem impressed by this new convert to the
communist cause.

But suddenly Gurewicz's grin disappeared and his expression changed to one of defiance and fury.

"You! All sitting in judgement over me. You say I do not
work, I who give you concerts for nothing! One day people
will have to pay God knows how much to hear me sing. All I
get from you is applause! 'It was great, Gurewicz' or 'What a
fine voice, Gurewicz!' But has any of you ever given me a
nickel? I am a singer, an artist. My art is my work! What do
you want me to do? Scrub floors?"

After a few moments Sobel admitted, "What you say is
true, but that's no excuse for cheating people and ..."

Gurewicz, who had worked himself into a passion, spat
out, "You hypocrite! You make me sick with your bourgeois
morality! If I have to go to prison I shall at least be rid of your
sanctimonious talk!"

There was something in what he said, although he had
cleverly distorted things to suit his own end. Most of those
present felt vaguely uncomfortable, for it was true, applause is
not enough to appease an empty stomach. In the end the

whole unpleasant episode was hushed up. The internees raised the money to pay Gurewicz's debts and Signor Gaspari was easily dissuaded from further proceedings against the culprit. However, this unsavoury incident also had positive sequels, for both Gurewicz and Lapidus were henceforth rewarded financially for the artistic contribution to the general amusement and welfare of their comrades. Gurewicz also confronted some uncomfortable truths about himself.

Schöntal's analysis seemed to have reached an impasse. Inhibition and resistance is common enough in analysis, but this time they seemed to have struck granite. He seemed to have completely dried up and was unable to produce any new material whatever. One day, however, he was agitated to a degree which suggested that his defences were due to crumble at last.

"I have these dreams, Herr Doktor. Frightening dreams and nightmares."

Henry made no comments, waiting for more to emerge.

"I see these men, huge men with huge penises." He blushed to the roots of his hair. "What does it mean?"

Henry knew very well what it meant, but it was better if the interpretations came eventually from Schöntal himself.

"Do you think, Herr Doktor, I may be homosexual?"

Henry decided that he would have to tread very carefully. 'Primum non nocere' he repeated to himself and resolved to give the analysis a break without pushing it any further before Schöntal had the chance to digest the material they had worked through so far.

At about this time, two events took place which afforded Henry an opportunity to get another glimpse into the frailties of the human mind. Though every member of their closely-knit community periodically showed some fluctuations of mood, Rauch was the only notable exception. His barometer never showed any change of pressure, no ups and downs. He continued to lecture everyone without losing a jot of his self-importance, making pronouncements with the gravity of someone who had had a revelation of the truth, the whole truth, and nothing but the truth. That laboratory in Milan, which he never tired of describing in minute detail, was his status symbol and the cornerstone of his success. This same brainchild, like Pallas Athena, the offshoot of Zeus's head, was not only the fruit of his endeavour, but also the very source of his strength and his sustenance. And then one day this self-inflated phoenix of near infallibility suddenly shrivelled like papier-mâché in a flame, never to rise whole again. It was all precipitated by an inconspicuous-looking letter. He read it and without warning his colourless face caved in suddenly, crumpling, as his distorted countenance assumed a mortal pallor. He became unsteady on his feet, swaying violently and gripping his heart with contorted fingers he shrieked, "Those bandits!"

Sobel caught hold of him. "What is it? What has happened?"

But Rauch did not reply. His eyes were closed and when he opened them again he murmured in a toneless voice, "Those robbers! They have ruined me!"

Instead of further explanations, he handed the letter to Sobel. It was written on a scrap of paper and came from his administrator.

"I have to inform you that your laboratory has been sequestrated by the State and taken over by a German research team."

Just like that. There was no preparatory introduction, no detailed information, no greetings, just that crude, stunning, knock-out blow. Evidently his administrator did not like him either. Despite Rauch's unpopularity, people could not help feeling sorry for him. They wondered how he would survive the shock. Yet survive he did, but only just.

The second change of personality of the Notarescan scene occurred under different circumstances. Henry became aware of it only gradually, as if the ticking of a clock or the humming of an electric fan had ceased. It happened while sitting on his balcony he became dimly aware that something was amiss, realising suddenly that an unusual stillness was surrounding him. The singing had stopped. Could Maria's infinite repertoire possibly have come to an end? Was she ill? He quickly got up and went in search of Albert.

"What's going on, I wonder? Has Maria lost her voice or something?"

Albert looked surprised. "I thought you knew. Her husband has been killed in action. She received the news three days ago."

Henry was shattered. *Poor Maria! The news everyone dreads in a telegram.*

He was nonetheless surprised at her silence. Having witnessed her hysterics during the suturing of her wound, he would have expected her to lament like some frantic mourner in a Greek tragedy. Instead she had become mute, inarticulate. A nightingale struck dumb.

Even Krohn seemed to have something on his mind recently. Though he continued to shine at bridge and pile up his fortune, his green money eyes, usually lively and perceptive, seemed to have lost their vitality and swiftness. Occasionally during the sacred rites of bridge he made mistakes, though he repaired them quickly enough to cash in his winnings in the end.

"Hey, you communist money-grabber, what are you going to do with all that lolly?"

As usual Krohn did not reply, except for a derisory lift of his eyebrows.

"He must be saving for the May Day celebrations," said Gurewicz. "That's when he will splash out."

To this, Krohn did not react at all, except that his eyes grew perhaps more opaque. Was he worried about his family? His wife and two daughters he had left behind? He was a deep one, unfathomable.

Sometimes Henry wondered how Sonia was getting on. Neither of them knew the other's whereabouts so communication was impossible. In the beginning Henry had missed her very much. Now that the passage of time had smoothed out much of her harshness, he could see her in a different light. She was right when accusing him of seeing the world only in terms of 'black and white'. Life was more complicated than that. Henry was sure, however, that Sonia and her daughters would be doing well. *She is a survivor; no need to worry about her*; and strangely enough, he never did. Gradually and painlessly she simply faded from his life.

Chapter 8

May Day

Henry made big strides in the theory of chess, thanks to Schöntal's expert tuition. Each game they played was recorded and afterwards dissected like a corpse in a post mortem. Invariably Henry's was the corpse they cut into fine shreds. It was beneficial to the progress of the psychoanalysis that each of them had an opportunity to exert his authority and superiority in turns. Schöntal was usually a dispassionate, but sometimes a fervid and harsh critic.

"How many times, Herr Doktor, must I tell you not to be in such a hurry? Think before you move! Nobody is chasing you! It's a tactical error to attack before you've consolidated your position!"

Henry was glad that Schöntal had a chance to work off part of his hostility, so commonly experienced by those who have to confide their innermost secrets even if they have chosen to do so.

So far Henry had abstained from making significant comments, confining himself mostly to listening. Only occasionally had he thrown in a word or two, a kind of catalyst, which might promote the flow of ideas. But now the time had come to throw some light on Schöntal's problems; to help him face up and come to terms with the traumatic experiences of his past. Obviously Schöntal's youthful sexual games with his sister were foremost in his mind, suffocating him with their nightmarish weight, so that was the subject to be elucidated first.

"I do not want to distort facts, mitigate or embellish them, but the trouble is that you are looking at the concept of incest, the sexual games with your sister, in an emotional, unscientific manner. Incest as a concept does not exist in nature. It is a man-made taboo, which does not apply to the animal world, where inbreeding between parents and their offspring as well as between siblings is common. Since inbreeding occurs in nature, it cannot be considered as *unnatural*, biologically speaking. However, animals have no code of moral conduct; thus it is man, not nature, who decrees that incest is immoral."

After a brief pause to help Schöntal absorb these ideas, Henry went on.

"At different stages of human development incest has been regarded in accordance with the rulings of the time. In historical times, incest was a common practice among the Pharaohs of Egypt, where it was customary for the Pharaoh to marry his sister; and remember that traditionally, the behaviour of a Royal House has always been a tone-setter for the rest of the population. Now, compare this state of affairs with the penalty of death imposed for it in Puritan England around 1650 and you'll see two diametrically opposed attitudes relating to the same subject. Even today disagreement continues in that incest is punishable in some countries and not in others."

Schöntal listened eagerly to the elucidation of his predicament in the unemotional light of reason and detachment, without uttering a word.

"Don't misunderstand me," Henry continued, "I'm not trying to justify incest, only to examine it from various angles. After all, we have to abide by the codes of the society we live in. Originally, 'incest' afforded an ageing father a taboo protection against his younger and stronger son, and often ended in the father's death; the typical Oedipus situation. And sisters are only extensions of mothers, as are all other women in general."

Henry had to be careful not to overtax his patient's capacity to absorb and digest, considering the extent and duration of his predicaments and so he broke off the session at this point.

April was upon them and with it, Henry's Easter dinner invitation, no everyday occurrence for a Jewish refugee. Eventually the great day arrived and to his degraded palate, conditioned to cheap food, Graziella's offerings seemed the ultimate in culinary perfection. The dinner started with home-made *tagliatelle*, followed by *pollo alla cacciatora* adorned with roast potatoes, peas, cauliflower and artichokes. The sweet *zuppa Inglese* was exquisite and so was the wine—a full-blooded Bardolino—which was served lavishly in huge goblets. Graziella's eyes were shining, her cheeks flushed with excitement. She was happy at the opportunity to repay her *dottore*, for all his kindness and attention.

"Mangi! Mangi, dottore! Please eat some more," she and her father pleaded with him. "There is still plenty left!" they insisted.

The wine had gone to the old man's head and he began to reminisce about the good old days, before the war. Graziella did not say very much, but her eyes were more than eloquent. They were radiant. She glanced furtively, and then, after a few glasses of wine, less furtively at Henry. Graziella beheld him with immense tenderness and affection, continuing to heap more and more food on his plate.

Henry could eat no more. He was bursting at the seams and did not want a repetition of the Ferramonti experience, when after that memorable *Rosh Hashana* celebration, he had brought up all that precious food.

"Basta, Graziella! Enough!" he protested, laughing.

There was no doubt that Graziella's health had improved recently. Her fever had almost subsided and, even more important, she had gained two kilograms in weight. If she continued that way, she had a fair chance of survival. When eventually Henry got up from the table to go back to his quarters, he was in an exalted mood and reconciled with this wicked world.

"You seem jolly," said Sobel, "and you smell of good wine."

Henry nodded. "I can't remember when I've eaten so well." He let himself fall into a chair, as his head was swimming. "It is a lovely day and hot for spring," he said. "Do you know what I'd love to do?"

"Well what?" asked Sobel.

"I'd like to walk barefoot in the sand. Somewhere by the sea. And then take a swim. How far away are we from the sea?"

Strangely enough, no one seemed to know. Unexpectedly Krohn came to their aid. "Chieti is about eight miles and Notaresco about fifteen miles from the Adriatic coast."

"Listen to that!" exclaimed Sobel. "Our bridge genius is also an expert in local geography."

Only rarely did Krohn take part in general conversation, so it was even more surprising that he had voluntarily condescended to give that information.

Slightly tipsy as he was, Henry became chatty and then pensive.

"Strange, we have been here for all this time and have never really bothered to find out where we are." He sighed. "It shows how little we care. Makes no difference whether you are a captive in Stockholm, Madrid or Monte Carlo; prison is still prison everywhere."

When mildly inebriated Henry always became half melancholy, half contemplative, tending to make sombre or slightly morbid pronouncements. He still felt the need to talk.

"I must confess, I didn't even realise we were on the Adriatic side of the peninsula, facing Yugoslavia. By the way, what's the nearest port?"

Nobody knew. Again it was Krohn who deigned to instruct them.

"Pescara," he said in a matter-of-fact manner.

"Strange how well informed he is," thought Henry. Who could make him out, this peculiar little monkey?

They were well into spring by now. Henry would sit out on his balcony to enjoy the early morning sunshine, the sweet scent of spring flowers from window boxes, the sounds of the little town coming to life as the trucks unloaded their wares or the church bells which rang out just across from his balcony, celebrating one religious feast or another.

One bright morning Henry was roused from his sleep by Gurewicz's sonorous bass-baritone.

"*Im wunderschönen Monat Mai, als alle Knospen sprangen.*"

This beautifully melodic setting of Heine's poem came flooding into Henry's room.

What the devil is he up to? thought Henry.

True, Gurewicz liked to sing while shaving but never as early as this. Then Henry realised it was May Day, celebrated the world round for a variety of reasons, political, romantic or plain spring-worshipping. Never mind the reasons, Gurewicz was right. No one should stay in bed on May Day, especially on a glorious sunny morning like this. He stepped out on the balcony to inhale the balmy air. The fragrance of jasmine, lilac and oleander, all blended together yet each discernible by its individual scent, lingered in the air. The bluish foothills, still shrouded in mist, beckoned from afar. How lovely it would be to climb them and behold the Adriatic in the distance. The hills were of course out of bounds....but never mind! At least they were free to move about the town, not like the poor devils in Ferramonti who could only gaze with longing at the distant peaks.

Maria's window on the opposite side of the street was shut. No spring rites for her. Death is as dead, and grief as painful, in May as it is in December. She had avoided the internees of late. After all, they were supposed to be enemies, and it was enemies who had killed her husband. Poor Maria! Now that she no longer sang, Henry wished to God she'd plague him again with her incessant warblings.

His door opened.

"Fancy a stroll?" asked Albert, brightly.

"Sure, and later we can go down to the bar."

They walked through the winding narrow streets, with Henry enjoying every single step.

"I don't want to sound morbid, Albert, but as I walk here, free to go where I choose, I can't help feeling sorry for the people in Ferramonti, especially the children."

"Who knows what tomorrow will bring? Let's enjoy today."

The little stream, swelled by the melting snow in the mountains, came rushing down, carrying branches and all kinds of debris in its course.

"This is a trout fisherman's paradise," said Henry. "At this time of the year the trout rise to the May fly."

Albert grinned. "I bet your fingers are itching for a rod and line. Remember the Traunsee in Gmunden, where we caught that big trout?"

"Of course. How could I forget?" Henry's voice was wistful as he recalled schooldays at the Chajes Gymnasium then holidays with Albert and their friend Willy Klughaupt in the Vienna woods. "But that seems a lifetime ago."

After a brisk walk along the stream's bank they reached the town limits and had to turn back. With a leisurely pace they made their way to the coffee bar and sat down under the arcade, fully exposed to the scorching sun. Graziella came out to take their orders.

"Buon giorno Signori!" She looked very neat in her white skirt and dark blue blouse.

"How are you, Graziella?" asked Albert.

"Much better, thanks to your friend, il dottore." She never referred to Henry by name, only as 'dottore', but the way she looked at him spoke volumes. As she left to fetch their coffees, Albert threw Henry a mischievous grin.

"I think she has her eye on you Henry!"

"How do you find her, otherwise?" asked Henry, slightly embarrassed.

"It's incredible! The girl is transformed. Holds herself upright and she's filling out. Must have gained a good bit of weight."

"She still has a cavity in her left lung, you know."

"Yes so you told me, but her morale is good. So surely that's half the battle?"

Architect Baumgart came by and stopped at their table.

"Have you seen Krohn? We want him for a game of bridge."

"What? Bridge on such a beautiful day!" exclaimed Albert.

Baumgart nodded. He looked sad and resigned. Ever since his wife had filed for divorce, he'd been only a shadow of his former self.

"Most likely," said Henry, "he is somewhere celebrating May Day. After all it is a red letter day in the communist calendar."

Baumgart shrugged his shoulders and went his way.

It was getting hotter. A blazing sun flooded the piazza with a sparkling radiance.

"Time for food!" said Albert. They had thoroughly enjoyed their morning stroll and were in high spirits. Climbing the stairs to the dining room they met Sobel. He seemed somewhat pensive and unusually distracted.

"Have you seen Mr Krohn?" he asked them.

"Why, you are the second person to enquire about him! Has he suddenly become so popular, or is something the matter?"

"No Albert, there's nothing the matter…except that none of us has seen him this morning."

"He's probably gone out for a walk. It's the 1st of May."

"Perhaps so," but Sobel sounded dubious.

Krohn did not turn up for lunch, so people began to feel uneasy, wondering what had happened to him. Their unease grew steadily with each hour and at 5 o'clock Sobel came into Henry's room.

"I am worried. I don't know what to do."

"What can you do?" Henry asked.

"It is my duty to report his absence."

There was a long pause. Neither of them said a word.

"Do you really think he has gone?" asked Henry eventually.

"I should not be a bit surprised. He is a dark horse."

"But why not wait? He may have lost his way, or perhaps he's had an accident."

Sobel scratched his head; a nervous, absentminded scratch.

"No, there's more to it. I'm beginning to put two and two together."

"What do you mean?" asked Henry, surprised.

"Do you remember how well he knew his local geography? No one else did. He even knew the exact distances. Why? What for?"

What Sobel said could make sense, retrospectively.

"Well what are you going to do?"

After rubbing his chin, adjusting his collar and sundry other delaying tactics, Sobel came out in the open.

"I think we ought to give him a chance. The more time we give him, the better his prospects. I'll wait until the evening meal. And if he's not back by then, I'll inform the Capo Polizia."

"Won't he hold you responsible for the delay?"

"I'll say we did not notice until this evening. It was a beautiful day … everybody was out. Besides, what can he do? Shoot me?"

The rest of the internees were not dumb either, having drawn their own conclusions. So far they had said nothing, but when Krohn was still absent at the evening meal, the tongues started wagging.

"The blighter! He's let us down."

"We shall all be punished because of him."

"I always said he was a phoney."

And so it went on, with most of them venting their indignation against the black sheep.

Sobel reported Krohn missing.

"How did Gaspari take it?" they enquired anxiously upon his return.

"He seemed more worried about himself, his own position."

"What about us? Is he going to punish us?"

"He did not say — so far. They are organising a search party immediately and have alerted the carabinieri in the whole province."

An atmosphere of doom and dread descended on them all. What had started as a promising May Day ended dismally with a sense of panic and heavy foreboding. Depressed and discouraged, they all went to bed early. Henry could not sleep for wondering what the consequences of Krohn's escape would be.

There was a knock at his door and in came Sobel, barefoot and in his pyjamas.

"Look what I have found in my pyjama pocket!" He held out a letter.

'Dear Mr Sobel, I write to you out of a sense of duty and hope that you and all the others will understand and forgive me. This was not done on impulse. I've planned it carefully for some time. This is why I needed to get the money. I just can't sit around here, a useless, passive spectator, while these Nazi-gangsters send the world up in flames. I must make my little contribution even if it kills me. I intend to join the Partisans in Yugoslavia. Should anything happen to me, please let my wife know after the war. I put the letter in your pyjama pocket, so that you should not find it before nightfall. By that time I hope

to be far away. Good luck to you all. Forgive me, I could not help myself. B Krohn. PS Burn this letter immediately!'

Henry was dumbfounded and shaken. He re-read the letter and handed it back to Sobel. "You'd better burn it, as he says."

"I will, and let's keep this to ourselves."

The anxiously-awaited reaction came the following morning: house arrest. All of them were confined to quarters, except Capo Sobel and the cook. Not everyone condemned Krohn. Some sympathised with him:

"He has guts! It's us stupid sheep that are to be pitied."

News of the recent events soon swept through the town. Most of the locals felt sorry about the house arrest. They were kindly people, now used to the internees and their ways. Henry worried about Graziella. She'd been due for an injection the day after Krohn's disappearing act but under the circumstances there was nothing he could do about it. Henry requested an interview with Signor Gaspari. Sobel arranged it.

"Signor Gaspari, that sick girl from the caffè– she was due for an injection today."

"So what do you want?"

"Please let me visit her and do my duty as her medical attendant."

Gaspari, a Capo Polizia only by name and not by vocation, could not make up his mind. By nature unassuming, in his private life henpecked, he was no authoritarian; visibly the wrong man in the wrong place.

He stroked his huge black moustache, the only thing that was remarkable about him.

"But you are an internee," he said at last. "She is not your responsibility."

"Every sick person is a doctor's responsibility. His own status or the patient's nationality do not matter."

Still Signor Gaspari was undecided. His stubby fingers drummed nervously on his desk.

"Va bene! All right!" he said in the end, clearly relieved to have come to a decision.

The next day the house arrest was partly lifted, on condition that all internees were back at their quarters at 12 noon.

The next day the concession was extended until 5 pm. On that occasion the *Capo Polizia* called on the internees in person and admonished them to behave themselves, like '*gentiluomini*'.

He was solemnly assured that no irresponsible lapses would in future disturb the peace. And next days reverted to normal in Notaresco. No one was happier about this return to normality than Graziella. In the beginning, when Henry had failed to turn up for her injection, she had been frantic with worry, working herself up to near hysteria. So, when Henry eventually appeared, she almost threw herself on him, managing to restrain herself only at the last moment. However, there was sufficient impetus left for her to squeeze both his hands hard, which considering her timidity and shyness was quite an achievement.

"Madre di Dio! You gave me such a fright! I don't know what I would do without...without your help, *dottore!*"

The old man was equally overjoyed, patting Henry affectionately on the shoulder and wiping away a furtive tear.

Chapter 9

Revelations

In contrast to Graziella's enthusiastic reception, Henry had lately had to contend with ill-concealed hostility and resistance from his other patient, Schöntal. Such periodic aggression and negativism was unavoidable in analysis, as Henry himself had experienced in his relationship with Dr Bernheim. To like those who drag our shortcomings, vices and weakness into the light of day is an almost impossible proposition. The topic of incest was discussed and dissected ad nauseam, in the hope that Schöntal would in the end *feel*, rather than *understand*, that he was largely absolved from guilt, biologically speaking. But the continuous harping on the same theme was not to the patient's liking and he reacted frequently with unhidden resentment and anger.

"You mentioned dreams about big men with huge penises, and expressed fear of homosexuality. What do you think is behind it?"

Schöntal shrugged his shoulders. "I don't know." He sounded sullen, disinterested and passive.

"You must make an effort. Don't leave it all to me."

But Schöntal did not reply. He remained uncooperative and resentful. When the silence dragged on for some time, Henry tried a different approach.

"What comes into your mind when I say homosexual?"

There was no answer, but Henry waited patiently.

"My sister," Schöntal said eventually.

"But what about her?"

"I don't know. But I'm sure she has something to do with it … I am afraid to touch women."

"Why are you afraid to touch women all of a sudden?"

"They all remind me of my sister."

"There you are! You have found the answer to your impotence with women. Every woman reminds you — is a symbol — of your sister, and so any sexual relationship with women has an incestuous flavour. Do you understand?"

Schöntal nodded, but did not utter a word.

"And there is more besides this defensive impotence," resumed Henry. "To make sure you are never tempted by women again, you unconsciously transfer your libido on to men. Do you follow me?"

Schöntal was now weeping silently, so Henry left him to experience the beneficial effect of tears.

After a while Schöntal got a grip on himself.

"I remember now something else," he said, almost in a whisper. "It happened many years ago, when I was a little boy. I had forgotten all about it until this very moment. Strange! I saw my mother in the bathroom. She was naked. It gave me a strange feeling. I wanted to touch her breasts. Odd, isn't it, how that scene comes back so suddenly to me?"

Henry remained silent and held his breath, for they had reached an important stage in the analysis, when it would be unforgivable to interrupt Schöntal's flow of words and ideas.

"Yes! I can see it clearly. My father was still alive. He told me to get out of the bathroom, but I didn't want to. So he smacked me hard and pushed me out. I hated him for this and wished he were dead."

Schöntal looked up, wiped his tears and shook his head in bewilderment.

"How strange! In all these years I've never once thought of that incident and now I can see it as clearly as if it had happened yesterday!"

When the session broke up at this point, Henry was at least as stirred and shaken as his patient. He was fascinated by the 'peeling of the psyche', the miraculous lifting of successive veils, as layer after layer was exposed and laid bare. For the first time he really grasped the significance of Jung's dictum: the patient comes to us with his neurosis in one hand and with a gift in the other. Cynics interpreted that 'gift' as remuneration; but to Jung the gift consisted of that rare privilege of getting a glimpse into the innermost recesses of a human being's tormented soul.

Once the tumultuous fermentation had begun there was no stopping its progress, for soon after when Henry was about to go out for a stroll, Schöntal suddenly burst in, without even knocking at the door.

"I hope you don't mind my intrusion, but I must talk to you. It concerns my father."

Henry was taken by surprise and exhausted from that dramatic session; he was not really in the mood, but nevertheless acquiesced.

"Well, what is it?"

"Something has just dawned on me," Schöntal spluttered out.

"Ever since my father pushed me out of that bathroom, I hated him. It was not just then that I wished him dead. It happened many times before. And when he actually died ...I was eleven years old by then...I felt it was because of me. That it was my fault, because I had wanted him dead!"

Schöntal became more and more agitated and had a strange look in his eyes, as if he were in a state of trance.

"All my life I have been guilty about something or other. I couldn't tell why—even before that thing with my sister. Now I know; it is because I felt I had killed my father. And this—probably—weighs heavier on my conscience than all the rest!"

After this last revelation Schöntal broke into spasmodic sobs and Henry, immeasurably moved, sat there, unable to utter a word.

This May weather was particularly pleasant. With a constant breeze coming from the sea and the cool air descending from the mountains, it was never too hot. At night glow-worms made their first appearance, minute lanterns sailing in the dark of the night. Henry had never seen so many before and was enchanted by the magic display of their phosphorescence.

Graziella seemed to be blossoming. Love had given her that badly-needed *élan vitale* and she continued to carry herself erect and to gain weight. The week after Krohn's departure, on a sunny day when the corn was out, Henry took her for a walk in the fields. He thought the fresh air and a little exercise would do her the world of good. She seemed to be walking in a dream, with a faraway expression and the aura of happiness about her. Though she never had the courage to express her feelings in words, these would have been superfluous anyway, as love shone so transparently from her. Love gives strength — even if it's only one-sided. She made herself a garland of corn-flowers and poppies and wore it gaily like a crown.

"Dottore, I think this is the most beautiful day of my life. I cannot tell you how wonderfully well I feel."

"There will be many more happy days for you in the fu-ture. But don't overdo it, Graziella. You must still take great care of yourself."

Henry felt sad that he was unable to reciprocate Graziella's feelings for him and knew he had to tread very carefully not to hurt her. He hoped that with the improvement in her health her infatuation would be gradually transformed into gratitude or better still, diverted. Anyway, it was no use looking too far ahead.

The next morning, Albert and Henry sat in the bar as usual, sipping an *aranciata*, while the old man was talking, as usual extolling the charms of the Abbruzzi. Over the months they'd got used to his Abbruzzese accent, and his chatter did no more to disturb their flow of ideas than discreet background music would do. They sat there relaxed, enjoying the sun on their faces and eyeing the multi-coloured display of seasonal fruits on the market stalls, brimming over with watermelons, succu-lent figs, grapes and vegetables of different kinds.

They didn't notice him at first, although he was waving frantically in the distance. But when the agitated figure came closer, Albert recognised him.

"Henry, that's Finzi waving to us. I wonder why he is in such a state."

Finzi reached their table almost out of breath. He looked upset.

"Thank God I found you! Have you heard the news?" and when they shook their heads he spluttered, "We are going back to Ferramonti. This very afternoon. At 5 o'clock!"

END OF BOOK TWO

Book Three

May 1942—November 1943

Chapter 1

Addio Notaresco!

It's strange how on a glorious summer's day, the human heart can feel so gloomy.

At first he was too stunned to feel anything at all. As the truck conveying them to the station sped through the sun-drenched landscape, Henry huddled in a corner clutching a big loaf of bread. It all happened far too suddenly to have properly sunk in. Gradually however, the violent jolts of the vehicle negotiating the difficult serpentine descent shook him back to full awareness. He glanced down at the loaf and smiled, wistfully.

Gazing back at Notaresco, it lay in a glory of light which seemed to flood over it from the surrounding hills. *Notaresco – brief sojourn,* he murmured under his breath, but gradually he began to steady himself sufficiently to review the recent events.

As soon as they'd learned the ominous tidings of their impending return to Ferramonti, Albert and Henry had shot out of the bar, dashing back to their rooms. In the momentary confusion and haste, Henry forgot Graziella and her father. Back at their quarters they walked into pandemonium. A babble of heated arguments, curses and lamentations filled the air.

"It's all that bastard's fault!"

"That bloody Krohn left us in the lurch!"

Sobel, patient and tactful as usual, tried to pacify them.

"You can't blame Krohn entirely. They move people about for reasons of their own."

"Just the same, we should have taken a firmer stand! We ought to have shown that none of us approved, most categorically dissociated ourselves from Krohn's escape!"

"It's all your fault, Mr Sobel!" yelled another, "You should have reported it as soon as he went missing, instead of waiting until nightfall!"

Sobel did not reply. He knew that their accusations and reproaches were unfair, but he also knew that scapegoats are found in times of crisis and misfortune for a reason.

"What does it matter whose fault it is?" exclaimed Gurewicz. "Instead of arguing, let's get packing."

"What's there to pack?" asked Lapidus. "Only my guitar. My pants and shirts I can chuck into the case in no time."

"They know that, the bastards. That's why they gave us no warning. All our earthly goods can be tied up in a bundle in five minutes flat."

"Perhaps they weren't taking chances of more escapes," remarked Rauch.

Because of all the medicines, boxes of phials and the rest of the paraphernalia, Henry asked Albert and Finzi for a helping hand. He suddenly remembered Graziella. What would happen to her? The least he could do was to leave her a supply of medicines.

"Would you two please finish the packing? I have to say goodbye to Graziella."

Albert looked at his watch. "I wouldn't if I were you. There isn't time. We are supposed to be out of here in twenty minutes. Besides, what good would it do to see her?"

It was true. The time announced for their departure was almost up. But how could he leave Graziella without a word of explanation and encouragement? Punctuality was never exactly an Italian virtue. There would certainly be some delay; he decided to make a dash for it. If he ran fast enough he could be there and back in ten minutes.

"I must go, Albert!"

He almost flew down the stairs and was about to run through the gate when he was stopped by a militiaman.

"*Nessuno esce di casa*! No one leaves the house!"

Henry protested "But I have to see somebody urgently."

The militiaman shook his head, repeating flatly, "No one leaves this house. Those are my instructions." Seeing Henry's distress, he added sympathetically, "Anyway, the transport is nearly here."

All the impetus and urgency suddenly drained from Henry. With sagging shoulders, chin on his chest, he just stood there, the image of helpless impotence.

"So be it" he murmured. Dejected and resigned, he trailed back upstairs.

A violent jolt bounced Henry back to the present. The truck must have hit a boulder or one of the deep craters in the road. No one even remarked on it. As if by mutual consent they sat in profound silence, each of them lost in his own web of misery. Henry regarded the loaf of bread tenderly and gave a deep sigh.

Both Albert and the militiamen had been right, for hardly had they finished packing when a loud hooting below announced the arrival of their transport. The *Capo Polizia* had arrived in person to supervise the 'dispatch of the goods', as Gurewicz acidly remarked. They had to assemble in front of the gate as the capo called each name.

Meanwhile a sizeable crowd had gathered in the street. The news of the internees' departure had soon spread through the town. Just as they were about to get into the lorry, there was a sudden stirring among the crowd, which parted to form a corridor through which moved a procession of elderly peasant women, all dressed in their traditional black. The first of them pushed a wheelbarrow laden with bread. She looked gravely at the internees, and then her expression softened into a toothless smile.

"Per voi! For you!" she said, pointing at the loaves.

Taken by surprise and not fully grasping the meaning the internees made no move. So the women took the initiative. They picked up the loaves and distributed them among the astonished internees. One elderly matron, her withered face deeply furrowed, approached Henry.

"May God bless you. *Che Dio Vi benedica!* My grandson is also a prisoner: in Tripoli with the *Inglesi.*"

Henry was in two minds. After all, bread was rationed. How could he accept a whole loaf? He looked enquiringly at the *Capo Polizia*, who nodded approval.

"Grazie, grazie tanto!" said Henry, and took the loaf. This spontaneous gesture from these simple folk brought tears to

many eyes. To offer loaves of rationed bread to internees, supposedly the enemies of the state, and in front of a police chief
— such a thing could only happen in Italy.

Suddenly the crowd became agitated, setting up frantic
cries of "*Buon viaggio! Buona fortuna!*" And there was also the
'nightingale of Notaresco', who had avoided them ever since
her husband was killed. Dressed in black, she came to shake
hands with Henry.

"*Arrivederci! Non addio!*" she said simply, and burst into
tears.

Somebody else was making frantic efforts to push through
to Henry, gesticulating and shouting "*Dottore! Dottore!*" It was
the old man and in his wake he dragged a tear-blinded Graziella by the hand.

"*Dottore*, what shall we do without you?" moaned the old
man.

Most of the internees were already aboard the truck. There
was no time for explanation, consolation or encouragement.
Graziella stood stricken in front of Henry, pale, tremulous and
wide-eyed, *like a wounded fawn,* thought Henry. On a suddenly
impulse he seized her by the shoulders, held her very close
and kissed her full on the lips. Just for an instant her arms
went round him too; then she went limp and her arms
dropped helplessly away.

"*Buon viaggio!*" shouted the crowd. Graziella remained motionless, unable to utter a word. Henry waved, but she
couldn't respond and the lorry chugged away.

All this had happened less than half an hour before yet
now he felt it had already receded into the remote past. No
one could have had a more heart-warming send-off; Henry felt
he would cherish the memory of that symbolic gift of bread as
one of the most precious moments of his life. But what of Graziella, what would become of her? A deep pain gripped his
heart. What could he do? What could anyone do? What did
the life of a single individual matter in this holocaust, with the
whole of mankind gone berserk? Notaresco was over. *Finis
capitoli!* He must brace himself to face Ferramonti anew.

Chapter 2

Albert settles in

They arrived early on a sunny May morning; it was already hot and sultry. What else could one expect in that godforsaken dustbowl? The return to Ferramonti brought back that day in July 1940 when the first transport had arrived, exhausted and bedraggled, not knowing what awaited them. At least now he had a good idea. The anopheles would be in top form at this time of the year. The thought of the regular ingestion of quinine gave Henry a sick feeling in the pit of his stomach, remembering the ringing in the ears and nausea it caused. How he would miss the cool fresh air of Notaresco and the freedom to visit the caffè!

Apart from the two guards at the gate there was no one about. Signor Rizzi's White House was tinged with pink by the newly-risen sun. Further down, the wooden hut of the provisions store seemed to be coming to life. Most likely that scarecrow Giuseppe with his foul-smelling mouth was getting ready to dump his third-rate wares on the unfortunate internees. *'Piazza de Ferrari'* looked as stony and barren as ever. But the place had grown considerably and some improvements could be seen.

As they disembarked, the door of the *Polizia del Campo* opened and several agents came strolling out. Except for Tommasini, all the faces were new. Tommasini must have recognised Henry, for he strode up to him, and for a moment it seemed as if he were about to proffer his hand but he refrained from doing so.

"Ah, *dottore siete ritornato*? So here you are again!"

"Yes Signor Tommasini, but not by choice."

Tommasini smiled.

"There are worse places in this war, you know."

Henry did not reply, though he was tempted to say that this place was bad enough. Something in Tommasini's behaviour had changed. He no longer appeared the cocky and arrogant Jew-baiter. After all, much water had flowed under the Tiber bridges since Italy's bombastic entry into the war.

"Can I, and my friend here, go back to *camerata* 3?"

"I think there are some vacancies there." He beckoned and they followed him. As they came closer, Henry's heart began to beat faster at the thought of seeing his old pals again. When the door was pushed open there was the familiar sight of cramped, snoring humanity before him. There, near the door, was still Batyushka's 'four poster' with the mosquito net neatly spread over it. A little further down slept Mario the cook, greying hair in disarray, his rosy cheeks puffed out, as if blowing an invisible bugle. Opposite him, snoring and huffing, lay Lubicz, huge mustachios vibrating, seemingly enjoying a life of their own. Dino's bunk had long been occupied by a newcomer. Henry's heart lurched; how he had missed his old friend especially the unmistakeable hum of his accordion. He resolved to find him and restore their friendship.

"*Gewalt*! Look who's here!" someone yelled suddenly. Little Wolf had spotted them first, and now he came running towards them in his underpants.

"How did you get here, *Herr Doktor*?" he asked, shaking Henry's hand vigorously. The *camerata* sprang to life. Szafran, Borstyn, Scholz, Lubicz, all jumped out of bed to greet Henry.

"He could not resist our attractions," boomed a familiar voice. Moishele the clown now evidently lived in *camerata* 3. "He had to return," Moishele continued, "like a criminal to the scene of his crime."

"More like a dog to his vomit!" laughed Szafran, always first to lower the tone. "Why didn't you tell us you were coming?"

"We didn't know ourselves until a couple of hours before we left."

Among the internees who had now risen from their beds were many new faces.

"Where have all the others gone?" enquired Henry remembering his arrival with Dino and Ossi with a heavy pang of nostalgia.

"No one knows," replied Trebitsch, the young man who had come with Laufman from Dachau two years previously. After shaking hands with Henry, Trebitsch, who was now the *Capo Camerata*, went on, "Some moved to another space here, many others were transferred to new places like you, to make

room for hundreds of new guests at the Five Star Hotel Ferramonti"

"Jewish refugees?" asked Albert disguising the shock of his
new living quarters.

"Yes, shipwrecked on a Donau paddle steamer!" Trebitsch
replied with a grin of admiration for the survivors of such a
crazy Exodus.

Albert and Henry were exhausted. "If you don't mind,
we'll talk later. I'm fit to drop."

"I'll get your bed ready, *Herr Doktor*," said Wolf. "Not your
old bed. I'm sorry, that is occupied. And one for our latest
guest!" Albert nodded at Wolf, grateful to have a place to collapse onto after the tiring and hectic recent events.

"Thank God for that. So I'm finally rid of my old mattress!"

Henry fell asleep as soon as his head touched the pillow. It
was midday when he awoke, just in time to join the queue.

Here we go! The blessed queuing again, he said to himself,
smiling wearily. After months of passable nourishment in Notaresco, the thought of the watery brew dished out by Lubicz's
steaming ladle made him feel quite sick. It must have shown
on his face.

Lubicz remarked, "I hope it's ok. I am sure we can't com-
pete with Notaresco, but we get by."

"I'm sure I will," said Henry, though he felt his stomach
churning at the sight of that thin concoction with its fragments
of suspect origin floating in it.

Somebody laid a hand on his shoulder. It was Dr Wunderstein, whom he had not noticed before. So he was still here
and, if possible, even shabbier and filthier than ever. His unshaven face breaking into a grin, his watering eyes shining
with excitement, he strove to greet Henry with that bad stammer.

"S-s-o you are b-b-b-back ag-g-ain!"

"So I am, Wunderstein. And how are you?"

"Not too b-b-b-bad."

Henry had always experienced mixed feelings of revulsion
and compassion at the sight of him. He reminded one of those
ancient ruins, which in decline and dilapidation still retain a
vestige of past splendours.

Albert, who had joined the queue, looked distinctly lost and forlorn. He contemplated the brownish liquid in his bowl, sniffing it suspiciously. This was his first encounter with the Ferramonti *haute cuisine.*

Henry could not help laughing.

"Come, Albert! It's not as bad as it looks!"

"I can't possibly eat this!" wailed Albert dejectedly waving his bowl under Henry's nose.

"You would be surprised what you could eat, if you were hungry — really hungry I mean."

"For me it's like descending from Paradise to Hell. I'd never realised it was as bad as this."

"You'll soon get used to it. My sad experience has taught me that man gets used to anything!"

"And those latrines! Open to view. How can you? In front of all the others?" Albert shook his head in the realisation that he had been spared this indignity for 2 years since his capture. Notaresco had indeed been Paradise in comparison.

"Wait until you're bursting. You'll find it's possible."

Henry tried to take stock of his new companions. Next to him was a man similar in build and appearance to Dino, except for a bushy black beard. He also turned out to be a doctor, and like Dino, he was all hair. But here their similarities ended, for whereas Dino had been of a jovial, extravert disposition and easy-going, his replacement had a sour, gloomy expression and demeanour of a misanthrope. Although he lay flat on his camp bed, Henry judged him to be much taller than Dino.

"My name is Kaufmann, Dr Kaufmann. Where are you from?" he asked in a sharp, disgruntled tone.

"From Genoa," replied Henry.

Dr Kaufmann got impatient. "But originally?" he growled.

"From Vienna, but I was born ..."

"Bah! I thought so!" interrupted Dr Kaufmann, "Obviously *Deutsche Kultur!*"

Henry was nonplussed, but decided to ignore this remark. He did not like his first impression and realised that the feeling was mutual.

In contrast to this grim personality, Henry discovered one bird of quite a different feather. Before actually seeing the man himself, Henry's curiosity was roused by the festoon of multi-coloured ribbons, romantically tied into a bow on a guitar, which hung from a nail above his bed.

"Who sleeps here?" he asked, thinking of Lapidus and wondering where they had put him.

Young Scholz, who happened to be around, started laughing. "So you have not met him yet? That's Dr Rosenkranz von Wien. From Vienna."

"What? Yet another doctor?"

"They come in dozens here."

"Well, why are you laughing? What's so funny about him?"

"Wait till you meet him. He missed his vocation."

"What do you mean?"

Scholz still wore an amused expression.

"Among singers he is the best doctor, and among doctors the best of singers."

"I see," said Henry, smiling, "a case of mistaken identity."

"He is mad about singing, and his voice is like an old goat's bleating. You wait till he picks up that guitar."

"Well, it takes all sorts," replied Henry with a benevolent shrug.

Albert sat hunched over his bed, miserable and brooding. Henry seized him by the elbow.

"Come on. Let's have a stroll round the camp."

As they were walking Albert remarked, "I wonder what happened to the Notarescan crowd. I feel a bit mean having dropped them at the gate like that."

"Don't worry, we'll find them soon enough. Let's face it, they can't hide here for long!"

As soon as they mixed with the crowd, Henry was struck by the prevalence of the Yugoslav tongue, which had replaced Polish, dominant at the time of his departure from Ferramonti. The camp's population seemed to have increased beyond expectation. Ferramonti was a little village by now, multinational in character.

A group of young Yugoslav women were strolling along, chatting loudly in their native tongue.

"They do not look Jewish at all," remarked Albert.

"Jews often assimilate their host nation's customs and looks."

"How could they assume their looks?" Albert was not convinced.

"I don't know, but there could well be a biological explanation. After all, camouflage is a very effective biological form of protection. Think of hares growing white coats in winter or insects assuming a bark-like appearance. With all the persecution through the ages, Jews may have developed this extraordinary means of self-protection, to avoid extermination."

Albert shook his head and smiled.

"I don't know why you always choose the most complicated explanations. There is a much simpler one: *Pater simper incertus est*. We know who the mother is, but the identity of the father is always open to question. After all, going to bed with the local population is also a form of biological adaptation!"

They had a good laugh, when suddenly Albert nudged Henry.

"Look at that blonde, blue-eyed beauty! She can't possibly be Jewish!"

Henry looked at the girl, and blushed.

"Yalda!" he exclaimed, "Yadranka!" The blonde girl waved and came over to them.

"This young lady is Yalda, Albert, well Yadranka actually," Henry smiled and bowed slightly as he continued his introduction. "She is from Yugoslavia, a history student."

They shook hands and exchanged the usual niceties and news.

"How are you getting on, Yalda? Still teaching history?"

"I'm afraid I stopped teaching lately." It was now Yalda's turn to blush.

"Why? What made you give it up?"

She blushed scarlet.

"I'm married now, and pregnant. I vomit a lot."

A burst of anger, and something like hurt vanity, got the upper hand, subduing Henry's discretion and habitual tact. He felt almost personally insulted by her revelation.

"What was the rush? Afraid of being left on the shelf?"

Yalda looked uncomfortable and turned her eyes away. But Henry's indignation was not exhausted yet.

"A baby, in this godforsaken place?"

Yalda seemed to stiffen suddenly and snapped back, "Babies can be born anywhere!"

"Yes, like weeds!" said Henry bitterly.

"Not weeds," retorted Yalda calmly, "but as end-products of love."

Albert, who was watching Henry's outburst with increasing discomfort and incredulity, sensed there was more beneath the surface than met the eye here. He looked at Henry curiously and under his steady gaze the latter collected himself.

"Sorry, I must apologise. After all, it's none of my business. So let me congratulate you."

Yalda took his proffered hand and held it in hers for a while.

"I know you mean well. But life goes on, in or outside concentration camps. We must have confidence and courage to face up to reality."

Henry, who by now had recovered his balance, smiled.

"I wish Mr Meiersohn were still alive. He'd be pleased to hear you."

"Who was he?" she asked.

"A very wise old man, and deeply religious."

"What has he got in common with me? I'm not religious."

"You'd be surprised, Yalda. Basically he said exactly the same with different words. 'The God of Abraham, Isaac and Jacob, who looks after the birds, will also look after me.'"

They shook hands again and Yalda went on her way, leaving Henry pensive and melancholy. It seemed a very long time since Yalda, in girlish curiosity, had first put her blonde head round the door of *camerata* 3.

A man with a flowing grey mane, hands clasped behind his back, eyes glued to the ground, was striding purposefully nearby. Even at a distance there was something about him which commanded attention. When he drew nearer he raised his gaze, revealing a fine head with an aquiline nose, piercing grey eyes and ascetic, yet sensuous, lips. In spite of the wrinkles and furrows he looked unbelievably vigorous and youthful. As he passed, he gave them a sharp penetrating look, which had an almost physical effect, like the tingling of an electric current.

"What an interesting-looking character!" Albert remarked.

A shrill sound rang through the air, followed by a prolonged whistle.

"What the hell is that?" asked Albert, startled.

"That's the good old *appello* I told you about," said Henry with a grin.

Chapter 3

A new palliasse

Back in the *camerata*, Henry saw there was a man tuning a guitar with loving hands; this was how he first encountered Dr Rosenkranz, a rosy-cheeked, blue-eyed, jovial man in his early forties. He had a sparse growth of beard, and altogether there was something eunuchoid about him, including his high-pitched voice. Right from the start he conveyed the impression of being an enthusiastic amateur.

"Enchanted to meet you," he said in his charming Viennese idiom, "I hear you also come from Vienna, the home of songs, Schubert and Beethoven."

"Yes, I lived there for many years, though I was not born there."

"Born or not born, once imbued with the special Viennese elixir, it is with you for life, like the lingering scent of a priceless perfume."

Henry smiled, amused by these highly-coloured baroque flourishes.

The roll call started, but no one paid much attention to it, most people displaying a couldn't-care-less attitude. *Tempora mutantur*, thought Henry, recalling Tommasini's hysterical antics of old.

Once the roll call was over, Batyushka Borstyn beckoned Henry over to his corner; in that spotlessly clean white shirt, blue dressing gown and red slippers, this lean aristocratic figure demonstrated that it was possible to preserve dignity and self-respect even in a concentration camp.

"Please, Dr Raupner, do come over and bring your friend along. This reunion calls for a celebration." He uncorked a bottle of wine. "*L' Chaim*....to life!"

Batyushka Borstyn smiled that very winning smile of his, in which his eyes as well as the rest of his face participated.

"I remember the day you all wanted to write Russia off. But the Big Bear is far from dead. He's growling and biting now."

"I wish he'd growl less and bite more," said Henry. "According to the last bulletins the Germans have reached the Don and are advancing on Rostov."

Borstyn was amused. "Let them advance, the fools! They're only digging their own graves!"

Henry could hardly share his euphoria, but not wishing to spoil the old man's fun, he remained silent. Borstyn however, sensing Henry's lack of enthusiasm, continued.

"I tell you Hitler missed the bus! He had his great chance and let it go."

"When was that?" asked Albert, fascinated by Borstyn's personality.

"In front of Moscow! When instead of storming it, he diverted his forces to the south. And, when Corporal Hitler changed his mind again and tried to take the Russian capital, General Winter played him a nasty trick."

"But why did he stop in front of Moscow?" Henry asked.

The old man threw up his arms.

"Why? Why? Why did Hannibal bypass Rome when it lay defenceless before him? Why did Attila spare Rome, when it was there for the taking? Why?"

"You tell us why," said Albert, mesmerised.

Batyushka Borstyn filled their glasses before replying.

"Why? There may be many answers. If old Mr Meiersohn were still alive, he'd have simply answered, 'Existentialists may point out that it's only the striving towards a goal that gives satisfaction, whereas fulfilment breeds a feeling of loss. Psychologists may bring superstitious fears, unconscious guilt, feelings of unworthiness into play. But most of all I believe that in the long run evil can never triumph. This I firmly believe is the unwritten law of the Universe."

"A law presumes a law-giver," retorted Henry, "so after all your answer is not very different from Mr Meiersohn's."

"My dear friend, the older I get the more I am convinced that we all hide our ignorance by saying the same things over and over again in different words yet we all believe it to be original."

A hand gently gripping Henry's shoulder made him jump.

"Oh! Linzer my old friend! How good to see you! I didn't know you were still here." Henry jumped up to embrace his old chum from Genoa.

"Good to see you too, my friend. I hope Mr Borstyn won't mind my joining your little reunion."

"You're always welcome, Mr Linzer. Sit down and have a glass of wine."

Linzer looked Henry over from top to toe and nodded approvingly.

"You do look well. Must have been well fed in Notaresco."

"We were talking about the war. How do you see the present situation?" Henry said, changing the subject.

Linzer smiled. "I may be good at buying and selling, but I hold no brief as a general. Just the same, I think the Allies are winning, slowly."

"Bravo!" exclaimed Borstyn, "You have summed it up precisely. Time is on the Allies' side, because of their superior resources. Hitler is fooling himself he'll get through to Baku and Tiflis to grab the oil. He never will!"

"Amen," said Linzer.

"Last winter," resumed Borstyn, "the Germans were near disaster when the Russians counter-attacked. It was a heroic, desperate offensive, masterminded by Marshal Zhukov, and will remain one of the great monuments to man's will to survive."

"Them German Panzers got stuck in their own shit," said a voice outside their circle, little Wolf's ponderous and irrefutable contribution to the discussion.

That night as he lay in the dark, Henry felt an acute pain clutching his heart. Poor Graziella! What was to become of her? In this orgy of blood and destruction, what chance had Graziella with death within and around her? It took a long time before his heartache allowed him to fall asleep. Having got used to his privacy and a comfortable bed, it was a shock to be once more sharing cramped sleeping space with all the accompanying noises. And this time there was no mattress to blame.

Chapter 4

The *Pentcho*

After a week, it was as if he had never left Ferramonti. Memories of Notaresco flitted in and out of his mind mostly during rare moments of solitary reflection. The numbers had swelled during his absence and the camp now had the air of a bustling Jewish community. Some entrepreneurs had even set up cafés with a limited menu; but the urge to recreate the culture of their homeland was strong and where better to meet new people, discuss the war and reminisce over coffee, even if it was often barely drinkable.

The change in temperature hit Henry hard as did the return to the blessed mosquitoes. How he missed that clear fresh air! Now he must get used to the regular doses of quinine and Atebrin, not to mention the side effects of nausea and ringing in the ears.

Ferramonti itself had undergone drastic changes, both in its social structure as well as in its population. The recent arrival of almost five hundred refugees from Bratislava had been something of a miracle and Henry was keen to hear about it. At the first opportunity, he met up with some of the newcomers who had arrived only a couple of months previously.

"Where do you all come from?" asked Henry as they sat one afternoon under the old tree in the *Piazza de Ferrari*. This was still a popular refuge from the heat and the accursed flies for *camerata* 3 and its regulars.

"We come from all over, we are Jews after all, but mostly from the Balkans! But our journey started on the Danube two years ago," said a young man who held out his hand to Henry who shook it warmly.

"Geller…from Prague," he said introducing himself. "On the good ship *Pentcho*," he added with a laugh.

"On a ship? Really?"

"Yes, well a river boat actually; we were on our way to Erez Israel."

Henry stared at him in a mixture of awe and admiration.

Wolf, who had joined the little group under the tree was keen to share the story. He was delighted to have Henry back in their midst and had for some time forsaken his broom.

"They caught them just off Rhodes," he exclaimed with a huge grin. "In a paddle boat! Such meshuggenehs!"

"Who caught whom?" Henry asked.

"Them *Katzelmachers*, them bloody Italians, caught their ship," explained little Wolf.

"And why would the Italians do that?" Henry asked, trying to work out what it was all about.

Geller smiled, glad to have a new audience for his tale which he never tired of repeating.

"It's a very long story," he began. "Two years long. Others can tell it better. If you want to hear the whole story you need to find Citron. He was with it from the very beginning but I warn you, it is a story that will only finish when we get to Erez Israel."

"Please tell us the story! Whatever you can!" urged Henry impatiently, adding with a wry smile, "And we have time….no one is going anywhere in a hurry!"

Geller obliged and making himself comfortable on the wooden bench he rolled a cigarette as he began the epic tale of the *Pentcho* and its incredible journey.

"Soon after Hitler's annexation of Austria in 1938, the Polish government deprived many Jews living there of their nationality and passport; this was done to prevent their return to Poland. At that time the Czech authorities were rather sympathetic and, turning a blind eye, allowed many stateless Jews without passports to cross the border. Perhaps the Czechs' sympathy sprang from a premonition of their own fate. Though this penniless first batch of refugees was soon found work by various Jewish organisations, their heart was not in it. They foresaw future events and felt that Europe under a Nazi regime was no place for Jews. But where was a Jew to go? Who wanted him, unless he had lots of money or an outstanding brain? Most of them had neither."

Just at that point, Kovacs, a man with a very imposing moustache came to find his friend and taking a seat under the tree, joined in the telling.

"There was a nucleus of Zionists," said Kovacs, "members of Betar, and it was they who hatched the plan to reach Palestine via the Danube and later by sea. You may ask, 'Why go by ship? Why not by train?' I can tell you! Firstly because it's cheaper, and secondly, what's even more important, because it is easier getting through the various frontiers without a visa, or even a passport. River transport is usually too slow for passenger service and is mostly confined to the movement of goods. Customs officers are mostly concerned with smuggled goods and less with the people on board. On the other hand, passport control is much more elaborate at railway frontiers. If your documents are not in order you must get off, the train won't wait. But if you hire a boat and they stop at the frontier you can still stay on board. You still have time to argue, barter, and if all else fails you can try the persuasion of *baksheesh*, a common procedure in the Balkans. You can't do that on a train surrounded by strangers."

Being the centre of attention appealed to Kovacs. He took his time rolling himself a cigarette, lit it, paused to stroke his moustache and continued. He knew his was a tale worth retelling and one which enthralled. Henry and Albert were spellbound by the sheer audacity of the plan. To sail down the Danube to Erez Israel? A plan that was borne of desperation with not a shred of common sense. Who were the masterminds behind this crazy venture?

"Alexander Citron was our leader," said Kovacs, pausing and pointing vaguely in the direction of the Yugoslav enclave. "He is easy to find...whenever you want, go over with the Yugoslavs, he can give you all the details. Much better than we. Anyway he is a fine young man with Zionist principles, a good brain and dynamic. He and another Betar member called Schalk, were together the brains and guts behind the *Pentcho*. They kept the whole thing going when others would have given up. Schalk had arranged collective transit visas for all the passengers. To Paraguay! Of course they couldn't say Palestine, you could not get such a visa at that time. Then came the business of finding a boat. There were regulations about passenger-carrying ships. Luckily the Czech authorities were not too bothered about the safety of Jewish refugees.

What if the whole lot were drowned in the Danube? They didn't care! Their only worry was if the boat blocked the passage of their ships and supplies so they wanted to get them out of the way as fast as possible! There was already plenty of anti-Semitism in Bratislava with twenty thousand Jews among the population, most of whom would not have ventured out alone at night for fear of being beaten up by thugs. You need to ask about our friend Lichtenfeld, God bless him wherever he may be. He knew a few things about life in Bratislava. Imi Lichtenfeld. Listen for that name. He is...or maybe was...a great hero!" Kovacs added pensively.

At first, Kovacz said, many refugees regarded the whole plan as sheer madness but when Hitler marched into Prague in March 1939, they had second thoughts. Suddenly Jews from Budapest and Belgrade became interested and wanted to join. If not, what would happen to them? Better to take a chance and hope to arrive at Erez Israel with God's help than to fall into the hands of the Germans.

"That's when I joined the group," said Kovacs "If I gave you all the details the story would never end." He made as if to wind up the story for the time being.

Henry looked at Kovacs then at Geller again.

"Please don't stop!"

Henry and Albert were full of respect for the bravery of these people who had set sail with their children, having sunk their life's savings into a venture which could have seen them all drowned. The indomitable Jewish spirit almost had echoes of the children of Israel's flight from Egypt and the parting of the Red Sea. Certainly another Exodus.

Geller took up the story again.

"So, Citron found Markeyevitch, a captain of a decrepit, rusty ship of the Donau-Dampfschiff-Gesellschaft, willing to undertake the journey down the Danube and to the Black Sea at a modest price. He was a one-legged Russian who was more often drunk than sober, a former officer of the Russian Imperial navy, with an addiction to morphine, the leg pain you understand...The crew, including the wife of Markeyevitch by the way, mostly from Greece or Turkey were drunk most of the time too. It was probably the best offer he had in years! Who knows, maybe he thought the boat would not get very far! And so on 18 May 1940 the first of us set off from Bratislava in a rusty tin can that would not have passed inspection. The plan as far as we were told, was to get to the Black Sea where a larger vessel would be waiting for us." Geller paused at this point to take a drink. He motioned to Kovacs.

"By the time we had sailed down the Danube and reached the Black Sea," Kovacs continued, "we had over five hundred passengers and this was one hundred more than Citron had agreed but an order came from Betar HQ to take new passengers just released from Dachau. The poor devils were mostly elderly, a miserable half-starved and sickly bunch. But there was just no room and almost a mutiny amongst the passengers. We were already like sardines, it was so hot, we could not breathe, there were bedbugs in our clothes, in blankets, it was disgusting. The only way the boat could stay afloat was to keep all passengers below in very close confinement. It was so overcrowded and dangerous that we feared it would topple over. At first people would prefer to be on deck but then when they rushed to one side to admire the view it almost capsized. Of course the children loved it; we tried to pretend it was a game to tip it back and forth. After this, Markeyevitch put stewards on deck who would call out 'nadrugu strano' to tip the boat back the other side if we hit a sandbank. The passengers could only take turns to come on deck for air one by one. There was hardly any food or water. There was no room for large supplies. We spent every day hoping and praying we would make it through the night, the boat was not seaworthy; it was 85 years old and ready for the scrapyard when we came along! And as we sailed down the Danube we needed to stop for water and more food but no! We were not allowed to even stop to refuel. Nobody would let us into the harbour. We stayed over 4 months on the Danube hoping to land, to get food for our children. We could even see the restaurants on the shores, see cafés and hear music. We wrote the word 'Hunger' on big signs in 3 languages in the hope someone would see it and bring us food but no one did. We were invisible."

A few more had joined them under the tree to see what was going on. They had heard the *Pentcho* epic again and again and never tired of its heroism.

"We had no radio, no proper lifeboats, no lifebelts, just an anchor."

Henry and Albert looked at each other open mouthed!

"Meshuggeners, madmen," whispered Henry to Albert who nodded, equally stunned.

Kovacz resumed his odyssey.

They reached the Yugoslav frontier posts. Most of them had been to Yugoslavia before, on holiday. But it was one thing to visit Split or Dubrovnik as tourists and another to enter Yugoslavia on board a rusty tramp steamer labelled a 'Jew Boat' with no money or documents. But to their surprise and delight some voluntary Yugoslav organisations had heard of their plight and sent hot food and a case of Slivovica.

"At times like these, when you're so downtrodden you feel lower than a worm's belly, the smallest show of kindness and goodwill can restore your faith in humanity. We thanked them from the bottom of our hearts and promised to remember their generous gesture as long as we lived."

The story continued. Endless problems with officials, a six week delay in Dobra where they thought they might be turned back. But it seemed the *Pentcho* had a guardian angel and each time, somehow they found either the fuel, the food, the necessary permission to continue. So finally they reached the Black Sea port of Sulina on September 14th. Here they imagined they would transfer to the waiting vessel for the last leg of their journey to Erez Israel, but no such ship existed, and when challenged, Citron and Schalk admitted it never had.

"The *Pentcho* steamed on through the Bosphorus. Then we had a problem. We had almost run out of drinking water and the Turkish harbour police would not let us drop anchor. They had been warned we were on our way and wanted to remain neutral. So desperate for food and water we entered the Aegean where on the island of Lesbos we had the greatest surprise! The sight of such a curious ship with a great big wheel, never seen before, brought everyone down to the harbour! The peasant women brought fresh fruit and sweetmeats to the wa-

terfront. A band in ceremonial uniform played tunes. People
were waving and cheering at us. They knew of our struggle
and thought we were heroes. It was unforgettable. Then a few
days later we were boarded by Italian naval officers in the
middle of the Aegean. They did not believe our story until
they saw the women and children. We had sailed over mines
and could all have been blown to pieces. They realised how
desperate we were to reach Palestine and the next day brought
us wine, fruit, vegetables and chocolates for the children. They
said we were the heroes of the war. We cried. They cried too."

At this point, Henry and Albert glanced at each other, both
stirred by this remarkable account of simple humanity, the
kind that knows no hatred. Greeks and Italians. No real sur-
prises there for these nations were born out of great moral wis-
dom.

"In the middle of the sea we ran out of water. Who could
imagine it? In the Danube there was plenty of fresh water to
keep the boiler going but now we were at sea and had to use
the drinking water supplies. Salt water would clog up the
steam pipes. Then Markeyevitch made the decision to use half
sea water to power the boat...but it was the only way to keep
moving."

He paused and looked at his audience; they sat still, transfixed, enthralled. He took a few puffs on another cigarette,
staring into the distance as he recalled the explosion which
rocked the boat and caused it to run aground.

"Again we were lucky! We found out later that the area was
heavily mined but our flat bottomed boat kept us safe. When
the engine died we were not too far from land. We made a sail
from all the blankets and sheets and with a little wind, the
Pentcho was able to sail into Kamillonisi, a little Greek island.
But it ran aground as we approached the shore. We were lucky
it didn't sink straight away; God again was merciful. We had
two days to offload everything from the boat until it sank. So
we escaped with our lives again."

"What happened to the *Pentcho*?" asked Albert. "Where is it
now?"

"The *Pentcho* who was so kind to us and kept us alive
stayed afloat until we had taken everything off her; we even

372 Ferramonti—Salvation behind the barbed wire

took the stove pipes so we could cook food. Then she went down." Kovacs whistled through his teeth slowly bringing his arm in an arc, pointing to the ground to illustrate the final path of the *Pentcho*, "In two pieces."

"How did you feel?" someone from the audience asked. "Were you sad?"

There was a silence. Kovacs and Geller looked at each other, each nodding to the other to take up the thread.

"Look, you know, we were so happy to be alive, out in the fresh air, on dry land, not to have drowned, to have saved all our belongings. That was what mattered. But the island was uninhabited and there was no food. We still had some macaroni, some onions but nothing else, we tried to fish but without nets it was not possible." Geller gave a shrug and shook his head.

Kovacs continued. He wore a bemused expression as if anticipating audience reaction.

"Next morning one of the women went to look at the wreckage. There was something big, like a red carpet where the boat went down but it was moving about in the water. You know what it was?"

Albert and Henry looked at each other. They had an idea.

"It was thousands and thousands of bedbugs....can you imagine it?" Kovacs shuddered as he recalled the infestations, the endless itching, the smell of the paraffin shampoos to rid them of lice.

"For Markeyevitch it was a terrible tragedy. The *Pentcho* was his livelihood and all things considered, he was a good captain. He navigated her through storms, through dangerous passages. It broke his heart to watch her fall apart and die."

The little crowd made sympathetic noises and felt a tug at their hearts for Markeyevitch's loss; they thought of their families and all was quiet for a few moments.

"And from there you came to Ferramonti? Henry was puzzled, trying to piece it all together.

"No—if only! No this was only October 1940! This was less than 6 months after we left Bratislava! But eventually we were rescued! After 10 days a ship—an Italian ship thank God— came for us. If it had been Germans, we would have been finished." Geller made a throat-cutting gesture with sound effects. "Some of our men sailed off in a small boat to find land and get help. Imi Lichtenfeld was one. Schalk another. Heroes! They nearly died but they saved us. God was looking after them….and us. Maybe now they are in Erez Israel, we don't know but we thank them every single day of our lives.

Then we were taken to Rhodes and left in tents in a football stadium for months. There was no food, it was freezing cold, raining all the time and we were living in mud and filth. After 3 days we still had nothing to eat. Then one of the men went to the officer in charge and said, "Shoot me or feed me — we are starving." So they brought us food! Figs and olives, then later a truckload of cabbages! That was our diet for 3 weeks! The local Jewish population helped when they could but there was a war and food was scarce for them too. But they did us a great *mitzvah*…they took all the children into their homes so they were fed and warm. Some of our kids even smuggled bread into the camp for us!

Then people began to die from the cold, starvation, malnutrition, dysentery. So on Christmas Eve they moved us to a shelter away from the cold rain into a basement building, the garage of the army barracks where we were at least dry and a little warmer but still hungry. The whole time in Rhodes we were hungry. Every day we went to sleep hungry. Every morning we woke hungry. This was life for a year in Rhodes!"

At that point there was a call for food and unappetising at it was, the regular serving of dubious nutritional value helped pass the time and give structure to the day.

Kovacs and Geller jumped up, shook hands again with the still awe-struck Henry and Albert, promising the rest of the epic voyage would be told another day.

Henry queued up deep in thought of the risks the Pentcho passengers had overcome and their endless courage. They wondered how they would have survived on figs, olives, onions, cabbages and oranges which became the staple diet of the *Pentcho* folk in Rhodes. They marvelled at the leaders of this ramshackle band of 500 and resolved to at least find this heroic Citron fellow and shake the great man's hand. It made their arrival from Notaresco seem like a pleasant excursion.

Chapter 5

Deutsche Kultur

The emergence of social classes, which hardly existed in the 'old days' of general penury, was largely due to the influx of the relatively affluent society of Yugoslavs and Greeks. This multi-national Babel of Poles, Germans, Czechs, Austrians, Hungarians, Yugoslavs and Greeks was further enriched by the arrival of Chinese, who added an exotic flavour to the community. Before the war there were many Chinese pedlars in Italy, nicknamed *clavate*. Most of them sold cheap ties: *cravate*. But unable to pronounce the 'r', they peddled their wares shouting '*Clavate! Clavate!*' Since Japan's entry into the war, these poor devils had become citizens of an enemy state overnight and had to be interned. But their stoicism, their courteous and elaborate ceremonials of conduct exerted a pleasing and almost calming effect on the turbulence of the camp's cosmopolitan population.

There was also a very active cultural life now. One morning Dr Rosenkranz asked Henry, "Are you coming to the concert?"

"What concert? I didn't know there was one."

"You'll need to get up to date with our cultural calendar here. We've all sorts of things going on. Today there's a '*Lieder Konzert*'. The singer is Elsa Kreisler. Used to sing in Graz."

"Any good?"

"Very good, a fine 'Heldensoprano', more dramatic than lyric."

"You seem to know quite a lot about singing," Henry said, more out of politeness than conviction.

"You are right there. Back in Vienna my friends used to say I should have taken up medicine as a hobby, and singing as a profession!"

Henry pretended to be surprised. "So you sing yourself?"

"I am a tenor," replied Rosenkranz (as if his high-pitched voice could have ever been taken for a bass-baritone).

"And have you sung here in the camp?"

Dr Rosenkranz seemed embarrassed. "Not yet, but I intend to."

"Well, I shall certainly come to hear you."

Henry went back to tidy up his bed, when to his surprise he recognised the older gentleman with the flying white mane and aquiline nose. He was involved in an argument with Dr Kaufman, who still lay resting on his *palliasse,* propped up on one elbow. The older man's eyes were flashing and he seemed vexed indeed.

"What you are saying, Dr Kaufmann, is nonsense! It is absurd to deny a nation's past culture, because of its present misdemeanour!"

In contrast to this man's outburst of indignation, Dr Kaufman remained calm and unmoved.

"I tell you Mr Mendelsen, that the race which calls itself the 'Master-race' is, has always been, and always will be, nothing but rubbish!"

Mr Mendelsen's fury grew with the younger man's insolent calm.

"And what about Goethe, Schiller, Lessing, Hoffman? What about Kant? Hegel, Fichte? Nietzsche? Schopenhauer? I should hope you have heard of them, Neanderthal that you are!"

"All rubbish and bullshit!" replied Dr Kaufmann. It was obvious he was simply out to provoke.

"I don't know why I waste my breath on you." Mr Mendelsen, quite beside himself, burst out.

"Nobody asks you to," replied Dr Kaufmann insolently.

"You are a dullard! The original man of clay! A Golem!" at which point Mendelsen stalked out of the *camerata.* Dr Kaufmann, a smug grin barely suppressed, remained in the same recumbent posture. In fact, Henry had so far hardly seen him in any other.

He threw an enquiring glance at Wolf and then both of them went out of the *camerata.* "What was all that about? Who is that man?"

"His name is Mendelsen. Supposed to be a painter of some repute, a German Jew, an assimilant. More German than a Prussian Junker."

Henry was puzzled. "He is obviously a cultured man. Why does he lower himself to quarrel with Kaufmann?"

The way Henry said it implied he did not think much of his colleague.

Szafran, who as usual had been listening uninvited, joined them. "They have these rows quite regularly. No one takes any notice any more."

"But why?" insisted Henry.

"It's rather complicated," continued Szafran. "Before he got a room of his own, Mr Mendelsen had the bed you sleep in now. He was his neighbour."

"Well, what of it?"

"Dr Kaufmann hates anything German, most of all 'Deutsche Kultur'. Mr Mendelsen tries to alter his convictions."

"Why does Mendelsen have his own room?"

Szafran grinned, his thick lips stretching from ear to ear. "There are various reasons. A painter of renown, so the Italians gave him a room to paint in. Besides, he is one for the ladies, even at his age."

Henry smiled. "I am not surprised. He is like a high voltage cable, bristling with energy, the old devil—but that still does not explain their rows."

Szafran gave one of his sly grins. "They are sharing more than rows but you'll find out in time. Anyway, Mendelsen must enjoy these skirmishes, or else he would not come back for more."

Henry, not much wiser after Szafran's ambiguous remarks, shrugged his shoulders and went over to the neighbouring camerata in search of Linzer. He found him sitting in front of his wobbly table, a pile of bills spread out.

Chapter 6

Deutsche Kultur—the concert

I t's becoming impossible to make ends meet," said Linzer. "They expect miracles from a provision buyer! Food prices gone sky high! And still the same allowance of five lire; how can one balance the accounts?"

Linzer seemed genuinely troubled and discouraged.

"And to make things worse," he continued, "there is this contrast with the Yugoslavs and Greeks standard of life."

"How come they are so much better off?" enquired Henry.

"There are several reasons. First, they came two years after us and have not yet exhausted their reserves. But more important, they have been able to bring with them their chattels, jewels and cash. Jews from Hitler-dominated countries were glad to save their skins. In Yugoslavia and Greece there was little Jew-hatred and so the friendly local population helped their Jewish co-nationals to escape the Nazis and salvage as much as possible."

"But where has all that comradeship gone? We took it for granted when Altman was here. We used to share the little we had."

Linzer had a wry smile on his lips. "You can't compare them with German or Polish refugees. Yugoslav Jews have never felt the full weight of anti-Semitism and so have not developed that strong tie and fellowship. They are really very nice people, but like all the rich, they do not understand the poor."

Later, when Henry examined his bowl of soup, he realised that the only way in which the provision buyers could balance their accounts was by a drastic degradation of the food; the watery brew with a few strands of runner beans and marrow had hardly any nutritional value at all. As he was working out the calories in his mind, somebody touched him lightly on the shoulder.

"Have you decided to come to the *Lieder Konzert*?" It was Dr Rosenkranz.

Henry had completely forgotten about the blessed concert. He was not really in the mood, but went over to Albert.

"Want to come to a *Lieder Konzert*?"

Albert liked the idea, for he was bored and disgruntled with life in Ferramonti having been used to Notaresco since the Italian declaration of war. To part with half a lire for each ticket was a major sacrifice, but as Albert put it, 'Man does not live by bread alone'.

After the usual afternoon nap to escape the sweltering heat, Henry woke up drenched in perspiration. Recalling the brisk air of the Abruzzi, he gave a deep sigh. He felt a fuzziness in his head, the combined effect of the heat and quinine. In his eagerness to cool down and clear his head, he went to the new latrine-cum-showers, but when the spray of water was released it stank so abominably that he could not stand it.

"Never mind," he sighed, "I'll just have to get used to it again."

Just before seven o'clock Albert and Henry set off for the concert, which was held in an overflow barrack, empty at that time. On their way they encountered a group of Yugoslav men and women, all neatly dressed and well groomed. Most men wore long trousers, sandals or shoes, and some even had ties. The women, in light summer frocks or evening dresses, looked like they were heading for a concert hall, and not to some shabby barrack in a concentration camp. Henry mused that Sonia would not have looked out of place. Against the elaborate attire of these people, Albert and Henry must have looked like a couple of tramps. In shorts, crumpled shirts and wooden clogs neither of them exactly delighted the eye.

It was very hot and stuffy inside. Mrs Kreisler, the concert artiste, made her entrance; Dr Rosenkranz was right. One could well imagine her with spear and shield as one of Wagner's warrior maidens. She announced her first song, Schubert's *Erlkönig*, the supernatural tale depicting the death of a child as he rides by night with his father. Her voice was powerful, expressive and carried well. The performance stirred many memories in the audience, who sat quite transfixed, and brought generous applause. Her next song, a powerful *Der Männer Sippe* from *Die Walküre*, was well received. Both songs being dramatic, suited her strong personality, more so than her third piece, *Dido's Lament*, more the domain of a lyric singer, which nevertheless had a poignancy which plucked at the heartstrings.

Henry let his eyes rove through the audience, a well behaved, dedicated crowd that could compare with audiences in any concert hall. As he leaned back to look over his shoulder at the rows behind, he was suddenly arrested by one face, the face of a woman, listening intently and wide-eyed to the performance. She'd be about thirty years old, despite her somewhat youthful appearance. But what had caught and captivated Henry's attention was the expression in her beautiful eyes — veiled, dreamy and yet sparkling with a strange lustre. For a few moments he continued to stare at the woman's face, fascinated by these strange expressive eyes. He could not possibly indulge for long in such an indiscretion and had to turn round again, wondering who the woman could be. Once or twice during the rest of the performance he looked back, trying to catch her eye, but she never noticed him.

"Well, what do you think of her?" asked Albert when the concert was over.

"Of whom?" Henry asked, startled.

"The singer of course! Who else?" retorted Albert.

"Who else indeed?" said Henry, smiling. "She may be better at felling trees than picking flowers."

Henry was anxious to get a closer look at the woman with the dreamy eyes.

"Why are you shoving? What's the sudden hurry?" asked Albert.

Henry did not reply. He was elbowing his way towards her. She was of slender build, willowy and lithe; somehow adolescent-looking, in spite of her age. Although not a traditional beauty, she held a compelling fascination for him. It was the radiance of those huge eyes — green eyes — a radiance which seemed to come from within - that made it so unusual. *The eyes of a visionary or an ecstatic*, thought Henry.

As he came closer, the man who stood beside her, a distinguished-looking man with strands of silver at his temples, put his arm around her.

"Well, it was not too bad after all. Didn't you think so, Sushka?"

People were pushing, eager to get out of the stuffy atmosphere, and Henry swept off in a different direction.

"Where's the fire?" remarked Albert trying to keep up. "You are in a strange mood!"

Henry smiled. "Never mind, Albert. Everybody acts strangely sometimes. That's what makes man such an interesting object of study."

No sooner had they entered the *camerata* than Dr Rosenkranz approached them, eager to get their impression.

"Well, what's the verdict?"

"I agree with you," said Henry, "her arm is more suited to wielding a sword than stroking a lyre, but she has power and drama!"

Dr Rosenkranz burst into his high-pitched laughter.

"So you noticed? I suppose it's the clinical eye."

Dr Kaufman, extended on his *palliasse,* must have caught part of their conversation.

He broke in contemptuously, "What was all that? More *Deutsche Kultur* rubbish?"

Henry ignored him. He did not wish to follow in Mendelsen's footsteps and get drawn into a slanging match. Luckily Moishele came in at that very moment.

"Have you heard the latest news?" he asked.

"No!" responded the entire *camerata* in eager anticipation.

"Neither have I!" said Moishele calmly, and then burst out laughing. No one ever minded Moishele's pranks. He meant no harm and lightened the atmosphere. Just the same, little Wolf felt cross at being cheated. His anticipation of sensational news, like some really big calamity befalling the German forces, had been frustrated.

"When are you going to grow up?" he asked, disgruntled.

Moishele went up to him and stroked his bald pate, something he often did, to Wolf's annoyance.

"Sorry to disappoint you, baldy. No news from the Eastern front. But now… come to think of it, there's *some* news."

"Another of your stupid jokes?" asked Wolf suspiciously.

"No jokes! There will be a visit from the Papal Nuncio."

"Who told you?" asked Szafran.

"Never mind. I have my special sources."

"What good will that do?" asked Wolf disparagingly. "All he does is sit on his throne and put out his hand, expecting everybody to kiss his apostolic ring."

"Last time he was here he did at least take our letters to send abroad," Borstyn reminded them, "so it's better than nothing."

An animated discussion ensued over the purpose of the visit.

"Let's hope he is not 'recruiting'. Remember Kanapek and the 'seven apostles'?" said Szafran.

"They wouldn't send a Nuncio for that."

"I tell you," said someone, "The Pope wants to jump on the Allies' bandwagon, now that the fortunes of war are changing."

"Oh! Stop talking nonsense!" yelled an irate voice suddenly. Everybody turned round. This unexpected cry came from Trebitsch, the *capo camerata*. It struck Henry all of a sudden that since his return to Ferramonti he had hardly noticed or spoken to Trebitsch, who seemed unduly quiet and monosyllabic.

"Stop talking nonsense!" Trebitsch repeated, "This is a serious matter! I've kept it to myself, but now I'm glad I can get it off my chest." He paused for an instant to control his emotions. "The fact is, this visit of the Papal Nuncio may have more weight than you think. I know, the Pope has been criticised for his lack of intervention on many scores. But let me tell you this: Himmler has asked for the extradition of all Jews in Italy, and so far only the Pope has opposed him."

There was a sudden silence as the full meaning of the new threat began to sink in.

"How do you know all this?" asked Borstyn in a hushed tone.

"Signor Rizzi told me in confidence two weeks ago. I kept it to myself, not to alarm you. I was in Dachau, I know what such an extradition would imply."

There was no reason to doubt Trebitsch's words. He was friendly with an Aryan German woman who, for reasons unknown, was also interned in Ferramonti and both of them had a special relationship with Signor Rizzi.

"But what has this to do with the Nuncio's visit?" asked someone.

"The Pope may wish to show his hand, his determination to reject Himmler's request. That's why—I hope—he has chosen this moment to send his Nuncio," replied Trebitsch.

Apart from Trebitsch, the only person to grasp the full weight of an extradition into Himmler's hands was Batyushka Borstyn. He'd gone white and his hands shook.

"It would be a disaster, a great calamity for all of us, if Himmler should get his way!"

One by one, as they began to fully realise what was at stake, their hearts felt the icy grip of fear, and they fell silent.

"What's the good of worrying about something that may never happen?" Moishele exclaimed in a brave attempt to disperse the dark clouds that had suddenly gathered over their heads.

He was right, of course, no need to bury oneself before one was dead, but unfortunately, fear cannot be dispelled by logic. The atmosphere remained subdued and grave. Most of them put themselves to bed, the refuge of sleep being the old comforter. Henry followed suit. Trebitsch's bombshell had shaken him. He lit one of Moishele's homemade cigarettes and reflected. Extradition. Maybe the devil is not as black as he is painted. After all, Germany was a nation of the highest culture. True, some were brutal and cruel, but even Trebitsch and Kaufmann came out of Dachau in one piece. Poor Yalda...to choose such uncertain times to be pregnant, and at her tender age! His mind began to wander and suddenly he saw again the radiant face with the dreamy eyes of the woman at the concert.

What an unusual expression, he mused, as he fell sleep.

Chapter 7

Mendelsen's exhibition

The afternoon nap was no longer an escape from heat, but from hunger. When he had first arrived in Ferramonti, more than two years before, Henry had been well covered and so had some bodily reserves. Even in Notaresco, where the food had been superior by comparison, it had still been of substandard nutritional value. So now, with yet further depletion of bodily reserves, he began to experience almost constant, nagging hunger pains. The few lire he had saved in Notaresco were soon gone. And the prices at the stores had rocketed not only because of inflation, but also because the Yugoslavs would pay anything to get the commodities they wanted. True, he still possessed a spare suit, some shirts, a wristwatch and gold and ruby cufflinks which he could barter for food, but victory was shrouded in the mists ahead, and he would have to bear his hunger until it became really intolerable. From his cufflinks, a heritage from Mundek, he would only part *in extremis*.

One day, during an energy-saving siesta, Henry was awakened abruptly by a fracas close to his bed.

"And I tell you, Mr Mendelsen, or should I say, Mendelsohn, that I have no intention of going to your exhibition!"

"But give me a reason! One single reason why you don't want to improve your education and taste."

"You, and your painting, smell of *Deutsche Kultur*! That's reason enough!"

Mr Mendelsen would not give up.

"Since you have passed your medical exams you must have at least a vestige of grey matter. How can you be so obstinate and stupid?"

"All I ask of you Mr Mendelsen — ex Mendelsohn — is to leave me alone!"

"Why will you insist on calling me Mendelsohn?" asked the painter angrily.

"Because it's your real name under that Germanic camouflage."

Mendelsen was livid. "You are a brute, an ape, still crawling around on all fours. I don't know why I even waste my time on you!" and he stormed out of the *camerata*.

"Goodbye Mr MendelSOHN!" yelled Dr Kaufmann after him, "Go hawk your *Deutsche Kultur* elsewhere!"

This is too stupid for words and such a bore, thought Henry.

"Anyway, when is this blessed exhibition?" he asked Wolf, who informed him that it would start that very afternoon.

Albert had also witnessed that show of bad temper and his interest was piqued.

"Why don't we go to the exhibition?"

Henry wondered whether Albert's sudden interest in art was genuine or just an attempt to escape the boredom of his new existence.

"Why not?" he replied, "It could be quite interesting."

Mendelsen's studio was situated on the fringe of the camp. It was a freak construction which had gone wrong for some reason and so, probably because of its uselessness, was allocated to the painter.

Henry hesitated.

"We have not been invited. Perhaps it is a private showing for a few select people."

"Don't be silly," said Albert, "and anyway, why should he object?"

To their surprise, the studio was packed but they realised at a glance that the public comprised the 'élite', the financial and intellectual cream of the camp. As they stood hesitantly by the door, Dr Rosenkranz, well to the fore of any worthwhile event, came up to them.

"Come! Let me introduce you to the *maestro*."

Mendelsen's scrutinising eye looked them up and down.

"I seem to know your face. Don't you sleep next to Kaufmann?"

"I do," replied Henry, smiling. "That is, I sleep when I am allowed to."

They exchanged meaningful glances.

"I hope you don't mind us barging in uninvited and ..."

Before Henry had a chance to say any more, the lady with the dreamy green eyes appeared. Henry stood there motionless. Mr Mendelsen, sensing the situation turned to her.

"My dear Su, may I introduce Dr...Raupner to you."

She looked vaguely at Henry and proffered her hand to shake his in a firm but brief contact.

"Su Springer," she murmured, but promptly turned back to Mendelsen. "I hope you won't mind me asking you a few questions?" Pointing at the paintings she said, "I see that you have created a cycle of *Madonna with the Christ child.*"

Mendelsen shook his head. "I prefer to look upon it just as mother and child."

Su's smile lit up her face. "What's the difference?"

"There is a very great difference. *Madonna and Putto* refers to one particular pair and event. The Mother and Child theme is timeless and universal."

While they were discussing the subject further, Henry glanced at the paintings, and as the room was only small he was able to encompass almost the entire exhibition. His first reaction to what he saw was stirring.

"You call yourself an expressionist. In what way does your school differ from others?" asked Su.

Mendelsen took one of the pictures from the wall. "If you look at this painting, you'll find a total disregard to proportions and ..."

Su interrupted him. "El Greco did that too. His figures are always elongated beyond normal!"

Mendelsen seemed rather annoyed at the interruption. "El Greco had a visual defect, astigmatism," he said firmly.

"Is that so?" said Su apologetically, "I always thought it was his way of infusing spirituality into his figures."

The master ignored her remark and continued. "What you may further note is the neglect of natural colours. The expressionist conveys his personal experience of an object, or a situation, and if that can be achieved by the use of unusual colours, regardless of proportions and perspective, he will use them."

Henry did not wish to appear too clever, yet he could not refrain from joining in.

"Gaugin painted his dogs red and had no perspective at all, as all his paintings are flat, yet he called himself an impressionist."

"What the hell is this? A conspiracy between the two of you?" asked Mendelsen, half amused and half annoyed.

They laughed, Su loudest, and in between she gave Henry a grateful smile for his moral support. Apparently she enjoyed teasing Mendelsen.

"Now seriously," resumed the painter, "the expressionist does not depict objects, but what these objects evoke in him."

Su thanked Mendelsen for his brief lecture, gave Henry a friendly smile and re-joined her husband, who was busy inspecting the exhibition. At this point Henry went to have a close look at the paintings. A mother and child cycle was no novelty, but this array on the age-old theme seemed to have a message of its own. The technique in each picture varied, to harmonise with its pronouncement. He tried to avoid intellectualising. Such an approach Henry believed to be advisable, both for the creative artist as well as the viewer, lest much spontaneity is lost; a spontaneity arising from the psyche's profound recesses, which enshrines wisdoms inaccessible to the rational mind. What struck him most was the expression of mother and child, which changed dramatically from picture to picture. By degrees the mother's virginal, angelic, Madonna-like expression changed to one of frivolity, lasciviousness and cruelty. And the same slowly progressive metamorphosis applied also to the child's countenance, which from innocent, spiritual, Messianic, underwent a gradual degradation until it reached a satanic expression of one begotten by Lucifer himself. One painting stood out. It was that timeless Mother and Child motif with the frozen look of eternity, an archetype par excellence.

"You have been staring at these pictures for quite a while. What do you think of them?" There was an inflection of irony, curiosity and patronage in Mr Mendelsen's voice.

Henry was caught off guard, but replied instantly, "These paintings are very strong!"

Mendelsen smiled. "Strong? What do you mean?"

"They hit you right between the eyes."

"Is that meant to be a compliment?"

"I believe it is. If a painting is capable of arousing emotion, no matter what kind, it has fulfilled its objective. Your cycle has done that."

As most people had already left, Henry felt less reluctant to monopolise the painter and confide to him his own reactions and interpretations, using his knowledge gained from his psychoanalysis to shed an archetypical light on the eternal theme of motherhood. At first Mendelsen seemed amused, but as Henry continued he became intrigued.

"Interesting," Mendelsen observed after hearing Henry's observations. "Obviously I was not aware of all that whilst painting, at least not consciously; but something in what you say touches a chord somewhere. This cycle really is one whole, with light and shade thrown in." He put his hand on Henry's shoulder. "Anyway, thank you for your observations. They are certainly thought-provoking."

When they left the studio, Albert, who had been listening to their conversation, looked at Henry askance.

"There is no knowing what weird thoughts go through your crazy head sometimes."

"Never mind, Albert. The world is full of cranks. Perhaps I am just one of them."

Chapter 8

Su asks for help

Once more the heavy rains transformed the camp into 'Ferramonti by the Lake'. Again swarms of migratory birds began to fill the sky, and the mighty oak in front of *camerata* 3 stood denuded and *triste*, its fallen leaves floating in the vast unbroken expanse of the Ferramonti lagoon.

It was in late August that the name of Stalingrad began to crop up with increasing frequency in the news. At first no great importance attached to it, except for the symbolic significance of its name. According to the war bulletins Stalingrad was about to fall at any moment; still the days went by and somehow the Russians managed to hold on to it by the skin of their teeth.

The food situation, for the less fortunate, was becoming desperate. Linzer was fighting a losing battle. From time to time he would slip Henry an extra piece of bread, a little olive oil or sugar, but this was never enough to quell the gnawing hunger, which by now had become his constant companion.

One day, idling about in the *piazza*, Henry was startled by the violent slamming of a door. Turning round he saw a woman, red-faced, fuming with anger and furiously muttering to herself. She must have come out of the Red Cross hut, since the glass pane in its door was still vibrating. As she lifted her head, Henry recognised Su. When she came closer he saw there were tears in her eyes.

"Good day Mrs Springer. You seem very upset. What is the matter?"

At first she looked at him vacantly, but then she gave him a smile of recognition. Pointing at the Red Cross hut she said disdainfully, "They call that a medical centre. It's a disgrace! They don't even have the most elementary things."

"What is it you need? Perhaps I can help?"

Su seemed to be turning something over in her mind.

"Perhaps you can. You are a doctor, aren't you? My husband is a diabetic. His insulin will run out next week."

Henry was perturbed. "Haven't you left it rather late?"

She stamped her foot. "Late? This is the third time in three weeks I have been to that travesty of a doctor! Each time he has promised me: 'Next week.' What am I to do?"

"If I am not mistaken, I have a box of insulin phials, but ..."

A glimpse of hope showed in Su's shimmering green eyes and she broke in, "You have some insulin?"

"Please let me finish, Mrs Springer. I do have some insulin, but most likely it is out of date."

Her face fell again. "How do you mean 'out of date'?"

"Insulin is not a very stable compound. It only has a limited effective life."

Su wrung her hands nervously. "How can you tell if it is still any good?"

"Usually the box is stamped with the date of expiry."

She was impatient. "Well, let's go and see what it says."

Henry did not like the idea of taking Su into his *camerata*. The 'old guard' still remembered Sonia; however, Su had already set off. As they entered the *camerata* inquisitive eyes were turned on them, especially that ironical pair of the nosy Szafran. The box of insulin, part of the Notarescan inheritance, was easily found, but as he'd expected it was a year out of date.

She looked utterly defeated. "What effect would it have if injected?"

"At best, none. At worst a toxic effect." Seeing her troubled face he hastened to add, "But I shall see Dr Sabatini right away and if necessary contact Signor Rizzi."

Su's face lit up and her eyes shone with gratitude.

"Thank you so very much, Dr Raupner. I shall not forget your kindness."

Henry was eager to get out of the *camerata*, as he felt the prying eyes burning on his skin.

"Where can I find you, Mrs Springer?" he asked, once they were out.

"I am in *camerata* 12, my husband is in *camerata* 19."

Henry was surprised. "Aren't you together?"

"No, Dr Raupner. We have no children so we can't have a family hut."

They shook hands. Su held his in a firm grip; her green eyes flashed.

"Thank you again," she said softly.

Chapter 9

Arnold Springer

The battle of Stalingrad had been raging now for weeks. Time and again Stalingrad was supposed to have fallen, but like a phoenix it continued to rise from the ashes. Now a new locality occupied the headlines with increasing frequency: El Alamein. At first there were only vague hints of a battle taking place in the desert. General Rommel had allegedly got the situation well in hand. Gradually however, the name of a British general began to be linked with that of the desert fox: a General Montgomery.

One evening, as Henry lay on his *palliasse* reading, he was startled by the sudden appearance at his bedside by a distinguished looking, middle aged man. There was something vaguely familiar about him, but Henry was unable to place him anywhere.

"Are you Dr Raupner?"

"I am," he said, sitting up.

His visitor looked rather doubtfully at the stool beside Henry's bed. "May I?"

"Please do. That stool wobbles a little, but it won't let you down." Henry recalled Ossi and Dino's enthusiastic carpentry with a stab of sorrow.

The man looked in his early forties, with greying hair and a somewhat anxious expression; he pulled up the stool.

"I meant to come before and must apologise for not having done so. You have been very kind to my wife and me. My name is Springer, Arnold Springer. You helped to get my insulin."

"There's no need to thank me for that. I only spoke to Dr Sabatini."

"Just the same, it was very kind of you."

Henry looked searchingly for tell-tale signs of diabetes, assessing the man at the same time. He had a kindly face, warm and open, though a little care-worn, which was hardly surprising at such times with or without a chronic condition.

"You shouldn't have gone to the trouble of coming specially to thank me."

"Well, that is not the only reason. My wife sent me to invite you to a little party with some Yugoslav friends."

Though Henry disliked parties with people he did not know well, he was pleased at the thought of meeting Su again.

"It will be a pleasure. When is this party?"

"Tomorrow. In the family hut of Mr Fleischer. He's a bank manager from Zagreb."

Henry didn't care for that at all. A bank manager was probably not his kind of person. A snob, in all probability.

"Are you a Yugoslav too?" he asked.

"I am. My wife is not. We met in Berlin during one of my business trips." His face assumed a melancholy expression. "Those were such happy days."

There was something disarmingly simple and direct about Arnold Springer and Henry took to him from the start.

"Have you been married long?"

Mr Springer paused. "Why do you ask?"

Henry smiled. "For no particular reason. Only, your wife mentioned you have no children."

"I see…anyway, though we have no children, we have been married for over ten years."

His face took on a pained expression, as if a sudden cloud descended upon it.

"I was not ill when we married. Had I known what lay in store for me, I would not have married at all, least of all Su, who is so vivacious…and loving."

The conversation had taken an embarrassing turn, at least for Henry, who was not prepared for such confidences. He searched for something that might cheer Arnold Springer up.

"Your wife is deeply attached to you," he proffered eventually.

"Why do you say that?"

"I saw how she cried when she could not get the insulin for you."

Springer's face lit up and the corners of his lips curled into a fine, tender smile. "She is a dear good soul, unselfish and generous."

But soon the corners of his mouth slid down again. "It hurts me all the more to have imprisoned her in this marriage."

Henry did not know what to say, feeling increasingly ill at ease. He was used to Italians blurting out their bath-and-bedroom secrets to complete strangers during a short journey, say, from Padua to Verona; but Springer was no Italian. So why?

By some form of telepathy, Springer seemed to have read Henry's thoughts, for he promptly gave him the answer.

"You are a doctor. I can be frank with you. You will understand. It was only six months after we were married that my illness was discovered. The doctors in Berlin called my diabetes severe. One heartless specialist even called it 'malignant'. But we'd found it was reasonably controlled with insulin."

Henry listened intently, wondering what he was leading up to.

"Soon after the illness started I developed disturbances of vision. I think they called it retinopathy; and not so long after that, other common diabetic disabilities appeared."

He sat there with downcast eyes, examining his fingernails. "Being a doctor, I need not explain to you any further. You will understand."

With these words he got up and walked away; he stopped at the door and turned, smiling. "See you tomorrow."

Chapter 10

Fall of Stalingrad

Hardly had Henry recovered from the impact of Springer's visit when in galloped Moishele, with an excited look on his face.

"Where is my friend Wolf?" he yelled, "I have some news for him."

Little Wolf, who was scraping his stubbly chin with a blunt razor, turned round with ill-concealed annoyance.

"What is it now, meshuggener? More of your daft tricks?"

"Now then, now then!" exclaimed Moishele, "I want to test your brains."

"Piss off, you fool!" hissed Wolf, resuming the interrupted shaving ritual.

But Moishele sat himself squarely on Wolf's bed, still retaining that air of elation. It was written all over his face that something unusual had happened, that he was dying to communicate to the others. In his shaving mirror, little Wolf examined Moishele's agitated reflection. Perhaps that idiot had some good news after all?

"All right then, meshuggener," Wolf said cautiously, "what is this nonsense about testing my brains?"

Moishele took his time, always the showman, delighting in the suspense he had created, not only in Wolf but also in others who began to gather round. Addressing himself to Wolf and hammering out each syllable, Moishele asked eventually, "What is the meaning of this sentence: 'attacks coming from all directions'?"

Wolf's mouth fell open to a gaping hole rimmed by soapsuds. He spread out his arms to the bystanders in a pleading gesture. "Listen to this madman! 'Attacks coming from all directions?' It means what it says!"

Moishele ceremoniously produced a newspaper from his coat pocket and began to read. "'Attacks coming from all directions were successfully repulsed'. Any comments yet?"

There was still no response from the audience, except for one person, Borstyn, whose eyes began to glow and then, when the penny had finally dropped, to shine excitedly. "Where is it happening?" he asked impatiently.

"In Stalingrad," replied Moishele, and focussing his sight on Wolf he asked mockingly, "Now then halfwit, do you still not understand?"

Wolf looked bewildered, unable to work out what this fuss was all about.

"They are surrounded! Encircled at Stalingrad!" exclaimed Batyushka Borstyn, unable to contain himself. He began to jump for joy.

Although little Wolf was still incapable of figuring it out, he relied on Borstyn's enthusiastic reaction and joined in his jubilation, with the rest of the *camerata* following suit.

"They're in the soup!" shouted Borstyn, hopping from one foot to the other with great elation, dancing around his four-poster bed. He reached for the big trunk and got out a bottle of Slivovica. "A toast to the gallant Russian army! And a toast to Moishele! Let's promote this clever man to the rank of field marshal!"

The Slivovica made its rounds. Such an occasion certainly merited a celebration. Eventually, when the excitement had died down, Borstyn addressed his fellow internees. "Gentlemen! This most memorable day is the turning point in the war! I assure you!"

These words were ringing in Henry's ears when, slightly tipsy and with a heart as wide open as the proverbial barn door, he eventually flopped into bed. But it was a restless sleep. He woke in the middle of the night. Something had been on his mind, though he could not quite put his finger on it. Somehow he felt that it was connected with Mr Springer's visit. The trouble was, he had not had sufficient time to get over the embarrassment of that encounter, when Moishele's sensational news had ousted and forcibly wiped out all preceding impressions. It was something in Mr Springer's demeanour, something in what he said, that had hauled him back from sleep.

Henry tried to recap their conversation, word for word: that he 'would not have married her' had he known what lay in store for him ... not Su, who was 'so vivacious'. He'd men-

tioned his diabetes, his retinopathy, 'and other common diabetic disabilities'. What common disabilities? Tuberculosis? He
did not look like a consumptive. Furuncles and boils? There
were none, at least not outwardly. 'I do not need to explain ...'
'you are a doctor ... you will understand.' In these last words
lay some significance which was puzzling Henry. What was he
trying to say? Why was he so embarrassed? And suddenly it
clicked. The answer was impotence! This common diabetic
side-effect would explain the absence of children after ten
years of married life, his embarrassment as well as his regret
for having married such a 'vivacious and loving' personality. It
might possibly also account for Su's girlish appearance and
contribute to that radiance stemming from banked fires. Having finally found the key to this riddle he turned over and fell
into a deep and restful sleep.

Chapter 11

La crème de la crème

Next morning, still elated from the good news, Henry was surprised that Moishele's brilliant interpretation of the war bulletin had not spread throughout the camp. Could it be that they had read a cryptic meaning, substituting wishful thinking for a cool appraisal of facts?

Anyway, his mind was set on other things, or rather one thing only: that evening's encounter with Su. Historical moment or not, he was dying of impatience to see Su again at the party. For such is the nature of man, that sometimes a bagatelle, light as the flutter of a butterfly's wing, can be closer to the heart and far more pressing than the conquest of the stars.

The party was to be held at 7 o'clock, which in late November meant that it would be dark already. But who cared nowadays? Gone were those rules and regulations forbidding the absence from barracks after sunset. Tommasini's 'sporchi Ebrei' were a faded memory of the remote past. With a wry grin Henry recalled those nocturnal forays, when crawling on all fours he'd made his laborious way to Sonia. No need to crawl nowadays he thought, smiling.

Henry decided to dress up for this occasion although his wardrobe gave little opportunity for stylishness. The last time he had smartened himself up was almost a year before, at Christmas in Notaresco, to meet Baumgart's family. But before he set off, he discarded his tie in protest against snobbery.

Oddly enough the Fleischer's family hut stood only at a short distance from where Sonia used to live, but it was bigger and had been recently lime-washed. On entering he found the place filled to bursting point and marvelled how they'd crammed so many into so small a space. The furniture had been removed and everyone squatted on cushions. A clean white cloth was spread on the concrete floor, with bottles of wine, dishes of sweetmeats and other delicatessen on it.

"So that's how the other half lives," thought Henry, with a mixture of irony and bitterness, mindful of Yadranka's comment on their first meeting. As soon as he entered the room,

Arnold Springer led him to the master of the house. They shook hands.

"Glad you could come to our little soirée," said Mr Fleischer, introducing Henry to his wife Tania, who pointed out an unoccupied pillow on the floor. It was very hot and stuffy inside, and the air was filled with the smoky scent of Turkish tobacco. Though Henry was anxious to catch a glimpse of Su, he did not betray his impatience. He sat there quietly, cross-legged, eastern style, wearing a social smile like the rest. Unobtrusively he studied the faces of the other guests, some of whom were familiar, others quite unknown to him. At the same time he discreetly kept a lookout for Su while eyeing up the delicatessen tantalisingly close by.

There, in the centre of the room, undoubtedly as the *pièce de résistance*, was Mendelsen. Only a turban was needed on that long unruly mane to make him into a Pasha. Seated beside him was Verushka, his pupil, a budding artist, exotic and attractive, who, it was whispered in the camp, was an expert in matters not only confined to painting. Mendelsen, his arm around her shoulder, was whispering something which provoked rippling laughter.

Further away, squashed in a corner, was the shorthaired, steely-eyed Mrs Feinberg, doctor of Jurisprudence from Vienna that Henry had encountered before his "holiday" in Notaresco. Henry caught her eye and she smiled back at him in recognition. In the time since his return, this was their first real encounter. Ferramonti had indeed grown into the 'Metropolis of Calabria', with each individual revolving in his own orbit of friends and interests. The word was that Hotel Ferramonti by the Lake boasted some three thousand guests.

Close to Mrs Feinberg sat a plump woman with long flaxen plaits. *Good God! Can it be?* Yes, it was Yadranka, in advanced pregnancy. She waved to him and so he got up to shake hands with her.

"Oh! How nice to see you, Yadranka! Are you keeping well?"

"Yes we are both doing fine and this little one," she patted her huge belly tenderly, "is due any moment!"

Fortunately she was Yugoslav, so her wealthier compatriots would take care of her.

"Which is your husband?" Henry enquired.

"He is not here. He's not Yugoslav and besides ...," she beckoned him to come closer and whispered, "he does not like bank managers. He says there are snobs!"

Pressing against Yadranka squatted another lady elegantly attired in evening dress. It was Mrs Kreisler, the opera singer. Evidently the gathering was not exclusively Yugoslav, but included only the *crème de la crème*.

Henry felt a gentle hand on his shoulder and turned round.

"You seem to be ignoring me." It was Su who addressed him so teasingly, her green eyes twinkling, as they always did.

"I'm sorry. I didn't see you."

"You couldn't. I was sitting behind you. Did you find the place easily?"

"Oh, he is well acquainted with this neighbourhood," broke in Yadranka with a sly grin. Apparently pregnancy had not tamed her humour.

Su looked blankly at them.

"Ask him! He knows what I mean," Yadranka added, laughing, a tinge of spite mingled with amusement.

Henry made a dismissive gesture and, turning away, enquired, "And how is your insulin stock, Mrs Springer?"

"There is still a month's supply left. I really ought to have thanked you for your kindness."

"Not again!" interrupted Henry, "Your husband has already done that. Most likely the insulin would have arrived anyway. It was long overdue."

"Just the same, it was very kind of you to take so much trouble for a complete stranger."

At this point their eyes met in a silent exchange of messages. Su was the first to lower her eyes. She must have understood the telepathic transmission intuitively. All this in only a split second, and when Su regained her composure, she pointed to the three girls sitting nearby.

"Have you met our camp beauties? These two are the Fleischer girls, Dana and Magda, and this charming young girl is Heidi, Mrs Kreisler's daughter."

Henry reached past Su to shake hands. Heidi Kreisler, a timid girl who looked about 14 years old, had a sweet, shy and unassuming manner, unlike the two Fleischer sisters who were vivacious and brimmed with the confidence of being on familiar home territory.

Seeing Henry's empty glass, Su got up to fill it and passed him a dish of titbits which Henry had been gazing at longingly. He took a handful, savouring the sweetness of the dried fruits while trying to chew nonchalantly. *Wine and dried fruits* he thought to himself. *This is the life of a bank manager!*

At this juncture there was a rattling noise.

"Please sit down everybody."

Apparently Mr Fleischer wished to make a speech.

Well, after providing all this wine and food he is entitled to, thought Henry.

Up to that moment, having only eyes and ears for Su, Henry had omitted to take a closer look at his host. The best way to describe Mr Fleischer, the former bank manager, was that he looked very *distingué*. Tall, lean and supple despite middle-age, with a sharp expressive face, he was certainly an impressive figure. His behaviour was debonair and polite, though rather affected; what Henry resented about the man was his patronising air, no doubt a result of his profession.

To draw the assembly's attention, Mrs Fleischer 'shushed' the chattering audience, her index finger over her lips like a kindergarten teacher.

She was a worthy complement to her husband; her appearance was dignified, her movements stately and measured, but like her husband she was somewhat condescending, formal and distant. Probably in years past she had been a very beautiful woman.

"Ladies and gentlemen! Friends!" began Mr Fleischer in his cultured voice.

"Needless to say, my wife and I are very happy to play hosts to such a fine gathering." At this point he made a slight bow towards Mendelsen, who returned the compliment with a slight nod and a glint in his eye.

"When we Yugoslavs decided to hold this party a few days ago, we were unaware that it would coincide with events of great importance."

Here he paused to rouse his audience's interest. In fact those who had been listening only distractedly pricked up their ears.

"Of great historical importance in fact, I should say. I cannot disclose my sources of information," he went on, "but I can assure you these come from very high up." He wrinkled his forehead portentously to impress on his audience the weight of the message he was about to deliver. Clearly he knew all about holding an audience in suspense.

Henry was getting impatient as he poured himself another glass of wine. *For heaven's sake*, he thought, *cut the cackle and shmooze and get to the point!*

"In days to come," Fleischer continued, "you will remember this party not only as a social event, but for matters of much greater importance, which I am about to disclose."

Henry felt he was nearing the limit of his patience and tolerance, especially as the wine was beginning to take effect.

"Ladies and gentlemen! Prepare yourselves for sensational news."

He paused again, took a deep breath, looked slowly around the room and announced, "I am honoured and delighted to inform you that the allegedly invincible German forces..."

Henry, losing his patience and self-control interrupted loudly, "Are surrounded in Stalingrad!"

Everybody turned to look in Henry's direction; a frosty stare from Fleischer transfixed Henry's insignificant person.

"Oh! How did you know that?" Fleischer, totally deflated, was trying hard to conceal his frustration and disappointment. Henry almost felt sorry for him, for at this moment he looked like a dejected little boy. "How do you know that?" Fleischer repeated.

"From a source high up," replied Henry, smiling, "from a Field Marshal."

Fleischer looked disbelieving and cross.

"A Field Marshal? What's his name?"

Henry could no longer contain himself and burst out laughing.

"The name is Moishele Perlemann of *camerata* 3," and subduing his mirth he added, "we knew this last night thanks to Moishele's acumen in interpreting war bulletins and we celebrated the event too." Henry raised his glass to toast the room with a broad grin.

The assembled guests broke into loud cheers and belly laughs brought on by the intoxicating wine and good news. Fleischer meanwhile tried to smile but was utterly crestfallen. Mendelsen seemed amused. He cocked an eye at Henry and gave him a wry smile. But what gave Henry the greatest pleasure and satisfaction was a gentle nudge from Su. So clearly neither she nor Mendelsen had any great affection for their host.

Once the hilarity over the comic episode had abated, pandemonium broke loose. The German debacle at Stalingrad lifted everybody's morale. Congratulations, *Mazel Tovs*, as well as Polish, German, Yiddish and Slav variants thereof, reverberated around the small room. The bottles of wine and spirits were soon exhausted and when Henry finally made his way back through the cold of the night, he was swaying like a drunken sailor, full of grog on the way to his ship.

Chapter 12

Tonsillitis

Overheated from the stuffy air and unaccustomed alcohol, Henry had caught a chill while trudging through the cold night back to his *camerata*. Next morning he felt feverish and sick. He had a sore throat and a splitting headache. Dr Rosenkranz inspected his throat.

"It's good old-fashioned tonsillitis. You'd better stay in bed and keep warm."

Henry needed no coaxing. He was perspiring profusely and shivering. As for keeping warm in bed, this was a joke for the single thread-bare blanket had more of a psychological than practical effect in keeping out the cold. He took some aspirin and Borstyn gave him a draught of vodka. Henry yearned for something hot, a bowl of real soup, but such luxuries were only for the upper crust. With regret he recalled those sweetmeats and titbits at the Yugoslav party, wishing he'd eaten more instead of concealing his hunger under a cloak of indifference for the sake of appearances.

Moishele brought him a newspaper to cheer him up, and after two years' experience of reading between the lines, Henry was uplifted by the wealth of good news which emanated from the bulletins. *Strange,* he thought, *how some rules of the gambling wheel apply to life in general.* About the Law of Series, he had learned the hard way, when as a greenhorn he had tried to play against the running of the wheel. He had to pay his penalties, when to his dismay uninterrupted sequences of twenty or more, of the same colour had occurred. However, no matter how long, each series had eventually to come to an end. So, now it seemed that the fantastic sequence of German successes had exhausted itself. Their series of *rouge, rouge, rouge* had run out. It was now *noir, noir* all the way. For almost simultaneously with the encirclement at Stalingrad came the good news of the British breakthrough at Alamein. Soon after, Tobruk fell; an Anglo-American force landed in French North Africa and Darlan surrendered the French fleet to the Allies. The over-extended colossus had clay feet after all!

Linzer came over to bring him an orange, which Henry peeled and ate immediately. It soothed his parched throat and Linzer was glad to be able to offer some temporary comfort.

"How are you?" he asked, putting a hand on Henry's forehead. "You still have a fever."

"Never mind! The Axis is cracking. This is the best medicine for me."

He had to stay in bed for two days, but then he got up, washed, dressed, shaved and even took his turn in the queue. But still feeling rather weak, he went back to lie on his *palliasse* to read a book.

"You are a fine one," said a voice unexpectedly beside him. Henry looked up. It was Su. "You are a fine one," she repeated, "Arnold and I have been all over the camp looking for you these last two days, and here you are, cosy and snug."

"I have been ill."

She screwed up her eyes to examine him closer. "You don't look well at all. Do you have enough to eat? Why did you not send for me?"

Henry was surprised. "How could I? Why would I? After all …"

"After all what?"

"After all I am a stranger. You have no obligation...besides, I'm well now."

She shook her head. "You are certainly *not* well at all."

Henry smiled. "Strange how women like to fuss."

She looked him straight in the eye, a smile on her lips.

"By the way, I found out, how you come to be so well acquainted with the Fleischer's neighbourhood."

"Is that all? So Yadranka has been gossiping again! I wonder if she has had her baby yet….."

"Never mind all that, let me straighten your pillow."

She bent over but recoiled at the touch of the pillow. "How can you sleep on that? It's soaked. And it stinks of mould!"

Henry was deeply embarrassed. "This is not the Ritz, you know."

For no apparent reason her face was suddenly irradiated by that magic sparkle in her eyes.

"It was splendid, you know. I mean, Fleischer, the other night..."

"I did not intend to be rude. He simply got on my nerves, drawing it out like that."

"You did quite right! He is a pompous ass. I was so thrilled I could have hugged you!"

"Why didn't you?" He looked straight into her dreamy eyes.

She didn't reply, but there was hardly any need. Her blushing face was like an open book.

"I must go now," she said abruptly. "Would you like me to send over some warm soup?"

"No!" Henry exclaimed vehemently, touchy as most paupers are, "but do come and see me again."

When she had gone, Henry murmured to himself, *Soup my foot!* Then, recalling the fuss Sonia used to make on the same subject, he added, *that's where I came in.*

Chapter 13

Playing with fire

Most of the internees were out of the *camerata* in the morning and Henry was able to relax on his *palliasse*. Su's visit had cheered him up no end. His throat did not hurt so much, so he lit one of Moishele's 'specials' and indulged in a little daydreaming.

But one man, sitting on the edge of his bed in a rigid posture, just staring at the ceiling, caught his attention. It was Przebylewski, whom he had hardly noticed in months. Now that few people bothered about *appello*, he was seldom seen in the *camerata*.

"How are you, Przebylewski? Hardly see you these days."

It was some time before Przebylewski detached himself from whatever he was contemplating.

"I'm alive," he replied in a flat voice, and continued to stare into space.

Moishele had been right, for a few days later, the Papal Nuncio did come to pay them a visit. He sat on his 'throne' in the centre of the *piazza*, a very imposing figure with his shining mitre and ecclesiastical robes. First he addressed the internees and then he graciously received those who felt the need to talk to him, in private audience.

Only Henry's comrades who had enjoyed the doubtful privilege of Trebitsch's confidence regarded this display of Papal diplomacy with grave concern; the rest of the internees were unaware of the Damoclean sword that hung over their heads. Now that Nazi Germany was recoiling under the Allies' hammer blows, it needed a diversion, a scapegoat, and Himmler was intent on providing it. What better target for their fury than the defenceless Jew?

Henry's comrades had honoured their promise not to alarm the rest of the camp for there was no point in creating panic. As he stood there, lost in gloomy forebodings, Su came up to him.

"Why, you have a face like a funeral. Seen a ghost?"

"Maybe I did," but noticing Su's preoccupied frown, he added lightly, "I was only joking. It's nothing. Really!"

"Are you better now?"

Henry nodded, unconvincingly. "You never came to visit me again. Why?"

"I don't like playing with fire."

"Neither do I."

"No?" she asked, looking him full in the face, "And Sonia?"

Henry was caught short by her direct question and that she had been checking him out.

"That was different. Too long to explain."

"Different?"

The crowded *piazza* with all its hullaballoo, was really not the place for this kind of conversation.

"Shall we walk?"

She did not reply, but followed him. They walked for a while in silence, when Su suddenly stopped.

"I do love my husband, you know."

"I never doubted it. I saw how you cried."

They walked on, slowly at a deliberate pace, when she stopped again.

"I've had many opportunities to start an affair."

"I can well believe it."

"But I never did, although ..." she hesitated, "although, odd as it may seem to you, my husband almost encouraged it."

"I can well imagine," said Henry imprudently, but as soon as he'd said it he wished he'd bitten his tongue for Su turned on him with hurt eyes.

"What do you mean?"

Pushed into a corner, Henry felt it was no use beating about the bush. So he faced those green eyes, which seemed to sparkle even more with anger, and put his hand lightly on her shoulder.

"I know," he said soothingly and with meaning.

"You know what?"

"I know all about Arnold ..."

"You mean to say Arnold told you?"

"Not in so many words, only a hint." He lowered his voice almost to a whisper. "I am a doctor, after all."

Her face crimsoned, as if in the deepest shame. There were tears in her eyes and soon with the heavy silence between them, they began to spill.

"Oh poor Arnold, how humiliating for him!" She walked away, leaving Henry in a state of confusion and regret.

Chapter 14

Luck is a fickle friend

The days passed. The Allies' fortunes were in the ascendant. The Axis cracks were multiplying. But in spite of their high spirits and jubilations, most internees were starving as well as suffering the winter's chill. By now the Allies' blockade had begun to bite deeply into Italy's economy and guts. Needless to say, things were much worse in concentration camps, except for the privileged few. However the rays of hope had a vivifying effect on mind and body. Apart from this, people were prepared to part with most of their belongings and convert them into victuals, now that victory was at last in sight.

"Clothes can be bought again, but not health," was the slogan and never had the bartering with the peasants across the barbed wires been more intensive. A wave of optimism and defiance was sweeping the camp.

But this prevailing high-spiritedness, almost escalating into euphoria, seemed to affect Przebylewski adversely. The more confident and forward-looking the rest of them grew, the more dejected he became. Ever since that acute attack of melancholia, he had not caused any major disturbance from what Henry had heard. In fact Henry had been surprised to still find him in the camp on his return from Notaresco more than six months ago. True, he was still a loner and odd, but he fell in with the daily routines. You saw him only very occasionally, for he spent most time wandering aimlessly through the camp, always alone. His wife, it was said, had left him, he had no friends; whereas others made plans for the future, he felt that he had none. For some reason he began to get on Dr Kaufmann's nerves.

"What are you staring at there, like a zombie?" he snapped one day.

Przebylewski did not reply. Most likely he hadn't even taken in what Dr Kaufmann had said to him, continuing motionless in the same frozen posture.

"You give me the creeps! If you don't move I'll make you sorry!" yelled Dr Kaufmann, losing his patience. Disgruntled and morose by nature and circumstances, he had to take it out on somebody.

"Don't you realise he is ill?" Henry said quietly to pacify him.

"Ill? Nothing that a good kick in the arse wouldn't cure!"

There was no point in arguing with him, for he very evidently needed an outlet for his own pent-up aggression. It was some time since his last tussle with Mendelsen, and evidently he needed a good row to let off steam.

Just then, talking of the devil, Mendelsen entered in person.

"Ah! Now look who is here!" Dr Kaufmann snarled, "The mighty Wotan himself!"

Mendelsen ignored the jibe. "I was not looking for you. I came to see Dr Raupner."

"So you are not talking to me all of a sudden, Herr Mendelsohn!" he bellowed. "You have come to see Dr Raupner from Vienna, from the *Deutsche Kultur!*"

Henry pretended not to hear. "You are looking for me, Mr Mendelsen?"

"Most likely one of his fancy exhibitions. Am, I right, Mr Mendelsohn?"

"Oh, hold your tongue, I've had enough of your boorish manners!"

But there was no stopping Dr Kaufman. "Now what do you think of your *Herrenvolk*? The Master-race, encircled by subhuman Mujika in Stalingrad?"

Clearly Dr Kaufman was talking through his hat, for no one would have ever dreamed of accusing Mendelsen of siding with the murderous anti-Semites. He did not even bother to reply, which proved irresistibly provocative under the circumstances. Dr Kaufmann's frenzy was nearing bursting point.

"Look at him! The great genius! A studio all to himself! Painting? Ha! The pocket Casanova! The old bag of bones! You think we don't know what goes on there? He likes them young, the dirty old goat!"

To everybody's dismay, Kaufmann jumped up to shove his clenched fist right under Mendelsen's nose. But the latter remained calm, at least outwardly; only the quivering of his nostrils betrayed his inner disquiet as he addressed Henry.

"We are having an evening of recitations at my studio, to-morrow at five. I thought you might like to come," and without deigning to look at Kaufmann, he departed.

"There must be more behind their altercations than meets the eye," thought Henry.

Dr Kaufmann resumed his usual recumbent position, but his chest was still heaving and he was pale as death.

Next day at five, Henry went over to the studio. He was not really in the mood for recitations; hunger constantly gnawed at his guts and recitations on an empty stomach held little appeal. But he looked forward to meeting Mendelsen, for whom he had a warm feeling of affection and admiration. When he entered, the recital was already in progress.

Das Glück ist eine leichte Dirne

Und weilt nicht gern am selben Ort.

Sie streicht das Haar dir von der Stirne,

Und küsst dich rasch und flattert fort.

Henry knew this Heine poem inside out; it was one of Mundek's personal favourites. He felt a twinge in his heart, like meeting an old friend unexpectedly after many years. It was so long since he had read any of Heine's poems, and for that matter, any poems at all. *Luck is indeed a fickle friend*, thought Henry.

One of the Danube Transport, Kuttner, was doing the declamation with finesse. Heine's *Die Wallfahrt nach Kevlaar* followed but after a while Henry began to lose interest. His eyes scanned the audience and he spotted the ubiquitous Dr Rosenkranz, Mrs Kreisler and the Fleischers; but right back in the corner sat Mendelsen, with Su and Arnold by his side. Henry's heart beat faster. Su seemed to be listening intently, relishing every word of the poem *Die Glocke*, Schiller's classic piece.

There was a light tug at his sleeve. Turning, he found to his surprise that Verushka, the young artiste and Mendelsen's protégée, was sitting next to him. She smiled at him and asked in a whisper, "How is Dr Kaufmann? Has he calmed down?" There was a puckish twinkle in her eye.

"Do you know Dr Kaufmann?" Henry asked, surprised.

Verushka nodded. "I know him all right."

At this point, irritated by this lack of consideration, Kuttner, gave them a look, which shut them up immediately. But like all things, good and bad, the poem came eventually to its appointed end. There was an intermission and Henry turned immediately to Verushka.

"How come you know Dr Kaufmann?"

"We're both from Grodno, in Poland."

Verushka had a perky yet sensitive face, with a sprinkling of tiny freckles. An urchin nose and a saucy expression in her dark blue eyes added to her *gamine* charm.

"He used to go on about the Germans years before the Nazi régime, ever since he came back from Königsberg."

"From Königsberg?" Henry asked, astounded, "What was he doing there?"

Verushka laughed. "Sorry, I thought you understood. The *numerus clausus*. He could not study in Poland. Königsberg not far from Grodno and all that."

"Oh, I see now. I'm beginning to follow your telegraphic style."

Verushka continued. "He only lasted two semesters. Could not take it. Those East Prussian Junkers, they treated him like dirt, the *Ostjude* from Grodno. He could not have chosen a worse place."

"And then?"

"Then he went to Italy to study."

"Did you keep in touch with him?"

"Not at first. I was studying art in Berlin. Later he wrote from Italy. He was full of enthusiasm about Florence, Pisa and Siena, the sculptures, paintings."

"Was he?" Henry interrupted her incredulously, "I thought he was not interested in art."

"He used to be, then. Anyway, later when I came to Italy to complete my study, we saw rather a lot of each other."

While they were talking, Henry saw from the corner of his eye that Su was watching him like a hawk. She had avoided him for over a week for some reason.

The interval came to an end and Mr Kuttner now began to recite poems from Baudelaire's *Fleur du Mal*. Henry, not being proficient in French, had great difficulty in grasping even the gist of these poems; but he kept quiet, wondering how many others in the audience were likewise hiding their ignorance in silence.

A side-glance revealed that Su was looking at him. He turned his head to meet her eyes. She smiled. He smiled back.

The last half hour had been rather heavy-going and Henry was glad when the recital was over. People gathered round Kuttner for the usual exchange of compliments and pleasantries. Dr Rosenkranz came up to Henry and clapped him jovially on the shoulder.

"Beginning to get the hang of our cultural life here?"

Henry nodded and as he did so encountered a sour-sweet smile from Fleischer, who proffered his hand in public avowal that there was no animosity in his heart.

Arnold Springer came up. "I am glad to meet you again. My wife told me you have been ill."

Su joined them and shook hands with Henry.

"That French recitation has given me a splitting headache. Would you mind, Arnold, if I went out for a while."

Arnold put his arm round her waist. "No Sushka, I would not mind at all. Perhaps Dr Raupner would be good enough to escort you."

"My pleasure, Mr Springer."

After some moments of silence, Su spoke up. "A very attractive young woman, Verushka. Don't you think so?"

"Yes, I would say she is."

"Have you known her long?"

"No, only by sight. It's the first time we ever talked."

They walked on in silence through the cold winter evening and Henry felt himself shivering.

"What were you and Verushka talking about?"

"She was enquiring about Dr Kaufmann, a colleague of mine."

They walked in silence.

"I have been thinking," said Su eventually. "I've been wondering if I understood you properly. I mean last time we talked."

Henry felt uneasy. "What was there to understand?" he asked, forcing indifference into his voice.

"I wonder what it was you thought Arnold was trying to tell you."

"I'd rather not discuss that, if you don't mind."

"But I do mind! What impression did he give you?"

There was no point in evading the issue any further. Sooner or later he would have to tell her anyway.

"My impression was that he was hinting at his impotence though he did not say it in so many words."

It was dark, but Henry could sense her embarrassment and he felt infinitely sorry for her. She did not respond for a long while.

"I think it is dreadful!" she burst out eventually, "So degrading and humiliating for Arnold—and for me. It makes me out like some mare on heat. But it is not like that."

"I know," said Henry before she could finish her sentence.

"It's not like that at all!" and her voice choked on a sob.

That was when Henry took her in his arms. He never could resist a woman's tears.

She clung to him with a desperate longing. Her warm body enveloped him. They kissed and Henry tasted the salt on her skin. And so it began.

Chapter 15

The Forgotten Man

Love may strike like lightning or grow imperceptibly like some tender plant. It may develop swiftly, unfurling blooms in profusion, which flourish before their time and wither prematurely. Between Henry and Su, first there grew an extensive network of fine rootlets, probing deeper into the core of their beings. They drew together hesitantly, tentatively, eager to explore each other's interests, likes and dislikes, hopes and disappointments. They trod softly, taking special care not to hurt each other. Only after that mutual alignment was established did their love come into such richness of bloom as almost to consume them. Unfortunately their physical craving for each other had to be frustrated. There simply was no opportunity to translate their passion into bodily union. Yet in spite of this ultimate barrier, their love deepened until they realised that they not only loved, but also truly liked each other, which is often the more difficult of the two.

Henry was particularly impressed by Su's devotion and concern for her husband. And strangely enough, Arnold seemed happy with this new situation. He never let it appear that he knew, but it must have been obvious to even the dimmest of wits that these two were in love. Arnold liked Henry and being acutely aware of his own physical shortcomings, was glad that Su had chosen to love someone he could equally like and accept. Nor was Arnold ever left out or neglected. Su doted on him. She worried about his diet, his insulin, his weight, looking after him like a new-born child. In fact, Arnold was her baby-substitute. For Henry, this was one of the happiest periods of his life, despite the somewhat delicate situation in which he found himself. He was hungry and penniless, yet walking on air.

One January morning, during their wanderings in the out-of-the-way parts of the camp, they came upon the Forgotten Man of Ferramonti: Przebylewski. He was sitting on a log, staring into space with his usual vacant expression. There was something spent and empty, rather than sad, about him. He looked truly pathetic. Henry, absently, patted him on the shoulder as he passed. He didn't stop, for in his exalted mood, at peace with the world, he was unwilling to disturb this, his inner tranquillity and harmony.

"Who's that?" asked Su, when they were out of earshot.

He recounted briefly the salient points of Przebylewski's illness, his previous escape attempt, his sadness at the lack of contact from his wife, his psychosis and how it manifested itself.

"He looked so pathetic and forlorn, poor man. Shouldn't you have stopped and talked to him?"

"Perhaps I should have. But he is often like this, far away."

It was one of those glorious Calabrese winter mornings, resplendent with sunshine and a warm southerly breeze announcing the imminence of spring. On such a morning it was a joy to be alive, especially if in love. As they reached the lower end of the camp, overlooking the Crati, they met a young couple holding hands who clearly only had eyes for each other. The girl looked radiant, full of the joys of spring as she walked with her beau; her sweet face glowed.

"Who was that girl?" asked Henry. "Her face looks familiar but I can't place her."

"That's Heidi, Mrs Kreisler's daughter."

Henry was surprised. "What a transformation!"

Su nodded, smiling, but Henry still disbelieving insisted, "Are you sure?"

Su chuckled, her green eyes dancing. "She's got a boyfriend now. And she's come to life...like me."

Tommasini took the evening *appello*, all smiles and all-pals-together. The roll call, which by now had become a formality only, attracted few people. Half the *camerata* was empty, Przebylewski among the absentees, but this no longer bothered Tommasini who had grown to accept the internees and even appreciate some of their finer qualities.

"That *shlemiel* Przebylewski is absent again," said Szafran to Henry. "He must be sitting somewhere looking at his old ghosts."

"I saw him this morning. He was in one of his faraway moods."

"Sometimes I don't see him for days," said Szafran. "He looks painfully thin, but then on this diet, who wouldn't?"

The sunny cloudless days in January brought frosty nights, even in Calabria, and so most of them retired early to bed. Soon the snoring, coughing and farting rose up all around him, but Henry's high spirits were immune to such crude realities. He lit a 'dandelion and mint' cigarette, enjoying even that distinctive aroma and flavour. In the mood he was in, he could enjoy almost anything. Someone got up to visit the latrine. By moonlight Henry made out the edifying spectacle of Lubicz in his underpants.

Henry was already slipping into the world of dreams, when suddenly there was a piercing scream outside, which had everybody up in panic. The door was flung open and Lubicz rushed in yelling at the top of his voice, "There is a man … a man dangling from the oak!"

They all erupted through the door at once, nearly taking it off its hinges.

"It's Przebylewski! Oh, my God…my God! Przebylewski has hanged himself!"

They cut him down, slackening the noose; they tried artificial respiration, but it was no use. Henry felt a physical pain, like a hard kick to his innards. An unspeakable depth of sorrow blanketed his spirit.

"Why did he have to do it right in front of our *camerata?*" demanded Szafran.

"To rub it in," said Borstyn, "To show us up for our blind indifference."

Borstyn's words found a resounding echo in Henry's guilt-ridden conscience. How right Borstyn was! Happiness can make one blind. So blind and deaf and egocentric! Impervious to other people's suffering. He hadn't even stopped to speak to him that very morning, so wrapped up, almost cocooned, had he been in his own complacent bliss. But what use was self-reproach or tears now?

A torch was brought and the sight of that cyanosed, swollen face with the bloodshot eyes, brought tears to his eyes; but Henry resented his own tears.

They won't whitewash you, he muttered to himself.

They buried Przebylewski close to the wall, next to Meiersohn and Ossi. Only a handful of internees came to the funeral
of the Forgotten Man.

Chapter 16

Life goes on

On a bitterly cold day at the end of January 1943, Henry 'celebrated' his 30th birthday. He had kept it quiet at first, even from Su and others, as he thought wistfully of birthdays past, celebrated with family outings to the Vienna Prater. He remembered the delicious foods, the tantalising smells of *Würstchen* and *Wienerschnitzel*, then back home to the aroma of his mother's wonderful *Apfelstrudel* which suffused the house. What would he give to taste such delicatessen now! And those trips to the Vienna Opera at Christmas to see Hänsel and Gretel with his sisters, his eyes full of childish wonder! His thoughts lingered on his elderly parents and his stomach lurched with fear. *Where are they? And my sisters Malka, Tushka and Roza? Brother Edi?* There had been terrifying accounts from the more recent arrivals in the camp but the tales they told seemed preposterous! He dared not dwell too long on their fate. Like the rest of the internees separated from their families, he lived in hopes of a happy reunion at the end of this blessed war but the darkest fears were only temporarily submerged.

But the best birthday present he could have asked for came late that evening as candle light faded. The news came bursting into the darkened *camerata* in great hollers of jubilation! Von Paulus had finally surrendered Stalingrad! The myth of Teutonic invincibility was now exploded. In seconds the camp was alive with the news amid much cheering, hand-shaking and back-thumping. There could have been no more fitting end to Henry's 30th birthday; the internees finally settled down to sleep, hearts full of joy and hope which more than made up for the emptiness of their bellies.

Henceforth the 'guardian angels' – the agents – walked about the camp like beaten dogs with their tails between their legs. Over the forthcoming weeks, the Axis powers crumbled in the North African campaign and the vainglorious Afrika Korps lost much of its plumage and lustre.

Only Signor Rizzi kept up some decorum. Meanwhile the camp strategists had the time of their lives as they rehearsed the Allies' future moves.

"They'll go for the underbelly, the South of France."

"Oh you idiot! What's wrong with Sicily and Sardinia?"

"You're both wrong," protested another, "Sicily and Sardinia are too obvious. Greece or Corsica, that's where I'd land, if I were Eisenhower."

"Then thank God, you are not!" snapped little Wolf.

Over the next weeks, out of this new and most welcome atmosphere of optimism came a spate of engagements and marriages. But people, being what they are, made unkind comments on most of these precipitate unions.

"That won't last long."

"I just hope she won't be wearing white, her dress might blush!"

"That arse of hers has done some mileage"

However none of the marriages attracted as much controversy, gossip and ill-feeling as the one solemnised between Klein, the little watch-mender, and the old dowager, who had been chasing him relentlessly ever since they'd arrived in the camp.

"That shrivelled old prune!"

"Such a baby-snatcher!"

"He must have been dropped on his head!"

The sneers, moral indignation and woeful prognostications escalated to a climax when eventually that ill-matched couple came to stand under the marriage canopy in one of several synagogues now in the camp. *Comandante* Rizzi who was nobody's fool, had picked up the stench of decay in Italian-German relations; somehow he'd found room to accommodate each religious faction within the camp. Anyway, when that couple stood under the ceremonial baldachin, some of the bystanders jeered ungraciously at the happy couple. It was generally felt that the only bonus Mr Klein got out of that union was a family hut-cum-workshop for watch repairs.

"Some bonus!" commented the cynics.

As spring advanced, so did many people's physical decrepitude, especially the longstanding internees, who had completed their third year in detention. Those poor devils had exhausted all resources and had simply nothing left to sell. Some developed swelling of the legs, others puffiness of the face, diarrhoea, bleeding gums, and other ills due to starvation and avitaminosis.

Su continually pressed Henry to accept some food, which he reluctantly did now and again. But he did not wish to scrounge or depend on alms and therefore decided to pawn his watch and Mundek's gold and ruby cufflinks. His decision was precipitated by the recent establishment of a non-profit-making organisation, founded by the wealthier elements in the camp. It differed from the usual run of pawnbrokers in that it paid the full value of the pledges, did not charge any interest, and then actively helped in the redeeming of the items. Some of the poor criticised the organisation as being only half-hearted charity.

"Why don't they just share their money with us?"

But such idealism was not in keeping with harsh reality.

When Su learned from the well-meaning Linzer what Henry had done, she was indignant and hurt. *Here we go again*, thought Henry, remembering the arguments he used to have with Sonia.

"I have accepted food from you occasionally, but I don't want to be totally dependent on it."

"Just tell me," persisted Su, "if it were the other way round, if I went hungry, would you just sit around and let me starve?"

"No, I wouldn't. But then things would be different."

"How different? We can afford it and wouldn't go short. Arnold would not mind ..."

"But I do!" snapped Henry. "In plain terms, it's bad enough to take a man's wife. It's even worse to take his food on top of it. I'd feel like a complete gigolo."

Chapter 17

Advances

The concentration camp was still growing. More Chinese, Greeks and especially Yugoslavs poured in at a quickened pace. Most of the late arrivals were gentiles. Among them were a number of experts in spit roasting. Some of them had their own money; others did the roasting for their wealthier compatriots, getting a 'cut' for their labour. The tantalising smell of lamb roasting over open fires drove the starving majority almost mad. But there were never any overt protests from the poor and hungry. They were too proud to show resentment though they may have cursed them in private.

The Chinese performed miracles of laundering. They washed with no soap, ironed with no irons and yet the end-product easily outclassed the most accomplished work of commercial establishments. How they did it, was a total mystery. When asked to explain their prodigious results, they would smile inscrutably, bow politely but never give away their secret.

The mending of socks, repairing of shirts and other such humble salvage jobs, remained the monopoly of the women from the *Pentcho* while the menfolk were making very acceptable clog-type sandals using scraps of leather fixed to a wooden sole. Another enterprising fellow had a regular queue for his private hot shower cubicle involving a couple of strategically placed sheets and a bucket of hot water. There were some disasters, like the oven that was built too close to one of the barracks, setting it alight! But by and large the majority of the camp's population had some way of turning their labour or skill into a marginal profit; like Klein, the newly-married watch-mender from Prague, or Spitz, the cleaner of hats. Most people, except for the doctors, had something to offer for cash; but the medics were the poorest and proudest of the lot. First of all there were far too many of them and even when their help was required, most would not accept any remuneration, not even from the richer Yugoslavs or Greeks.

"That, if you'll excuse my saying so, is not pride but sheer pig-headedness and stupidity," ventured Borstyn.

"Perhaps so," replied Dr Rosenkranz the songster, "but that is the way it is with us. We'd never take alms from beggars; and here in Ferramonti, if they're not beggars today, why, they will be tomorrow." This, from a man who was himself poorer than any church mouse!

In Ferramonti's Babel of nations, with now over three thousand internees, it sometimes took weeks before one encountered an old friend or acquaintance. So, when Henry bumped into Schöntal one day, he was genuinely pleased to have come across him again.

"How are you keeping?" asked Henry, who had a soft spot for this unassuming and luckless young man.

As usual Schöntal avoided looking Henry directly in the eye.

"I get by," he replied half-heartedly.

"Have you made any friends in the camp?"

"Only gaming partners at chess."

"Any girlfriends?"

He shook his head. "I prefer chess."

"Do you think you've benefited from my amateur analysis?"

Schöntal hesitated before answering; like all good chess players he liked to think things over first.

"Sometimes I think I have … and sometimes I don't." He paused to reflect. "At least I know what's wrong with me. I understand myself better."

Henry felt this was yet another human being he was neglecting and asked himself how far a man's responsibility extends towards his brethren.

"Now, promise to get in touch if ever you feel like talking things over with me."

Schöntal nodded assent. But he didn't come; and Henry, caught in the web of his newly found love, made no effort to find him.

Sobel, on the other hand, had adapted well to Ferramonti. He had made many new friends and was as popular as he'd been in Notaresco. Rauch too seemed to have found his feet again. No doubt the prospect of victory, leading to the recovery of his laboratory, contributed to the re-emergence of his old pomposity. But poor Baumgart was a shadow of his former self. After the divorce he had gone downhill rapidly, physically as well as in morale. Lapidus, an occasional visitor to *camerata 3*, was located in another part of the camp, where he gave guitar lessons for a few lire and composed his Ferramonti variations.

But it was Gurewicz who had taken both the limelight and the jackpot in Ferramonti. His voice had made a great impact. He was in great demand for upper-crust parties, and his frequent concerts were richly rewarded with adulation and money. His was a truly meteoric rise to stardom. While still a likeable rogue at heart, he had learned one of life's most valuable lessons after the financial scandal in Notaresco. Thoroughly chastened by his fellow internees' refusal to abandon him, he was a changed man thereafter.

One day in May, a fantastic rumour travelled through the camp. A young Jewish couple who had allegedly escaped from German-occupied Poland, had come all the way to Italy and were supposed to have arrived in the camp. No one in Henry's *camerata* had actually seen them, so perhaps it was just a 'bonk' — a rumour — after all.

Finally, when Henry managed to locate the couple, he got the shock of his life, for they were people he'd known well for years. Oh yes, life could be stranger than fiction! Sigmund and Myra Weismann were the pharmacists whom he had known in the good old days in Viareggio. With his sister Anna and husband Frederick, they had spent many a pleasant hour at *Fappani's* or *Gianni Schicchi's* sipping their espresso, or dancing through the night at the *Gatto Nero* in Viareggio's pineta.

Sigmund, very much down to earth, was a man of ruddy complexion, blond and blue-eyed; a typical *'goy'*. Myra, fair-haired, shapely and sporty, loved to dress up in revealing outfits, and had the reputation of being 'hot stuff'. In those days both of them were bronzed, bursting with health and the zest for life.

"Myra! Sigmund!" exclaimed Henry, half crazy by the impact of this most unlikely encounter. They embraced fondly, hugging each other, much to the bystanders' bewilderment.

"To meet in this bloody place! Unbelievable!"

Henry regarded them with the greatest tenderness and compassion. Gone was their old deep tan. Gone Myra's buxom figure. Gone that self-assured expression on Sigmund's face. They looked pale, thin, haggard and exhausted, yet, bursting with joy-tinged relief.

"How did you get away?" asked Henry when they had quite exhausted themselves with their frenetic salutations.

"It's a long story. We're just going to take a shower and meet you later in your *camerata*."

"Watch out!" called out Henry, with a wry smile. "The showers stink!"

Chapter 18

Stinking showers

Later that day, the Weismanns recounted their tale under the oak tree. A crowd soon gathered, Arnold and Su among them. Sigmund Weismann sat himself on a stool, not far from the very spot where Janos Kovacz had recounted his Odyssey of the Danube journey a year before.

"My friends," he began, "you just don't know how privileged among Jews you are to be in Italy." He stopped, overcome by his memories. "Whatever you saw or heard of Nazi brutality before the war was only a prelude, a taste of things to come. Compared with what has followed, that was child's play. Believe me."

Sigmund went on to enumerate places and names the internees had never heard before: Eichmann, Einsatztruppen, Treblinka, Auschwitz. The audience was dumbfounded, unable to grasp the significance at first. More names followed: Majdanek, Theresienstadt, Sobibor, Belsen. They listened, stunned, in total disbelief, shaking their heads slowly as they tried to process the chilling messages they were hearing.

"What followed, my friends, was massacre, mass murder, extermination in cold blood."

He paused because more and more people were arriving, pushing to get close, desperate to hear news, any news at all, of their homelands, their families. And when order was restored he went on. "First they shot them or bludgeoned them to death, after having forced them to dig their own graves, like in Babi Yar where they killed thousands upon thousands of Jews. But this was too slow and cumbersome a process for the Final Solution."

He stopped again to master an upsurge of emotion.

"Have you heard of extermination camps? Gas chambers? Giant incinerators? You haven't? I'm not surprised. They keep it quiet. Only the sick brain of the would-be master-race could conceive such monstrosities. And all done methodically, meticulously, to achieve the minimum of wastage of material and time. So very German."

"*Deutsche Kultur!*" exclaimed Dr Kaufmann, but his exclamation was drowned in a louder yell, which came from young Scholz.

"No, I don't believe it! I have lived in Germany for eighteen years. Brutal, arrogant, even violent they may be—but mass murderers? No! Never!"

Weismann gave him a doleful glance. "I can't blame you for not believing. I didn't believe it myself, at first."

"And I won't believe it either," said Su in a low but steady voice. "I have lived most of my life in Berlin and have seen Nazi thugs harassing Jews and beating them up. Sure, they can be cruel and savage, but the majority of the German people are decent normal human beings. They would never allow such terrible things to happen. Not organised mass murder. Never! With all their faults, they are Europeans, not savages!"

"*Deutsche Kultur!*" Again it was Dr Kaufmann who yelled at the top of his voice. There arose a great commotion, arguments, and counter-arguments, intermingled with the sobbing of some.

Sigmund raised his hand. "Please, calm down. You asked me to tell you and I'm trying to do that. If you don't want to believe me, that is your affair. Shall I go on?"

They asked him to do so.

"When we arrived here, you made jokes about the stinking water in the showers. To us it smelt sweeter than all the perfumes of Arabia. Do you know what a shower means over there?"

He looked intently at the crowd. No one said a word, so he went on.

"A convoy arrives. Hundreds of men, women and children. They have been travelling, crammed into cattle trucks, no food, no toilets, no windows for days. They are filthy, hungry and exhausted. The children, babies, little ones are terrified and crying. Officially their journey is for 'Resettlement', so, like a flock of sheep they willingly follow the Nazi officials into a huge hall, labelled Ablutions and Showers. They are told to strip. Suddenly the doors are slammed, hermetically sealed and, instead of the water spray, cyanide, cyclon and other diabolical gases are released from the showers. They bang on the doors, they cry and scream in agony; within minutes they are all dead. Babies and children too. Then, after a depraved search of the corpses for gold teeth and rings, their bodies are cremated in huge incinerators, until nothing but ashes remains. Ashes, and the sickening stench of burnt flesh. It hovers perpetually over that Inferno, which transcends even Dante's most horrendous imagination."

Henry was shocked and nauseated to the core. Were such things possible? It sounded like the ramblings of a madman. With a side-glance he caught Borstyn's face, drained of all blood, with an inexpressible horror in his eyes. So, he believed it? A young woman was crying quietly; but Mrs Feinberg was weeping aloud, sobbing unashamedly, that woman of iron, the ice-cool lecturer in Jurisprudence. Good Lord, she believed it!

Trebitsch, who had been listening with mounting tension, exchanged a significant glance with Henry. Was this what was waiting for them if Himmler's demand for their extradition succeeded? Henry felt a cold shiver running down his spine. He thought of his elderly parents, his sisters, their husbands and their young families. Surely they did not meet such a horrific end? Gassed in showers? Even children? The room was silent, the air hanging heavy with unspoken dread.

With a heavy heart, Henry felt it was time to change the direction of the narrative, lest an emotional typhoon swept them all away.

"For now, just tell us how you managed to escape."

Sigmund gave Henry an understanding look and went on. For two years they'd been on the run, hiding and sleeping rough. Somehow they'd managed to get false papers. Their gentile appearance helped; but it was mostly a matter of luck, for many others, just as Aryan looking, had been apprehended and killed. Occasionally they worked on farms or refuse dumps, but the important thing was to keep moving, lest people began to ask too many questions. While hiding in a forest, they accidentally ran into a group of the Polish Underground. It was from them that they'd first heard of the Final Solution.

"So all you know is only hearsay," called out young Scholz almost triumphantly, "You haven't actually seen it with your own eyes."

Sigmund Weismann produced a sad smile with a trace of irony in it.

"Had I been there to witness it, I would not be here to tell the tale. But I got the same description of identical facts from many independent sources."

Again there ensued a heated debate and when it died down Sigmund continued.

"A Jewish uprising in the Warsaw ghetto flared up only a month ago. Myra and I happened to be in the vicinity."

An intensive Jew-hunt had followed in its wake. Terrified, they'd hid for three days in sewers without food or water, suppressing their natural revulsion for the rats. Eventually, when they stepped out into the light of day, they walked along the track of a railway line — a foolish thing to do, as railways are closely watched because of sabotage; but they were too far gone, too tired and bewildered to know what they were doing. However, this very stupidity proved to be their salvation.

"You know the Italians sent troops to the Russian front. One day, hiding from a patrol behind some bushes, I spotted an engine. I couldn't take my eyes off it. Suddenly I knew what it was: two large letters, F. S., *Ferrovie dello Stato*. This was an Italian engine. The engine driver and his mate climbed out of the cab and sat on the grass verge, sharing a bottle of wine. Myra and I decided we had nothing to lose. My heart was thumping… I crawled over to them. First they were suspicious, but when Myra came out of hiding, when we both spoke to them in Italian, they took pity on us."

Now it was Myra's turn to break down, sobbing her heart out at the memory. Sigmund tenderly put his arm around his weeping wife, stroked her hair and continued.

"They were simple, good-hearted Italian folk, who hated the arrogant Germans, for whom many of their compatriots had been killed in vain on the Eastern front. We had nothing to give them or bribe them with, all we had was our lives and the rags we wore. But there was no need for bribery. They offered to hide us in the locomotive and smuggle us out of Poland and into Italy. Myra kissed their hands and wept." He paused to steady his quivering lip as he recalled. "And I cried too."

Reliving all this, the tears sprang to his eyes and he had to wait until he could collect himself again.

"There isn't much room in an engine cab. We had to be stowed away among the coal. Sometimes we had to dive into the tender for complete cover and almost suffocated. It took nine days, with endless shunting and stops. An eternity! Our hearts were thumping and almost bursting with anxiety. When finally they dropped us at the outskirts of Verona, we kissed the Italian ground and wet it with tears. We kissed the soil… literally! And so should you! For you do not realise how fortunate you are! You are alive because of Italy my friends, make no mistake."

Chapter 19

Deaths come to Ferramonti

After the North Africa campaign was over British and American troops, emboldened by their success, could not be brought to a standstill. They needed an outlet for their energy and high morale; in July 1943 the invasion of southern Sicily began. Right from the start this campaign went well, despite Il Duce's threat that he would lay out allied corpses on the beaches if they attempted an invasion of Italy.

Ferramonti, in southern Calabria, was close to the Sicilian battlefront, and to airfields whence frequent sorties of Allied aircraft to the mainland began. The first sight of American Flying Fortresses was overwhelming. The internees, who had never seen anything remotely approaching the size of these gigantic bombers, gazed at them mesmerised. These squadrons flew in broad daylight and their 'V' formations, reminiscent of the flight of wild geese, were a masterly display of synchronised navigation. The drone of their engines was sweeter than music to the internees' ears.

"The cheek! The *Chutzpah!*" exclaimed Szafran, brimming over with admiration. "Fancy flying like that in full daylight!"

In time they got used to the frequent sorties of these huge metallic hulls, glistening in the sun. But their deep satisfaction was not only derived from stargazing, for a joyful sight also unfolded on *terra firma*. Just outside the camp, where the main road ran, columns of retreating German motorised units held them spellbound. They watched this parade of a beaten army with mixed feelings of joy and awe, for it needed only one salvo to flatten the entire camp. Sigmund Weismann's report had sharpened their alertness to the Hun's inhuman atrocities, and therefore they watched those retreating German columns with growing apprehension, an apprehension escalating to panic, when German soldiers paid a short visit to get some water for their overheated vehicles.

As for Sigmund's report, this had received a mixed reception. Those who had families in Poland refused to believe, out of a need for self-preservation. They could not bear the idea that their loved ones had been murdered and burnt to ashes.

Although Henry had no reason to distrust Sigmund, he still could not fully accept that the same nation, who had given the world so many poets, philosophers, artists and musicians, could have plunged back to pre-historic levels of savagery. Most of his family had fled to Poland after the annexation of Austria. The idea they had all been murdered was too impossible and agonizing to contemplate.

The camp authorities, already feeling the Allies breathing down their necks, made vast improvements to the camp's sanitation, improvements which were received by the internees with both amusement and contempt. The internees were now being allowed to cultivate the dusty ground to grow anything that could survive the harsh conditions. Shoots of maize could be seen pushing their way through the barren soil with sunflowers and other small meadow flora competing for nourishment.

With the Sicilian campaign progressing well, another epidemic of marriages and betrothals broke out. One relationship of special interest and approved unanimously was that of young Heidi, Mrs Kreisler's daughter, with that same young man whom Henry and Su had met with her, on their walk in the spring. Heidi was now blossoming from the love and affection this relationship bestowed on her tender soul. She was still the same unassuming shy girl, but there was now an aura of happiness about her.

The jubilation following the fall of Palermo in late July had hardly abated, when three days later, it was whipped into a new frenzy by the bombshell news that Il Duce had been toppled by the King. People went mad, almost berserk with joy, for this was the crowning moment they had patiently waited and prayed for throughout the years of imprisonment. It felt like heavenly retribution.

To celebrate this joyous occasion, a concert in grand style was to be held later in the month. The shaky camp authorities had no guts to object so time was set aside for planning. The place was alive with meetings, secret rehearsals and stage preparation, with much to-ing and fro-ing of instruments and the buzz of excitement, as performers attempted to keep the programme under wraps. The camp boasted a vast number of extraordinarily talented internees. A community of several thousand Jews brought excellence on so many artistic levels; conductors, composers, pianists, violinists, saxophonists, vocalists, writers and poets amongst many. A newly formed jazz band, which made more noise than music, was also included. At the last moment, more for the sake of devilment, Dr Rosenkranz was also invited to make his contribution. He was over the moon.

The concert took place on a balmy August evening. Wooden benches tightly pushed together formed a makeshift stage with a grand piano accompanist to one side; for a few precious hours, the audience could overlook their humble surroundings and lose themselves in artistry. Even the camp authorities were there. After a varied programme of recitals and poems, Gurewicz received thunderous applause, in particular from the Italians, for his swaggering rendition of Don Giovanni's frivolous aria *Finch'han dal vino*.

Despite Gurewicz's fine performance, it was Dr Rosenkranz who contributed most to the public's high spirits. His voice so much resembled the bleating of sheep that people were in tears of laughter! At the end, he'd earned himself very generous applause from a public truly grateful for his contribution to their amusement. No one really knew what he'd been singing but it didn't matter. The evening ended on an utterly hilarious note with the drummer, a born comic, enthusiastically smothering the sound of any other instrument in the jazz band.

"Come with us," said Arnold after the concert, "the night is still young." They wanted to prolong the feeling of elation the music had instilled in them

"Yes Henry, do come," Su joined in, "I'll make you both a cup of tea, real tea."

It was pleasant to relax in the evening cool after the stifling heat of the day. Arnold and Henry took a stroll, chatting amicably in the bluish twilight, as they contemplated the soirée and the sudden feeling of hope. Seeing an acquaintance in the distance, Arnold excused himself and strode off towards his friend. And then, without warning, there came the faint drone of an aeroplane, which grew louder and louder. Suddenly from nowhere, a fighter plane appeared flying very low, almost touching the rooftops of the barracks. Flames sprayed out from it. Henry looked up in horror.

"That plane's on fire! It's going to crash!" he yelled in warning.

His eyes followed the plane with great trepidation, as he expected to see it hit the ground any moment. But instead of crashing, the aeroplane rose again and disappeared into the distance. Henry's eyes were still glued to the horizon when a sudden heartrending scream brought him back to reality. What he saw was bloodcurdling and horrible; writhing in agony, a man lay in a pool of blood only yards away.

"Arnold! Arnold!" screamed Su, coming out of the *camerata*, "Arnold, where are you?"

She went frantically in search of him. It had all happened so swiftly, so unexpectedly. Henry was still trembling in shock, baffled by what he had seen; he still did not realise that the plane had been machine-gunning the camp, not crashing. In the semi-darkness the glowing tracer bullets spewing from the plane looked like tongues of flame and the low strafing dive, like an imminent crash.

The man lay on his belly, his buttocks a mass of mangled flesh and blood. His eyes had the terror-stricken expression of a beast at slaughter. Henry was horrified, terrified and shaken. Cold sweat covered his forehead and for a long minute he was incapable of movement.

Then Henry heard Su. "Thank God," she cried, "I found him. He's all right...he's all right." She grabbed her husband, throwing her arms around him, almost crushing him with relief.

Wailing, moaning, crying and cursing everywhere. Desperate, panic-stricken people desperately looking for their loved ones. In front of Henry's barrack a young woman lay sprawled on the ground.

By the time Henry managed to shake off his stupor, Kaufmann and Rosenkranz had already knelt beside her. She was bleeding profusely and in a state of shock. The bullet had entered the pelvis after perforating the lower abdominal wall. She was in desperate need of a blood transfusion but Dr Sabatini, biting his lip, trembling and beside himself, was not equipped for such an emergency. The nearest blood bank was in Cosenza. Dr Sabatini did his best by sending a dispatch rider immediately to collect blood of all groups. The woman was still alive by the time he returned, but before her blood could be cross-matched, she had died. Su sobbed her heart out. Henry wept silently inside himself.

Four people died that night and several others had been wounded, some severely. The young woman's tragic death had torn at the heartstrings as it turned out that she had survived the Pentcho ordeal and only recently married. But there was another loss which was pathetic in its own way, the death of Mr Klein, the watch-mender from Prague, whose marriage had been so much disparaged. He was shot right through the heart inside his new married quarters, while mending watches, and had died instantly. That strange death by a stray bullet fired at random reminded Henry of an old Polish proverb: 'The fool shoots, but God carries the bullet'. Mr Klein was deeply mourned and many now regretted the ruckus they had caused at his marriage ceremony.

Only one person managed to make the tasteless wisecrack, "God is merciful, maybe it was a happy release!" That person, of course, was Szafran.

The next few days following the disaster were chaotic. First the survivors had to take care of the dead and bury them, before they could start caring for the living. The little Catholic cemetery in Tarsia became crowded with Jewish intruders. *No numerus clausus here*, Henry thought.

Once the burials were over, a delegation went to see Signor Rizzi to protest that the concentration camp was now too close to the battlefield in contravention of the Geneva Conventions. The delegates were in an ugly mood and demanded the removal of the camp to a safer location or its complete disbandment.

Comandante Rizzi, minus all the old arrogance and playacting, bore himself with dignity. In fact there was more decorum about him now than he had ever shown during his tenure of office. He still sported his riding breeches and boots but he no longer wielded a riding crop. His whip-hand empty, he looked less imposing, thinner and drawn. Listening to the delegation's request a sad expression, as well as a vestige of the old sardonic smile, spread over his countenance.

"Remove the camp?" he said eventually, "We cannot even move our own personnel. There is no transport! Everything has been requisitioned."

"Then why not disperse the camp?" asked someone with an authoritative air.

Signor Rizzi looked at him searchingly, a frown on his face. "Where would you go without transport? Here at least the children have a roof over their heads."

"But after what's happened," protested the same man, "we cannot be expected to remain in the front line! It's preposterous!"

"I agree with you," replied Signor Rizzi, "you should not have to ... and I wish I could help! Unfortunately I can't. Besides, it is most unlikely that such an accident could ever occur again."

"Accident?" exclaimed the man, truly outraged, "You call this an accident?"

The *comandante* looked rather surprised. "You can't seriously think it was anything else? Certainly none of our planes. It was an unfortunate mistake. I have already been notified by higher authority. A pilot of the Allied air-fleet, probably inexperienced, mistook this for a military camp. I thought you knew."

In fact most internees had guessed as much already, but had been reluctant to admit such a possibility. On the other hand, it was immaterial who the culprit was once the people were dead.

There was a long silence; neither a calculated nor an embarrassed one, for there was simply nothing more to be said. Since there was no transport their request could not be met and that was that.

Depressed and disheartened, the delegation left Signor Rizzi's office. They knew he had spoken the truth. As Henry made to follow the others, the *comandante* caught his eye, beckoning him to stay.

"You came here with the very first transport, didn't you?"

"Yes, I did have that honour."

"It seems so very long ago. Things have changed since then." He took a deep breath, possibly half a sigh. "We counted our chickens before they were hatched. The fortunes of war are fickle."

Henry didn't make any comments. It could easily have been his turn now to take his revenge and humiliate the man with whom he had several uncomfortable skirmishes in the past, but he simply did not have the urge to repay him in the same coin.

Chapter 20

Exodus to the hills

Out of the blue, Henry developed a high fever. It descended upon him without warning. His temperature shot up, he ached all over and perspired profusely; yet in spite of the summer heat he was shivering. An icy cold seized his body and made his teeth chatter. His back felt as if it were splitting in half. The fever rose sharply and he became semi-conscious and delirious. This was malaria, no doubt. He knew it before *plasmodium vivax* was confirmed microscopically. The recent tragic events and the upheaval that followed had thrown things out of gear and he'd neglected to take his quinine regularly. Several other people, Albert as well, developed malaria. Now he had to take massive doses of quinine and stebrin, which caused nausea and distressing deafness in both ears. The left side of his abdomen was particularly painful due to an enlarged spleen.

Su did not spare herself and did her utmost, nursing him, wiping the perspiration from his face and giving plenty of cold drinks. After four days the high fever abated, leaving Henry exhausted, drained of all energy. This was no time for arguments and false pride, so he gratefully accepted the soups Su prepared for him, and for Albert.

Meanwhile life in the camp had become completely disorganised, largely due to the continuous incursions of allied aircraft, aimed at disrupting the retreat of the Axis forces. This resulted in a complete breakdown of the camp's few communications with the outside world. In consequence the food situation became desperate, even for those who could afford high prices. The risk of further 'accidents' grew enormously, when to the internees' dismay an anti-aircraft battery was placed on a hill, quite close to the main road, just outside the camp. The discovery of that battery had a dramatic effect. Riots and tumults broke out, largely fomented by women, because of the fear for the safety of their children. They kept the flame of insurgence alive until the men, urged on by their womenfolk's near-hysterics, threatened the camp authorities with violence, unless this battery was removed. The Italian officials lived in fear of their lives, for no one could tell how far people's frenzy might go, once their very existence was endangered. Agents and officials began to vanish, until in the course of twenty-four hours none of them was left except Signor Rizzi and the *capo polizia*. The disappearance of these men was followed by the desertion of all sentries and it was then that the internees, driven by hunger, broke into the provision stores and plundered whatever they could lay their hands on. Next they smashed their way to adjacent stores and helped themselves to blankets, sheets and anything of value that they could possibly barter for food.

And then the exodus began. There was no one to stop them. Signor Rizzi and the *capo polizia*, left on their own, didn't even attempt to stem the tide. While the pandemonium of this exodus was raging, Henry lay helplessly on his *palliasse*, cursing his luck in falling ill at such a critical time. Apart from his own predicament, he resented being a drag on Arnold and Su. People were abandoning the camp in hundreds, but the Springers would not go without him. He begged them, literally implored them to go with the others, promising to join them as soon as he had gathered sufficient strength, but neither would hear of it. Only a handful remained in *camerata* 3: Borstyn, Wolf, Dr Wunderstein and Albert among them.

"Mr Borstyn," said Henry one day, "why don't you go with the others? Albert and I are now well enough to look after ourselves."

Batyushka Borstyn came to sit by Henry's bed and smiled. "The life of an old man matters very little. To have seen this Nazi pack on the run is the highlight of my life. Besides, I like my four-poster bed. Where would I go? Climbing hills? I'm too old for that."

"What about you, Mr Wolf?"

"Somebody has to look after the shop," and though there was no need for it, he reached automatically for the broom to sweep the floor. "If the *Malach Hamavet*, the angel of death, is after me, he'll find me anywhere. But I don't think I'm ready for the chop yet. First I must see Musso and Adolf hanging by their balls."

"And you, Wunderstein?" asked Albert, "Why are you still here?"

Dr Wunderstein replied with a sheepish grin, but did not say anything. His stammer had become worse lately, if that were possible, so he avoided the effort of speech altogether. But little Wolf, who so often hit the bull's eye, unceremoniously replied, "He stuffed his mattress with thousand lire notes. It would be too heavy to carry around."

At that moment the door was flung open and in rushed Su, full of excitement, her eyes shining with joy.

"We have found a solution to our problem. Arnold has found a cart, an oxcart. It will take us and the luggage up into the hills and you can ride on it."

He lay on top of the pile of luggage, occasionally leaning over the side of the cart to watch as they crossed the Crati. At the height of summer the darkish green water was only shallow — two feet at the most, but even so the flow was rapid, almost torrential, so that Su, gathering her skirts in one hand, had to hold on to the wagon with the other to keep her foothold. It was the carter's idea to ford the river. He thought that having left it rather late, they'd have a better chance of finding both food and shelter on the river's far side. It was doubtful whether any of the hundreds of refugees who had left the camp before them had dared to venture to the other side, burdened with luggage and children. After all, they could not know the river's fords and shallows as he did. Halfway through the ford the wagon stuck. Unlike Arnold, who rolled up his trousers above the knee, the driver, without bothering, just jumped down into the water to help push the cart. Both Arnold and Su pulled as hard as they could while Henry felt useless as an additional burden. Eventually they got it moving again and once they reached the other bank they took a winding path leading up to the hills.

At first there was only a moderate incline, but soon the path got steeper until even that powerful pair of sturdy oxen found it hard to drag the cart over the bumpy road. Gradually the vegetation, luxuriant near the river's edge, became sparser, the soil dustier and the air hotter. It was a weary ascent. To lighten their burden the carter walked in front of the oxen, pulling the reins attached by a metal ring to their nostrils, and cracking his whip as he spurred them on with yells and curses.

"*Op op! Avanti! Porca miseria!*" He was a jovial little man, dark skinned, a Sicilian, who did not seem to take life too seriously. Progress was slow. However in time, as they got higher up, the air cooled, the grass became greener and the landscape friendlier, with occasional carob, fig and mulberry trees. Still, there was no sign of human habitation. Anopheles bred in the valley, so the higher people lived, the less their risk of malaria. The oxen showed signs of exhaustion and panted heavily. Henry felt sorry because his weight added to their toil. Eventually, when they reached a point of drastic steepness, it became obvious that the oxen would be unable to accomplish the savage climb.

The little Sicilian spread out his arms in a gesture of helplessness and regret. "*Non é possibile.*"

There was no alternative but to unload and for Henry to get down. After the luggage had been unloaded, the carter paid and the oxen turned round, the cart vanished rapidly on the precipitous downhill run.

"You'd better lie down under that tree and watch the baggage, while Su and I go scouting for a roof over our heads."

When they had gone, Henry crawled towards the tree and sat there, leaning back against it. Only then did he suddenly become aware of the exhilarating sensation of freedom, for he had been too engrossed in the tribulations of the journey to savour it fully. But now, left on his own to let his eyes rove undisturbed over the scenery, a piercing feeling of immense joy came over him. He was free!

But for all that, thinking of his friends he had had to leave behind, a drop of gall seeped through. At first he had refused to go with the Springers, but his love for Su had prevailed in the end. It was mostly Albert, like himself stricken with malaria, who preyed on his mind. But Borstyn had assured Henry he'd look after him. Besides, Albert was his friend, he'd understand. Immersed in these reflections, Henry was only dimly aware of the passing of time. In this first day of freedom, any feelings of regret were bound to evaporate quickly. He looked into the overhanging branches of the mulberry tree and smiled happily at the sight of the creamy, turgid berries which gleamed invitingly in the foliage; and all he had to do was get up, raise his arm and pluck them! If only he were strong enough! He was free to do exactly as he liked. A little further away, a fig tree bent under its succulent load. How beautiful the panorama! How graceful the winding curves of the Crati! Even the camp, that goddam desolation, looked harmless, almost friendly from afar. A grasshopper landed on his knee. He caught it and held it for a while. There hadn't been any grasshoppers in the camp. How could there be, there was no grass. Multi-coloured butterflies fluttered around an over-ripe fig, attracted by the syrup oozing from its skin. The world was so beautiful that he came near to tears. He felt slightly faint. Maybe he was feverish again, for his head was swimming and he was shivering.

And suddenly a strange, eerie mood came over him. He trembled at this mysterious, liberating and frightening thought: what if he were really dead?! If it were only his soul experiencing all this beauty around him. Perhaps he too had been killed in that air raid, or had died of malaria.

Automatically his hand went into his pocket in search of the little box containing quinine and he swallowed three of the pills.

"Thank God! We found a place!" Arnold's sudden exclamation shattered Henry's reverie and brought him back from no-man's-land, where he had been drifting, debilitated by his fever. Looking up, he saw Arnold and Su, as well as a peasant woman, leading a donkey.

"This kind woman," said Su "has offered us a roof over our heads."

Emerging from his trance-like state, Henry stared at the peasant woman, a middle-aged matron, wearing a multi-flounced wide skirt and an even wider grin on her sunburnt face. *"Buona sera Signore, state bene?"*

"We explained to her," said Arnold, "she knows you cannot walk far, so she brought her donkey."

Henry felt embarrassed. He had never ridden a donkey before, nor for that matter, anything else either. They hoisted him to his feet and then helped him to mount the animal. Apart from its pricked ears, which swished about, following their voices, it stood stock-still.

"The reins! You mustn't drop the reins," the woman called out. This was a large donkey of a dirty brownish grey, quite devoid of the cuddly appeal of Maria's little Ciuccio. But it had those mournful eyes, grave and pathetic, which all donkeys share and which pluck at the heartstrings. Henry patted its neck and picked up the reins; as he did so, Petruccio promptly responded and walked. "Now keep hold of those reins!" the woman repeated and turning to Arnold added, "I'll walk with him and then I'll come back with Petruccio to fetch the things, *i bagagli*."

After a short uphill ride they came to a tumble-down cottage of rough, unhewn stones. It was certainly no palace, but at that instant, the little refuge on the brink of collapse beckoned more invitingly than any Waldorf Astoria.

Anastasia helped Henry dismount and led him to a low stone bench in front of the cottage.

"*Siediti*! Sit down! I'm going to fetch the *valigie*," and cupping her hands over her mouth she called out, "Zaira! The ropes!"

A little girl came out carrying a coil of rope.

"This is Zaira, my daughter. Ask her if you need anything."

She then hung the coil round Petruccio's neck and off they went. Zaira sat herself some distance away and simply stared at Henry. She had a black mop of tousled hair, a deeply suntanned round face, flashing white teeth and a pair of huge burning black eyes, which seemed to fill most of her face. As she continued to stare at Henry without uttering a word, he tried making conversation.

"Do you have any brothers?" Zaira shook her head.

"Any sisters then?" The same reaction.

"Where is your father?" Zaira just stared at him, but did not answer. "Does he live here?" She shook her head. "Is he dead?" She nodded.

"Do you go to school?" Again the same denial.

"Why won't you talk to me?" Henry finally asked, in as friendly a tone as he could muster. But she made no reply. *Strange girl*, he thought, and stopped quizzing her.

So he sat in silence, contemplating the magnificent interplay of light and shadow of the setting sun. After some time, voices drifted up from the distance, and looking down he saw Petruccio with their cases roped to his flanks. Arnold and Su followed in his wake. This was a sturdy animal, clearly used to heavy loads, a beast of burden, earning his meagre keep with hard labour. As soon as he saw Zaira he started braying and she ran off to meet him.

"Well, we pulled it off!" Both Arnold and Su were on top of the world. Proud to have successfully concluded what had begun as a very uncertain venture. Anastasia led them into her cottage. It had only two rooms, of which she offered the larger to her guests. The walls were roughcast with faint traces of whitewash and peppered with holes, large and small. But this did not bother them in the slightest.

While Anastasia and Su busied themselves preparing some kind of sleeping arrangement on the floor, both men were asked to sit outside as they were only in the way. Henry, who insisted on dragging himself to the stone bench unaided, now felt utterly weary and exhausted. It had been a long, long day and although everybody had done their utmost to spare him exertion, he was nevertheless drained to the limit. After all, it was less than a week since his first attack of malaria; when the straw-mattress was improvised in one corner, he let himself flop onto it fully dressed. He'd intended to have a nap on this heavenly palliasse of sweet smelling straw, but instead he didn't wake until the following morning.

Chapter 21

Hilltop Happiness

Though covered in perspiration, he felt a lot better and ravenously hungry. Su had left the room in great disorder, so as not to wake him. The place was really in an unholy mess, with clothing and all their possessions littering the narrow space. There were no curtains and the bright morning light flooded the room. A glass of milk stood beside Henry's mattress. He tasted it, recognising the flavour and smell of goat's milk, and blessed his good fortune in being so well looked after at this critical time, when he most needed it. He savoured the richness of the milk, the first proper milk he had drunk in such a long time.

The door opened gently, and quietly Su's head poked round it. "You are awake? Fine! I brought you an egg and a cup of coffee. Real coffee."

She sat down on the floor beside him with a radiant smile in her sparkling green eyes. "Guess where this coffee comes from? Abyssinia! Her husband brought it back from the Ethiopian campaign. Almost a sackful of coffee beans. He died of consumption four years ago. She is of Albanian stock, like most people here. She's got a few sheep and goats. Keeps chickens. But Petruccio is her most cherished possession."

Henry had to laugh at the way Su rattled out all this news, non-stop. Apparently the two women had been chatting all morning.

"I see you haven't been idle, gathering all this information. I never knew you were such a gossip!"

Su smiled and took his arm. "Come on, come outside for some fresh air! It's so lovely out there!"

The others had plenty to do, unpacking, tidying up and improvising a meal. Henry lay back on a blanket in the shade, looking at the clouds, while engaged in the familiar pastime of 'cloud-casting', projecting shapes onto them. One cloud looked like a clown, the other like Sleeping Beauty. Further down, another cloud looked just like a galloping horse. Strange, he had never indulged in this playful game in all the time in the camp. The clouds were the same, but not his disposition. As he was lying there, giving his thoughts and fantasies free rein, he realised he was being watched. Zaira, partly hidden by a hedge, was staring at him.

"What are you doing there, Zaira? Come and talk to me."

But as soon as he'd opened his mouth, she ran off.

"Lunch is ready, Sir!" Su called out. "Now don't get up, we'll all eat out here." On an improvised tray she carried a steaming bowl and dishes. Already, from afar, Henry caught the appetising smell of chicken soup.

"I can't believe it," he called out, "wherever did you get that?"

"Simple! Our landlady keeps chickens...now she has one less!"

"It must have cost a fortune!" protested Henry, "And I have nothing to contribute."

"Don't be silly!" intervened Arnold, "Poor folk don't exploit refugees. Besides, even if the cost were tenfold, I'd still have bought it to celebrate our freedom."

In his dependent and helpless state, Henry could not protest too much. But one day, he resolved he would repay all their kindness. And so he stopped being 'poor and proud', and during the next few days he ate is fill. Soon with the wholesome food his health improved and he began helping with little chores, exercising his legs in short walks, then gradually increasing his efforts as time went on. There were also other unmistakeable signs of restored vigour. When they first arrived, although all three of them had to share the same bedroom, he was too ill to feel embarrassed and too much taken up with unpleasant bodily sensations, to pay any attention to the others. But after a few days, the sight of Su in her nightdress, the occasional glimpse of naked thighs, or her breasts, had a disturbing and often tantalising effect. It was no good pretending. While in the camp they had never had the opportunity to enjoy each other fully, for those snatched encounters had left them utterly dissatisfied. But at least they'd had a chance to be alone with each other for a part of the day, whereas here all three of them had to stick together continuously. They went on walks together, ate together and shared the household chores together. There was no escape from togetherness. In spite of this they enjoyed their idyllic existence, which in many respects was quite out of this world; a unique refuge of peace and tranquillity in a world gone mad. Only one thing troubled them: they had no news whatever, being completely cut off from all the other internees. To be oblivious of the world for a while is one thing; to be totally in the dark about recent events in the middle of war, is another.

One fine morning, two women in traditional black garb, shawls covering their heads, dismounted from their mules and came scurrying over to Anastasia muttering and gesticulating wildly as they cast meaningful glances at Anastasia's guests. Their local dialect, *Arbëreshë*, was difficult to follow, but Henry caught the word *'Messina'* repeatedly. Eventually, Anastasia came across to her lodgers with a sombre, pre-occupied look on her face.

"Gli Americani ed Inglesi hanno preso Messina, Messina has fallen!"

Evidently Anastasia was every bit as scared as the two other women. It was not difficult to understand why, for Messina lay only a stone's throw from Reggio Calabria, separated from the mainland by its narrow straits. Consequently the Allies were hammering on the gates and could be expected to break through any moment. From time immemorial invaders and adventurers of all descriptions had left a terrifying reputation imprinted in people's memory and folklore; a reputation of plunder, destruction and rape. So now, who was to know how these *'Inglese ed Americani'* would behave, especially towards the womenfolk. Su, seeing their fright, hastened to reassure them.

"Don't be frightened Anastasia! The English and Americans are civilised people, *gentiluomini!*"

Her words had some effect, but couldn't quite dispel a fear deeply rooted in the history of the region. One of the visitors began to cry, rocking to and fro, while the other two tried half-heartedly to comfort her. For some time all three women continued to converse animatedly, the volume of their voices alternating from a shrill pitch of panic to almost inaudible whispers and sighs. They crossed themselves, invoking the protection of local saints and the blessings of the Virgin. Then the good ladies remounted their mules to continue their journey and the dutiful spreading of alarm and despondency.

"How on earth did they get the news?" Arnold wondered.

"Some sort of bush telegraph, I suppose. Or perhaps they've been dropping leaflets, psychological warfare and all that," replied Su.

Henry was frustrated. "I do wish we knew what was going on. Hysterical women are not the most reliable source of information."

Arnold seemed to be weighing something up, then he declared abruptly, "I am going down to get some facts from the camp."

"No, Arnold!" protested Su, "They're all cooped up too. Where would they get news from?"

"They are bound to be more in touch with the world than we are up here."

"In that case, I'm coming with you."

"You are not going anywhere, Su. There's no point in both of us *shlepping* ourselves all the way down and back."

"But," protested Su, "what if something happens to you?"

"Oh do stop fussing!" Arnold retorted, impatiently. "Treating me like a child! I had my insulin. I can look after myself!"

Henry felt uncomfortable. "Then let me come with you. I'm feeling a bit stronger now."

"You stay where you are," snapped Arnold. "Do you want your fever back again?"

And so Arnold went.

Henry's conscience troubled him; how could he possibly mind being left alone with Su after the perpetual threesome? Truly he felt well enough to accompany him, but if Arnold declined, why insist?

"I'll tell you what," Su said, "let's have a picnic. I'll boil a couple of eggs and there is some mortadella and bread. It'll do."

Her eyes lit up; she beamed with excitement. The three of them had been on a short walk before, but had not ventured further afield because of Henry's convalescence. Maybe without realising why, she suddenly felt a sense of light-headiness, and what better symbol of freedom was there than a picnic, a return to happy days of childhood.

Setting off with their picnic basket, they came across Zaira feeding the chickens. She neither acknowledged their presence, nor spoke to them, but just stared at them with those huge black eyes.

"She gives me the creeps," said Su.

"A very odd child," agreed Henry, without paying much attention to Zaira, for his mind was elsewhere. His eyes brimming over with emotion, he surveyed Su who seemed lovelier than ever with a deep tan from the few weeks of rustic life and her spellbinding green eyes, glowing, full of joy.

"Shall we go a little further?" she asked, "I don't fancy sitting in this blazing sun."

Apart from the panoramic views there was not much to gladden the eye. It was mostly a barren hillside with occasional trees and brown patches of grass. As far as they could see there was no arable soil, no vineyards, at least not at that altitude, but maybe higher up? The day was sultry and as far as they could tell, the monotony of that landscape was not likely to alter, no matter how far they went.

"You know, there's no point in dragging ourselves much further. Let's just go as far as that hillock; we might at least get a better view of what's beyond."

So they walked on but on reaching their target an unexpected sight surprised them. At the foot of the hillock, in the midst of barren land, was a large vegetable plot, full of cauliflowers, lettuces and tomatoes. It was incomprehensible. How could this scorched earth produce such a wealth of succulent vegetables? Intrigued and mystified, they climbed down to look. As they carefully explored the terrain, they came upon a trickle of water emerging from the base of the hillock. Tracing its source they found themselves at the entrance of a cave. This cavern was deep and cool, with water seeping from its moss-covered walls and dripping in minute droplets from the vault above. The moist cool airiness was a blessed relief, after the sweltering heat outside. The deeper they ventured, the darker and cooler it became, until at last the water no longer filtered, but fell in heavy drops from the roof, splashing their faces as it soaked them with delicious showers.

Abruptly, as if by a predetermined, telepathic signal, they halted, turning face to face, and fell into each other's arms. Here in the cool depths of the cave, months of restrained desire spilled over in an uncontrollable flood of mutual passion.

Long after the fire had burned itself out, they lay close, caressing and murmuring tenderly. Therein lay all the difference from that relationship with Sonia; he had little to say to her, once he was drained of passion. Here with Su, he was privileged to experience the communion not only of the body, but of the deepest recesses of their minds and souls.

That cavern was a blessed discovery to which they would return more than once.

Chapter 22

The Doctor and the Donkey

Arnold returned from the camp that evening, breathless from the steep climb but full of excitement. They sat on the stone bench as he relayed the news. He firstly confirmed the fall of Messina. The Sicilian campaign was virtually at an end, and the invasion of the mainland was expected any day. The camp was buzzing! He had encountered many old friends who had returned to the camp because they could find no suitable accommodation. They had enquired about Henry's malaria and were at pains to send their best wishes for a speedy reunion. Arnold emphasized how lucky they were to have found such a good friend in Anastasia. One sight in particular had gladdened Arnold's heart; the sight of the road outside the camp, littered with abandoned German vehicles. With no time for repairs, lorries, armoured cars and tanks had been left stranded. One very large tank, immobilised in the middle of the marsh quite close to the camp, stood out. It must have strayed in search of a short cut and got bogged down.

Comandante Rizzi and the *capo polizia* were gone. A replacement *comandante* had been sent but there were no agents or sentries at all from what Arnold could see. Certainly rules and *appello* were a thing of the past.

The next day, all three were out walking when they came across a young shepherd grazing his flock. Whilst they were talking and exchanging news, Henry noticed a huge abscess on the shepherd's neck and offered to lance it. The young man, on learning that Henry was a doctor, agreed enthusiastically, and went back to the cottage with them. Henry incised the abscess, drained it, plugged the wound with an aseptic dressing and put a plaster over it. The young shepherd, who had been watching the whole procedure with awe and respect, thanked him profusely and went his way. Next morning however he was back, with a basketful of eggs — and his sister.

"*Dottore*, my sister has such a bad cough, *una tossa cattiva*."

Henry examined her, listened to her chest with a stethoscope, concluded it was only mild bronchitis and gave her an expectorant from his Notaresco supplies which he had salvaged before leaving. Henry's first reaction, as usual, was to refuse remuneration of any kind.

"*Grazie dottore, mille grazie.* You can see we have no doctor here. Most of them are in the army; the others are in places with more money. We are only simple people. Please, you must accept these eggs."

Henry gave in. After all, even this poor shepherd was richer than he. Incredibly from this small beginning, swift developments were to follow. In no time the news of a doctor in their midst spread like wildfire in the hills; what had started as a charitable act, a trickle, developed into a flood of astonishing proportions. Within a few days, patients began descending on Henry from far and near; men, women and children, on mules, on donkeys and on foot. The suddenness of this change of circumstances was unbelievable! Unbelievable, for this unexpected avalanche of patients brought a change of fortune with it. Provisions and money began to roll in and Henry, who up to then had been living entirely at the Springers' expense, was now able to repay their kindness with interest. He was overjoyed! What his patients lacked in wealth they made up in numbers, and in no time Henry was swamped with coins, bank notes, and edibles of all descriptions: eggs, sausages, olive oil, fruit, vegetables, home-made pasta and flasks of wine. He could have opened a provision store! Many of his patients had chest complaints, tuberculosis and recurrent attacks of malaria. It was therefore fortunate that Henry had a good stock of quinine and calcium gluconate as well as other drugs, laboriously carried from Notaresco.

Anastasia was proud beyond measure of having offered hospitality to such an important personage. Her prestige among the local population increased immeasurably as well. Many of the peasant women eyed her with ill-concealed envy, begrudging her privileged position and good fortune, for in their eyes, a doctor in the house was the ultimate status symbol and luxury. Anastasia basked in that newly-found glory of '*infermiera*', bossed people about, arranged appointments, giving herself airs.

The only person unmoved by all the hullabaloo was Zaira. Unconcerned, she looked right through the crowd, but continued to transfix Henry with that same strange basilisk stare, whenever she got the chance.

Henry never asked for a set fee, preferring to leave this to his patients; even so his bundle of banknotes grew fatter.

"You'll soon be another Dr Wunderstein," said Su jokingly, beaming at him. She was happy for his sake at the reversal of the humiliating position he had been in for so long. Now he was able to provide for the Springers, play host to them almost lavishly. In fact Henry's store of provisions grew so fast, they were unable to keep pace with it, as much of the victuals were perishable. Naturally Anastasia and her daughter benefited by it too and were glad of the unexpected windfall that had come their way. Even Petruccio got his share of treats.

The visits to patients too ill to come to the cottage provided an opportunity for Henry to widen his knowledge of the native population and environment. Most people were of Albanian origin and spoke a dialect called *Arbëreshë*. Outwardly they did not differ from the indigenous population, except for the customs, festivities and traditions they firmly adhered to after an exile of over four hundred years. The majority were Greek Orthodox. It was mostly the women who betrayed their foreign origin by their eye-catching trinkets, bracelets and amulets, many handed down from generation to generation. Their skirts always seemed bouffant, padded out by several layers of petticoats. They were friendly, modest and hardworking people, although there were also some fierce types among them, huge strong men, with flying whiskers, the descendants of brigands of not so long ago.

Some of the journeys took Henry high up in the hills, where the air was much cooler and the vegetation richer. Here oleander, olive and fig trees grew lavishly amid vine-covered slopes. With the emergence of richer pastures, cattle and even horses made their appearance, among the many pigs and turkeys. It was an entirely different world from the lower reaches. The cottages, similar to Anastasia's ramshackle dwelling, tended to be clumped together, conglomerating into little hamlets, or even small villages. During such journeys Henry would ride Petruccio, because Anastasia insisted on walking in front. In vain did Henry protest that being much older, and a woman at that, it ought to be her riding the donkey, but she would not hear of it. She retorted that it was an honour for her to lead the *dottore, un Santo*, who went about healing the sick and poor.

Petruccio played him up on several occasions. During the first two journeys, when Henry was entirely inexperienced, he'd suddenly bucked and thrown him for no apparent reason. However, one day, out of the blue Petruccio flatly refused to budge. At first Henry tried friendly persuasion, stroking his neck and whispering into his ears, and when this did not work, he pulled the donkey's tail and dug his heels into his ribs. But still, Petruccio wouldn't give an inch. Anastasia turned round and, surveying the uneven struggle between the obstinate donkey and his inexperienced rider, shouted, "*Le redini*! The reins! Pick up the reins! He won't move if you've dropped them."

In fact, as soon as Henry did so, the donkey started off. Now he recalled Anastasia's repeated reminder at the first encounter. Evidently this was the way donkeys were trained here.

"Mountain people can easily have accidents," she explained, "and if a rider falls off, the donkey just stays still, until the person comes round again and picks up the reins." Simple but obvious.

Arnold, who was a sociable person, visited the camp frequently to exchange news and keep in touch with his Yugoslav friends. What else motivated his frequent visits was a matter for speculation for it required a good deal of exertion. Overtly, he insisted it was imperative to be well-informed and prepared in these uncertain times for despite the peace and tranquillity up in the hills, one had to plan ahead.

Because of the heat, Henry did his domiciliary visits early in the morning and saw ambulant patients at the cottage, late in the afternoon. The rest of the day he liked to enjoy in peace and Anastasia saw to it that he was not disturbed. She was an extremely effective watchdog, a Cerberus who could bar the way to any intruders.

On several occasions the lovers returned to 'their' grotto. But occasionally, when Arnold was down in the camp, they made love in their room. Both of them knew, without saying it, that their idyll could not last and so gave free rein to their yearnings for each other, enjoying the thrill of their intimacy as and when they could.

On one such afternoon, while lying in each other's arms, a sudden terrifying explosion rocked the foundations of the cottage. For an instant both were petrified. The ear-splitting bang had clearly come from deep down in the valley. Su wriggled free from Henry's embrace and sat bolt upright, trembling, as if in mortal fear. Then she started to scream frantically, "Arnold! Arnold!"

Henry, taken aback, remembered instantly that very same frenzied reaction after the machine-gunning of the camp.

"Arnold! Arnold!" she cried again, an edge of hysteria in her voice. She was up and dressing herself feverishly. "I must go down there! Immediately! If anything should happen to him...!"

A sobered Henry scrutinised her, a little piqued. "Why this rush? Why should anything have happened to Arnold?"

"I don't know. But the bang came from down there. I just have this awful feeling. I must go."

"Then I am coming with you."

She rushed out headlong, nearly knocking over Zaira outside the door. She ran so fast Henry could hardly keep up with her, wondering how she kept her balance, for he stumbled and nearly fell repeatedly on the stony incline. Finally they crossed the Crati; they reached the camp gasping for breath.

"What happened?" gasped Su, to the first man she saw. "That bang, that explosion?"

The man's face looked solemn.

"There has been an explosion, a terrible accident. ..."

"Who? Oh who?" she yelled, beside herself.

"A young couple, I think. They'd gone out of the camp for a stroll.

"Who were those poor people?" asked Su, aghast.

"I don't know. The girl died, only a youngster. I think her name was Heidi."

Chapter 23

Allies in Calabria

One September morning, the young shepherd burst into the cottage with news of the Allies' landing in Reggio Calabria, which his friends high in the mountains had witnessed earlier. Although anticipated, it nevertheless hit the trio like a thunderbolt. After the initial shock had worn off, their hearts soared sky high with indescribable relief; this was finally the moment they had been dreaming of, throughout the last three years. The Axis was defeated, the allies had come to save them! Hallelujah! Henry imagined the ditties that little Wolf would now be singing! There was much merriment! From the stone bench, they looked down into the valley, imagining the jubilation in the camp, their friends and the emotional response to such great news, chattering with light hearts about their lives, their plans, their hopes. They wished they had gone down to the camp straight away but it was getting too late in the day to visit and return before dark. Out of consideration for their hostess's anxieties, they chose to forego too ostentatious a celebration, but there was no harm in an extra-special supper, courtesy of Henry's mountain medical services, with extra helpings of *vino*. He was proud to be able to put food on the table for this extraordinary repast which both Anastasia and her daughter were invited to share with them. Anastasia put on her best Albanian costume and Zaira, appreciating the sense of occasion, combed her hair and wore a clean dress. Calabrese children drink wine freely, and under its influence the tongue-tied Zaira loosened up to join in such toasts as '*Pace!*'– '*Prosperity!*' – '*Salute!*' and so on. Apart from this she said very little, but her fierce burning eyes seemed to sparkle with an even more intense glow than usual. Strangely, that almost impudent stare of hers now seemed to encompass both Henry and Su. Intrigued by that unnervingly queer expression in her eyes, Henry secretly searched his mind for a fitting adjective to define it and suddenly he had the answer. *Knowing – yes, knowing eyes. That's it!* And in a child of her age, such knowing eyes had a most unsettling connotation but this was soon overshadowed by the festivities. He only wished that Dino the optimist were here to celebrate with them but he had long since left Ferramonti to God knows where.

Early next morning the three of them went down to the camp, eager to share the excitement with their friends. Gaily tripping their way down those sheer slopes, Henry recalled that laborious ascent with panting oxen, weeks before. At that time a world of uncertainties lay before them; now it seemed things had worked out better than they could have dared imagine. The cares of the last three years seemed to have been lifted off like a leaden cloak.

"We shall remember these hills," remarked Su, wistfully, stopping for a breath half way down the hill.

"Of course we shall," said Arnold, putting his arm round her slender waist.

As soon as they'd reached the outskirts of the camp they stopped and looked ahead, dumbfounded, spellbound! For there, recognisable even from a distance, were soldiers in the traditional khaki shorts and shirts of the British Forces. In their eagerness to talk to their rescuers, they started to run and that initial joy escalated to delight, when the first soldier they met smiled, extended a friendly hand and said, "Shalom."

Henry could not help himself, nor was he ready for his own reaction to that simple greeting. He fell to his knees and sobbed in an outpouring of relief, mixed with grief and the release of so much pent-up emotion. His body shook as he wept, as if the suppressed trauma of his captivity was being uncorked from a bottle. He knew this was *catharsis* and did not fight it.

His reaction was by no means unusual, for when he had recovered his customary equilibrium, friends began to appear from all over to greet him, describing how the arrival of the Allies would be remembered to the end of their days. There had been such hugging and embracing, back-patting, handshaking and weeping, which eluded any attempt at description. The children had been dancing for joy, basking in their parents' new happiness, even though its true meaning escaped many of them.

From the moment of their arrival the 8th Battalion of the British Army had liberally handed out all the 'Riches of the

Empire': tea, sugar, condensed milk, corned beef, egg powder, custard, flour, soap, cigarettes, blankets, shoes, clothes and even cosmetics for the women. Henry's heart skipped a beat at the sight of those round tins, containing fifty cigarettes at a time. All this was simply wonderful! The British saviours! Great Britain living up to its name! Henry's heart swelled with gratitude. No more hunger, no more wooden clogs, no more huddling to keep warm under a thin moth-eaten blanket. The cigarettes were the icing on the cake! And there was even chocolate!

On entering his old *camerata*, Henry was greeted with great cordiality. Albert, now looking hale and hearty after his malaria, seemed to have forgiven him for his abrupt departure. Most of its occupants had by now returned from their diverse hideouts in the hills and everyone was eager to describe his own trials and tribulations during the exodus.

Little Wolf, resting on his broom, listened to their tales impatiently. "You could have saved yourselves a lot of bother if you'd stayed here," and turning to Albert he added "Wasn't it nice and quiet without this lot?"

So they all joked and teased each other, glad to be reunited despite all the protestations to the contrary. With decent food in their bellies once more and the sense of anxiety lifted by their liberators, there was nonetheless a far worse cloud hanging over them all which they tried not to dwell on.

Linzer came in beaming and vigorously shook hands with Henry.

"So you're back too?" he said, glad to see his protégé in good health again.

"I only came to see how things are. I'm not staying."

Linzer gave him a penetrating look, like a torchlight exploring dark recesses.

"And how are the Springers?"

"They are fine," Henry replied, giving little away.

Then, in a softer voice Linzer added, "By the way, your friend Weismann was telling the truth about the *Einsatztruppen*, the gas chambers and incinerators."

"How can you be sure?" whispered Henry, in shock, a sudden choking in his throat as he thought of his parents, his brother Edi and his 3 older sisters.

"I talked to Captain Shulmann, the intelligence officer of this Brigade. They have secret information from their own agents down there. Their reports confirm everything the Weismanns told us. If anything the truth is even worse. It's being hushed up in the ruling circles of the West."

So the happiness was short-lived; the icy clutch of pain around his heart had only been waiting round the corner.

That same evening, on the way back to the cottage, the three of them were torn by conflicting emotions. There was jubilation in their hearts because of their liberation; there was also an agonising pain and despair over the fate of their loved ones. None of them voiced their fears aloud, although each of them was acutely aware of each other's distress.

"Why is it," reflected Henry, "that at life's most significant turning points, there has to be a Janus head with its eyes twinkling on one side and weeping on the other?"

Back at the cottage, they sat on the stone bench to catch their breath and watch the sun go down, a regular evening ritual as they reflected on the day's events. It was now almost dark, except for the light from those magnificent constellations, those hanging fiery stars of southern skies. For a time they sat there in silence, absorbed in thought, until Henry, remembering his tin of cigarettes, struck a match to light one.

"Well, the time is ripe," said Arnold, "soon we'll have to leave. To get back to reality."

"Not just yet," pleaded Su, "where will you find a place as peaceful as this? It's like paradise!"

"I know, Sushka. I like it too. But we can't stay here for ever. We must be practical and get ready to leave the camp altogether."

Su did not reply. She only sighed. Henry mused on Arnold's remarks. He was aware that things were coming to an end and that the idyll with Su would soon be over. He'd have to brace himself to face the pain of separation. But as for leaving the hills, this was a different matter. The Springers had sufficient funds to leave the camp whenever they wished. This was not so in his case. Before he could venture out into the world, he'd have to earn more and build up some reserves. Here in the hills the unexpected opportunity had presented itself; he would have to stay on for a while. But he kept these thoughts to himself.

Chapter 24

Partings

Most mornings, Arnold insisted on the long trek down to the camp, allegedly to get information about formalities for their eventual departure from Ferramonti. Henry suspected Arnold was camouflaging his true intentions; he was a generous man, and it was most likely that he wished to give the two lovers time on their own, now that their romantic days were numbered.

At first Henry felt guilt at allowing a diabetic to undertake such frequent exertions, but love is egotistic, and so he soon began to rationalise that it didn't do him any harm. In fact the exercise seemed to have done Arnold the world of good, for he seemed fitter than ever.

The two lovers were acutely aware that they must soon part; this not only saddened and distressed them, but also intensified their burning desire for each other. It was like lovemaking under the sentence of death.

This being another sweltering day, they preferred to stay where they were, to make love in their stuffy little room. They had an insatiable hunger for each other and throwing all inhibitions overboard, they gave free rein to their desires. Their complete freedom from restraint was enhanced by the Calabrese *vino* they'd drunk liberally to quench their thirst in the oppressive heat. Suddenly, in the midst of this Bacchanalia, Henry's heart missed a beat. He stopped dead, as if petrified, for just above them, in one of the walls' many holes, he caught a glimpse of something moving. By God! It was dark and easily recognisable as a human eye. There was no doubt about who was spying; the 'knowing eye'. Henry whispered a hurried warning into Su's ear and the lovemaking ceased abruptly. Both got up as casually as they could, pretending not to have noticed anything unusual, and got dressed.

In the long run, plying between the cottage and the camp proved to be too laborious for Arnold, and he began to show signs of impatience.

"I wish we could stay longer here, Su, but it isn't a realistic proposition. We have to move."

She did not reply. What could she say? They packed their belongings to return to Ferramonti.

On the eve of the Springers' departure all three sat silently on the stone bench in front of the cottage, sharing the melancholy of *Paradise Lost*. Arnold broke the silence.

"And what are your plans, Henry?"

"I shall have to stay on here for a time to earn more money."

"But you will visit us in the camp, won't you?" Su asked, her voice trembling with emotion.

"Of course I will!" he replied, lightly.

"And when we leave the camp, you will join us?"

"Yes Su, as soon as I can."

Su, elbow on her knee, chin resting in her palm, went on brooding. "We shall be the advance party, the scouts, and as soon as we have found a place to settle, you must come too. Promise?"

"Yes, I promise."

But in his heart of hearts, Henry knew as he spoke that this promise must be empty and void. Something inside him repeated the old adage: "You can't bathe twice in the same waters." He was not one for throwing sand in his own eyes. For some time he had realised the true nature of the 'Triangle'; how things really stood had begun to dawn on him since the air raid, when Su, panic-stricken, had run to Arnold, without stopping to check on Henry. And again the truth was driven home by the explosion, when she had shrugged off his embrace, running headlong in that frenzied downhill scramble. He could not blame her for these reflex reactions for they were those of a mother for her child. Arnold, sick and impotent, was the infant-substitute in her childless marriage. Nevertheless, mother-love or not, it set him far below Arnold in her scale of priorities. Su was an honest human being. She loved Henry, no doubt; it was not just the physical relationship which bound her to him. But Henry was still young enough, still at that uncompromising stage of 'All or Nothing', where love was concerned. He could not play second fiddle even to mother-love. Now for the first time he really envied Arnold, for in spite of his physical incapacity, it was to him that she was tied by that indestructible silver cord that springs from a loving mother's heart. This was why Arnold could afford to be so generous; he knew she truly belonged by his side.

No one could have been happier than Anastasia when she learned of Henry's decision to stay on. Now she would have her *dottore* all to herself; to clean, wash and cook for, as well as assuming the role of receptionist, guide and general factotum. Zaira did not share her mother's enthusiasm. Basically, her attitude had not changed much, except that she no longer stared at him. She seemed to avoid him altogether and never looked him in the eye again.

Occasionally, Henry had to extend his operational field beyond his immediate surroundings. Twice he had been called to isolated hamlets in the mountains to assist at difficult births. He had little experience of obstetrics, but luckily Nature did most of the job which Anastasia credited to him. The way she put him on a pedestal was embarrassing and no matter how far they journeyed, she would still insist on walking in front of Petruccio guiding her *dottore* to the sick.

Henry would frequently visit the camp to meet his friends and receive food rations, cigarettes and clothing which were now regularly supplied to the *refugees*, as the Allies now called them. On one such visit in October, while enjoying the luxury of a proper cigarette under the tree in the piazza, Henry's eye fell on a face which somehow looked familiar. That pale face belonged to a tall, dark-haired internee, engaged in an animated conversation with a young woman of tomboyish mien. Henry recognised her as Verushka, Mendelsen's gifted pupil and now that he was focussing again on the man's features something suddenly clicked. It was Dr Kaufmann, minus both his beard and his habitual misanthropic frown. He looked different altogether in appearance, bearing and expression. Henry had seen him mostly horizontal, with a disgruntled face under its luxuriant black beard. No wonder he didn't recognise him.

"Good heavens, what a transformation!" mused Henry. His confusion must have shown on his face for Verushka, recognising him, grinned and winked.

He stopped his friend Linzer as he headed for the *camerata*.

"Hey, I've just seen Dr Kaufmann. What's come over him? He looks a new man."

Linzer gave a knowing smile.

"Why are you surprised? It's the old story: the King is dead, long live the King!" Linzer walked into the *camerata* with Henry hot on his heels.

"Are you talking in riddles again?" he asked, glancing round and recognising a few old faces.

"Surely you know Mendelsen is dead, don't you?" he said turning to face Henry.

Henry gasped. "Mendelsen dead?"

"Dead as a doornail," Szafran called out, nosy as ever, from his bunk.

"How did it happen? An accident?"

"No accident," replied Szafran, sitting upright to give and witness the full impact of his bulletin.

"The old Casanova had a hernia. He kept it quiet. Didn't want to ruin his reputation as a ladies' man, you know how the old goat was. It got strangulated. Maybe all the rushing and climbing, the big escape." Szafran paused, gesturing towards the hills. "Anyway," he continued, "you know what it's like here in Hotel Ferramonti, no proper medical facilities, just useless Sabatini and a scrawny old nurse! By the time they'd got him to surgery it was too late. He died of peritonitis. They buried him in Cerisano a week ago!" Szafran waited to see the effect of his report.

Henry was shaken, for he was fond of the old lion. He sat on his old bunk, trying to make sense of this depressing news. Poor Mendelsen! He had travelled half the world for his art only to end his days in a poky army hospital in no man's land just as the fortunes of war had turned. The great man deserved a more fitting end.

Tout passe, tout casse, tout lasse, he thought. *Poor dead Mendelsen; another casualty of this damned war.*

"And another thing," called Szafran sitting up again, "that young woman, his fancy-piece, they call her Verushka. Not a bad bed-warmer I hear! She stayed with the old man when they left the camp. So, when he died, back she comes to Dr Kaufmann, like a bitch on heat. That's why he's so pleased

with himself." Szafran stopped and sucked his teeth for a moment. "And who wouldn't enjoy a piece of that?"

"Oh yes....and listen to this ....that other woman," Szafran
continued his tale, not satisfied with his demolition work,
"that friend of yours, the one who came with her husband all
the way from Poland? Well, she's got herself pregnant and not
by her husband. No! God forbid!"

Batyushka Borstyn, on tenterhooks throughout, lost his patience and shouted across the *camerata*, "Enough mudslinging,
Mr Szafran! I do not understand how you can take so much
delight in other people's misfortunes. It is disgusting!"

Szafran got up at that point and sauntered out the *camerata*
leaving a bad taste behind him.

Chapter 25

Ghosts

During a fitful night's sleep in the *camerata*, his head swirling with the distressing news of Mendelsen, Henry could not help but reflect on his arrival in Ferramonti three years earlier. His mind went straight to poor Ossi and a dreadful ache filled his chest. Such a dashing young man taken in his prime and for what? A game of football. He thought with warmth tinged with sadness, of Dino; his unbridled enthusiasm for life, genius at cards and chess, his accordion playing, his clowning and his antics! All were so badly missed. Dino had been moved around the same time Henry had returned from Notaresco but no one had any further intelligence. Henry could only hope they would meet again after the war, if they survived. He wondered briefly what had happened to Sonia. Where was she now? Had her husband joined her? He remembered the shared meals, like manna from heaven during times of great hunger; he thought of her sweet little girls, how this life of worry and instability would impact on them. And now he must face the separation from Su. She had been his lover, companion and friend and now he was to lose her. He wondered, could he bear yet another loss? *How much can the human psyche take before something inside cracks?* he asked himself.

Then the black cloud seeped into his half-waking half-sleeping mind; the constant unsung chorus to every waking moment. What had become of his beloved elderly parents, his sisters, his brothers, their children? Did they meet their end in gas chambers, poisoned and screaming? Or bludgeoned to death by some savage in the woods around Lvov? They were elderly people, no threat to anyone! He shuddered, shivered and felt sickened at the thought.

After the night of such mental turmoil Henry was glad to leave the camp with all its demons at sunrise and set out for his long climb to the cottage. But first he had to cross the Crati. This however, was no longer the same shallow river. Unusually heavy autumn rains had transformed it into a powerful torrent, increasing not only its depth, but also the force of its swirling waters.

When Henry approached the river, a turbulent mist rising in wreaths was hovering over the water. There was something weird and unwholesome about the general atmosphere. Henry, who was an excellent swimmer, realised that his feeling of eerie unease was not rational; nevertheless, he was unable to free himself from an uncanny dread, the more as being alone, there was no one to come to his aid, should anything happen to him. To cross the river he had to strip completely and carry his shorts, shirt and sandals well above his head, for in some places the water was up to his armpits. He also had to struggle against the force of the torrential current. On reaching the other bank Henry heaved a sigh of relief and lay on the bank, utterly exhausted. The battle was with more than the forces of nature. He felt this was a journey he could not repeat too often and so his visits to the camp all but ceased.

The day of the Springers' departure drew near. Henry returned to the camp once more for this joyful yet melancholy event and together they celebrated in a sombre key. Su, pensive and subdued, had a continual struggle with tears.

"Now don't be silly, Su," said Arnold, gently. "This is an occasion for rejoicing, not tears! We're out of prison, and Henry will be coming to us soon! Let's have a smile. This isn't a funeral."

Su tried her hardest to oblige, but those usually luminous eyes could not regain their lustre for they were veiled with unshed tears.

As for Henry, he felt a resigned sadness and emptiness because he knew in his heart this was the end. But no matter what, life would go on and somehow he would survive. He had come to accept the fleeting nature of happiness and to anticipate its departure.

After the Springers left for Bari, Henry threw himself wholeheartedly into his work. At first he found it very hard going for he felt lonely and lost. Anastasia tried her best to keep his spirits up. In the simplicity of her heart, she had sufficient female intuition to sense the emptiness and sorrow which had crept into Henry's life with Su's departure. So she did what she could, preparing special *Arbëreshë* delicacies for his meals, anticipating his every wish.

The number of his patients increased steadily; Henry felt torn emotionally because of his intention to abandon them, once he had saved up enough to leave.

In the evenings, after work, Anastasia would engage in an elaborate ceremonial, preparing *petulla*. First she'd kindle a fire of dry sticks under the tripod and bring a cauldron of olive oil to the boil. Next she'd prepare a batter of flour, eggs and milk which she would throw in, a ladleful at a time. When the mix turned a light brown, she would fish out the little pieces of fried batter with a wooden spoon, murmuring strange incantations. From the irregular shapes of the doughnuts she would then divine Henry's future, which according to her was always as sweet as the honey she spread over them.

Sometimes Anastasia would tell him strange tales of witches and spirits, of the Wild Hunt of Alaric the Goth, whose secret burial and treasure lay under the waves of the Busento, a stone's throw from the Crati River. Anastasia would also extol the bravery—despite their cruelty—of the Calabrese *Briganti*, fearsome men, who not so long ago terrorised the mountains.

In any spare time, Henry would go off for short walks to places of sentimental associations, the grotto and the vegetable plot. Occasionally he would go down to the camp to enquire about news and collect his mail and cigarette ration. On his last visit there, he found a letter from the Springers, urging him to join them in Bari.

"Don't become a miser and do join us," wrote Su.

This was the second reminder he had received from her. But it was not only the need of more funds that held him back; he had no wish to rekindle a flame already doomed to die.

One evening, after a long solitary walk, he sat down to rest leaning against a spreading fig tree. Watching the familiar Calabrian sunset, he lit a cigarette and began reminiscing, reliving meaningful episodes, until he was quite lost in contemplation of the past. A deep physical melancholy filled his heart as he saw once more Przebylewski hanging from the piazza tree; Ossi, black hair wisps over his death-mask tinged with dust and a milky froth at his lips, Meiersohn the pious, dead on his bunk, the writhing bodies killed by friendly fire machine guns, even poor little Tikvah, removed from her cool watery home to die in a bucket. His sorrow deepened into fear as he imagined the Jews being murdered at this very moment. Maybe even his parents! It was hard not to feel despair and dread for what lay ahead for him and for those he loved…or had loved.

Though he'd got so carried away in recall and meditation, one faint sound succeeded in breeching the barrier of his temporary detachment, making him strain his ear; his inner ear at first, for outwardly it was as yet hardly perceptible. Gradually the sound began to penetrate his consciousness as the distant tinkling of a bell. At first he was unable to fit this silvery sound into the mosaic of recollections, but nevertheless, he continued to strain his hearing, until the sound touched the right cord in his memory. Anxiously, full of anticipation, he scanned the countryside whence the sound came. And there, he caught his breath, he finally made out in the evening dimness the rotund silhouette of a little woolly donkey with the dark outline of a female rider on top.

"Ciuccio!" he yelled out, "Maria!" and was off like a shot to meet them. He was beside himself with joy for in his present despondent and unhappy frame of mind it was unbelievably uplifting to meet a familiar face.

"But how did you get here, Maria?" Henry asked, recovering from the excitement of this unexpected encounter.

"I told you, didn't I? I live in these hills, the other side of the Crati. Don't you remember?"

Henry would have liked to embrace Maria like an old friend. Instead he put his arm round Ciuccio's neck. Maria seemed embarrassed, for this was Calabria, and it was against all Calabrese custom for any married woman to meet a man on her own; and in the dark at that. Henry sensed her unease.

"You must be tired, Maria. Do you live far?"

She pointed in a direction Henry had never bothered to explore because of the dismal prospect. "Not far from here. A little house."

Although Maria certainly did not wish to be seen at this hour with a stranger, her need to exchange a few friendly words with an old acquaintance must have got the better of her.

"Why didn't you come to work anymore?" she asked.

"Some people escaped from the camp, so they stopped the working party."

For a moment she kept silent, not knowing what to say. "I've had no news from my husband for over a year. Perhaps he is a prisoner with the *Inglesi*. Maybe he's dead. I don't know."

"I'm so sorry. It must be very difficult for you, Maria," he mumbled helplessly.

"I don't know what I'd have done without my Ciuccio." She stroked the little donkey, which looked more pathetic than ever.

"You must tell me more some other time," said Henry. "May I come to see you?"

As soon as he'd asked this, he realised that he had transgressed the established local code and taboo, and wished he hadn't done so. She hesitated but in the end she overcame her qualms.

"I work all week. Up there in the vineyards. It's all right if you come on a Sunday afternoon."

With these words she moved on and soon both of them were lost in the darkness. Moved by this chance encounter, which stirred up from the dust of oblivion those labouring days in the forest, Henry gazed after them long after there was nothing more to see.

Chapter 26

Maria

The days went by and autumn moved into November. Henry's urge to step out into the world again became more pressing. He had to save enough money to be sure he wouldn't be stranded once he left Ferramonti. First of all he had to redeem Mundek's cufflinks. This was a must, a *sine qua non*! Next he would have to equip himself with the most elementary clothing, lest he be taken for a tramp. He had set himself a target of roughly three thousand lire, a sum which would buy him a minimum of garments and ensure a livelihood for a month or so. As he spoke English reasonably well, he hoped to find some gainful occupation with the Allied Forces and possibly enlist as a doctor.

Gradually he began dropping hints about his future plans and was both saddened and troubled by Anastasia's disconsolate reaction.

"Oh why? Aren't you happy? People need a doctor so badly here!"

Henry asked himself the same question many times, especially as he had made up his mind not to intrude on the Springers. But after years of confinement in the narrow space of a concentration camp, he felt the need to spread his wings; and this world of hills was too constricted and too removed from the swift succession of historical events. No doubt, he'd never find a more peaceful and idyllic place and regret his decision ever to leave it; but just now he felt a compelling urge to throw himself into the stream of the world outside—even though that world had gone mad.

Once the decision was taken, it was no use prolonging the agony. Besides, it was wiser to cross the Crati with his belongings while it was still passable. He reckoned he'd reach the financial target he had set himself in a week or so; and then he would go.

So he told Anastasia of his decision and she was heartbroken.

Meantime he would have to tie up loose ends, intensify the treatment of some patients, notify others of his imminent departure and leave them instructions on how to continue treatment on their own. He felt mean and wretched about it all, but it couldn't be helped for he had been an involuntary prisoner too long, to be now voluntarily imprisoned by his own sentimentality. The last few days he worked almost non-stop. People, having got wind of his departure, sought his help at the eleventh hour. He saw them all and did not spare himself. By this feverish activity Henry tried to redeem himself and find absolution from his guilt.

Only the day before he left did he cease work altogether, to attend to his own affairs. He packed his few belongings into a suitcase, crammed some remaining medical supplies into a box, leaving household remedies behind, so that Anastasia might play nurse a little longer. Then he proceeded to take stock of his provisions, which had accumulated over the weeks. There was a strange medley of perishable and durable victuals, most of which he would leave for Anastasia anyway.

Only one item stood out because of its fragility: a basketful of eggs. And suddenly, the sight of these eggs provoked a chain reaction in his mind. So he picked up the basket, put a flask of olive oil and some tins of corned beef into a box, and went off. True, it was neither a Sunday nor an afternoon, but that could not be helped. He had forgotten all about it, during the strain and pressure of the last days. He only knew the direction, not the precise location of the hut, but she had said it was not too far and so he hoped he'd have no difficulty in finding it. And before long, it stood in front of him: a tumbledown dwelling, poor and derelict. He hastened to knock at the door. There was no response. Should he just leave the provisions in front of the door? That might be too risky. Besides, he wanted to say goodbye to both of them. So he decided to wait. It could not be too long anyway before Maria came home, for it was getting dusk.

Henry sat down at some distance from the hut and waited. The November evenings were cool now even in Calabria, and when the sun finally disappeared behind the mountains, he shivered slightly.

It was dark. Still no sign of Maria or Ciuccio. She would be very tired from work and he still had some packing to do; he would just say farewell, give her those provisions and go. And then he heard that unmistakeable silvery tinkling. As the donkey and rider came nearer, Henry could not resist a childish impulse, and he jumped suddenly out in front of them.

"*Gesu Maria!*" exclaimed Maria, alarmed but recognising Henry, she soon regained her composure. "You frightened me!"

Henry laughed. "I wanted to surprise you," and as she dismounted he added, "I'm going away tomorrow and came to say goodbye. Here, I bought you these."

Maria took the basket and the box without examining its contents in the dark.

"I must go now, Maria. You're surely tired anyway."

"Now that you are here, there's no need to rush off. Why didn't you come by day, on a Sunday, as I told you?"

There was no edge to her voice though.

"Sorry, I couldn't. Had too many things to do."

`Maria hesitated, not knowing quite what to say or do. "Well, since you are here, come in and have a glass of wine."

"Are you sure? You must be tired."

"Never mind. You can take Ciuccio into his shelter over there and give him some hay and water?" she asked.

Henry was glad to be entrusted with that menial task, for he loved the shaggy little donkey and while he fed him, he stroked his neck and pressed his face against those powerful mandibles.

Maria lit a candle inside and when Henry had finished with Ciuccio he went in. It was a simple room, but clean and neat. Apart from a wooden table, there was a massive wardrobe, hand-carved in places, peasant fashion—two chairs, an iron bed and a kitchen stove. The whitewashed walls were bare, except for some religious prints and the pièce de résistance was an icon, watching over the bed from a little niche above. Evidently Maria was Greek Orthodox too. Bunches of dried peppers, garlands of onions and garlic hung from a beam above the little stove. The room was fragrant with the scent of rosemary and bay.

"I see you've brought me a whole basket of eggs."

"Yes I did. And for good reason too. Remember my first day....you gave me that egg? I wanted to repay such kindness with interest."

"There wasn't any need, but thank you all the same. I'll fry some of the eggs for us."

Using dry sticks, straw and a pair of bellows, Maria lit the stove. In minutes a large omelette adorned with slices of red pepper and tomatoes was on a platter, and a coarse linen cloth on the table; she bade Henry sit down. Then she placed a hunk of dark bread, a carafe of water and a flask of *vino* before Henry, gesturing him to eat.

"I'm afraid I can't offer you anything else," she said apologetically.

Maria seemed very hungry. She bolted her food in silence, keeping her eyes on the plate and taking frequent gulps of wine.

"So you are leaving the hills?" she asked, looking him straight in the eye. "You don't like it here?"

"I do, but I have been too long like a caged animal; I want to see the world again."

"And where will you go?"

"Anywhere, as long as it's away from Ferramonti."

The meal cleared, Henry made a move to leave.

"Now I must go, Maria." He stood up. She did not reply, remaining seated, looking down at her work-worn hands.

"You must?" she asked sadly. "It's so long since anyone came to visit me. It's so very lonely here."

Henry did not know what to do. He began to feel strangely on edge.

"I'll stay a bit longer, if you really want me to, Maria."

There followed a long silence.

"You shouldn't have come here at this time of day. But now that you are here, why don't you stay and have another drink."

So he sat down again and poured himself a glass of wine.

"Do you remember, Maria, all the haggling and bargaining we did in the forest?"

"Surely I remember!" she said, laughing, "The rubbish you all used to bring!"

"But you were always fair, at least with me," remarked Henry.

"Oh yes, I used to favour you, because you didn't push yourself."

Again they sat in silence for a while; a silence of recall. Ciuccio's braying came mournfully from his stable.

"Shall I give him some more hay?" asked Henry.

Maria shook her head. "No need. He sometimes likes to feel sorry for himself. Like a man — *come un Christiano*."

"I bet you have forgotten that you did invite me here ages ago."

Maria sighed. "Yes, I remember I invited you, but that was for after the war, when my husband was here."

Henry regretted his remark. "Are you sorry I came?"

It was then that she looked up at him, smiling; that kind of eloquent smile which comes naturally to all women, irrespective of social class or education, a timid smile, yet tender and inviting. It would have been unkind and heartless to ignore its message. So they looked at each other, testing; and when Henry felt sure he'd not misread her message, he got up and took her in his arms. She melted into his embrace. This was no fervent lovemaking, but gentle almost mutually compassionate, with each trying to escape their loneliness; forget a while the miseries of life like the playfully tender brushing and rubbing of heads of two packhorses, freed from their burdens after a hard day of labour.

They lay quietly on that rustic iron bed, enjoying the mere nearness of another human being.

"You shouldn't have come here by night," said Maria with a vestige of after-the-feast remorse. "Had you planned it that way?"

"No, I didn't ... Well, maybe I did, without realising it. You know Maria, I always liked you...when we worked in the woods."

Maria gently pressed his arm, acknowledging the compliment.

"I know and I liked you too."

When Henry eventually got up to dress she became alarmed.

"*Per amor di Dio*, for God's sake, be careful! Don't let any-one see you! This is Calabria! If anyone should find out, it would be the end of me... and you!"

They hugged each other for a while, more like good friends than lovers.

"Take care," whispered Maria at the doorstep, "goodbye and good luck. *Addio*."

As he hurried through the cold night, Henry pondered over the subtle intricacies of the human psyche. He wondered what Dr Bernheim would have made of that episode.

Chapter 27

Ashes to Phoenix

Next morning Henry took his leave of Anastasia as tenderly as he could. She cried bitterly, wiping her tears on her apron, insisting that it was *arrivederci* and not *addio* on the one hand, but then realising how unlikely another meeting would be, that she would never forget him. He knew they would not meet again but that the gratitude he owed was something he could never repay as long as he lived. She, with her small home and big heart, had confirmed what he already knew about Italians and the Calabrese in particular; their riches were not in material goods but in their honesty and humanity. She stood by the stone bench, sorrowfully waving Henry down the hill while Zaira simply stared after him, stroking Petruccio who brayed his own particular lament.

Back in Ferramonti, Henry was impressed by the many changes that had taken place. AMGOT, the American Military Welfare Organisation, had taken charge of the camp's administration. It also issued identity cards after a thorough interrogation of each internee, to eliminate the possibility of espionage. The former Italian camp authorities were allowed to co-operate, especially after Italy's unconditional surrender. The replacement *comandante* carried out the duties assigned to him by the Americans with an air of resignation, yet with a measure of dignity. The new administration saw to it that not only the internees' stomachs, but also their cultural and social needs, were catered for. To disperse a concentration camp of that magnitude would take some time. Each case would have to be dealt with individually. It was therefore important to make the internees' life as rewarding and constructive as possible, for they had to be re-educated and prepared for normal existence.

Thanks to the selfless and dedicated efforts of Mrs Feinberg, now officially on AMGOT's staff, the needs of the children were given high priority. Kuttner, Gurewicz and Lapidus became the King Pins of Entertainment, aided by ENSA, the British organisation responsible for leisure and amusement of the troops. Linzer, who only knew a few words of English, had the cheek to offer himself as an interpreter; surprisingly, he was accepted.

Some people did not fare so well. Poor Mrs Kreisler was a broken woman following her teenage daughter's tragic death, just as the rosebud was about to bloom. Another unhappy person was Sigmund Weismann, humiliated and hurt by his wife's infidelity. People like Szafran would crack cruel jokes.

"He had to come all the way from Warsaw to get a bastard."

Poor Myra, five months pregnant, was confused and bewildered. She had lost her bearings and her head. After all the privations and sufferings, after years on the threshold of death, an overpowering hunger for life had overwhelmed her. She had fallen prey to that sudden resurgence of energy, that indomitable zest for life: libido.

Henry had no intention of staying in Ferramonti a day longer than was absolutely necessary. The wealthier element had already left the camp. Others, less enterprising, had preferred to play safe; as long as their bellies were filled they were prepared to hang on and who would blame them after the extreme deprivation they had endured?

Before obtaining the relevant documents for his official release, Henry had to be interviewed by an intelligence officer of the Palestine Brigade. Captain Shulman subjected him to a gruelling interrogation and painstaking cross-examination on his entire life history but once satisfied, he became friendly and communicative. He was about thirty five years old, tall and lean, dark of hair and complexion, with an alert, intelligent face and needle-sharp brown eyes. Originating from Lithuania, he had emigrated to Palestine as a *chaluz*-pioneer soon after graduation from high school, much against his parents' wishes; they had planned a legal career for their son. Captain Shulman was a proud Jew, devoid of any ghetto characteristics.

"This is the last time they'll ever abuse and slaughter us," he said emphatically.

"Who's going to stop them?" asked Henry sceptically.

"We shall," Shulman replied. "This time we'll fight to survive! It is time to eradicate from the 'goyim' mind, once and for all, the idea of the Jew as the eternal scapegoat! That image of the toothless, spineless Jew, the sacrificial lamb, ready to be butchered, has to be wiped out!"

There was no need to preach to the converted, for Henry had always resented the passive, semi-masochistic meekness of his martyr-prone co-religionists. Unfortunately he doubted whether Jews, at least those he had known, were capable of physical combat. *Millennia of oppression,* he thought, *have squeezed out all the vigour of brute force, to sublimate energy into intellectual, spiritual and artistic achievements. But as for fighting...?*

"I very much doubt that our brethren have it in them to fight," he said at last, "not on a physical plane, at least."

Captain Shulman looked at him critically, almost with scorn.

"You talk like a ghetto Jew! Had you seen our chaluzim — better still our freeborn *sabra* in Palestine — you'd think differently. Remember, before the *diaspora,* the dispersion, the Israelites were always a warlike nation. Our history abounds in battles and wars. We fought the Philistines, Babylonians, the Assyrians. We drove the Greeks out and for many years we even defied the might of Rome."

"True," replied Henry, "but that was thousands of years ago."

"Never mind the years! The genetics are the same. That warlike genetic heritage lies dormant, throttled by oppression and the over-ethical philosophy of orthodoxy. If you were a *chaluz,* a farmer, you'd know what difference soil and environment can make to the same seed. Sown in the open, exposed to sunshine and rain, the seed will shoot up vigorously and develop into a robust, healthy plant. That same seed, planted in darkness, in arid soil with hardly any water, will only grow into a caricature of the former; sickly and weak. For thousands of years our seed was sown in blood, derision, humiliation and pogroms. I wish you could see our *sabras,* born and bred in freedom. You'd see the transformation."

"There are not enough *sabras* as yet; and unfortunately the rest of European Jewry is affected with the same malady of scepticism as I am."

"European Jewry? What European Jewry?" yelled Shulman. "We have our intelligence there. When this war is over, there will hardly be a Jew left! Belsen, Sobibor, Treblinka, Majdanek, Auschwitz and the rest will see to that! Only a handful of the fittest will survive; but those who live through this mass extinction of the Jewish nation will be possessed by such a fury and hatred, they'll fight for their existence to the end!"

"If only a handful of European Jews survive, how are they ever going to be an effective fighting force?"

Shulman smiled. "Ever heard of the wonders of pruning? Hitler will prune the tree of Israel almost to its roots so that it will shoot up again, stronger than ever. That seasoned nucleus of European survivors, together with our *chaluzim* and *sabras*, will form a tremendous force, spiritual and physical!"

Captain Shulman, usually calm and collected, had worked himself up into a state of high passion. So he lit himself a cigarette to soothe his nerves and continued.

"Numbers are not all-important. Remember the Battle of Marathon? It is the spirit that matters. Ideas cannot be suppressed for ever. Ideas unite people and weld them together into a battering ram."

Henry's lips curled in a sardonic smile. "No doubt ideas do unite; but once united, people usually kill the idea. Look what Robespierre made of the ideals of the French Revolution! What Stalin did to Communism! Look at the caricature the Christian world made of the teaching of Christ! Love thy neighbour! Offer the other cheek! Would all the agony, destruction and killing be conceivable, if Christians practised the idea of Christianity?"

"You are a stickler, Dr Raupner! A pessimist, keen on polemics; but up to a point you are right, of course. Nevertheless, I believe that any idea, which has lasted almost 2600 years, deserves a special place and consideration."

"Two thousand six hundred years? How do you arrive at that figure?"

"Nebuchadnezzar razed Jerusalem to the ground and carried the flower of Israel into Babylonian exile in 586 BC, almost 2600 years ago. Do you recall the lament of the captive Jews, '*By the Rivers of Babylon*'? Look up Psalm 137. 'If I ever forget thee, oh Jerusalem, let my right hand forget her cunning, let my tongue cleave to the roof of my mouth'. We wailed that lament almost six hundred years before Christ, we still sing that same song two thousand years after Christ's death! Some endurance! Some hankering after the homeland!"

"I grant you, this perpetual, stubborn craving for Jerusalem is unique and transcends the intensity and constancy of any idea I know. Still..."

"Still what?" Shulman interrupted, "A Jewish home in Palestine for our down-trodden brethren is the only solution; and we'll have to fight for it! We are not *conquistadores*, like Hernando Cortez, departing from our own rich homeland to pillage, plunder and murder other people for their gold! All we want is our ancient home and to live in peace; in peace and dignity! And if we have to die, let's die on the battlefield and not in gas ovens, not in mass graves, shot down like dogs!"

Henry listened in silence, captivated by Shulman's heartfelt plea and wishing to God he could raise his own spirits to the same pitch of faith and optimism. Alas, he couldn't.

"And don't delude yourself!" Shulman went on, "Palestine is not a land of 'Milk and Honey'. Stones and sand, bogs and malaria, that's what the first *chaluzim* of old found — those tough and dedicated pioneers — who gave their very lifeblood for a dream, the idea of a Jewish Homeland."

"I only wish I could share your enthusiasm and optimism, but I can't. The world around us has never lifted a finger to lighten our burden for two thousand years. And now Hitler is exterminating us."

"Hitler will have done us a service!" Shulman broke in, "A favour, though at an agonisingly exorbitant price! He'll succeed in shaking and waking not only us, but also the sluggish complacent conscience of the world's nations. Only monstrosity of such magnitude could achieve that! The sheer dimension of his crime will bring about the miracle of rebirth: the realisation of that age-old dream of Palestine as a natural homeland!"

Shulman had to pause. Although he had left his parents years ago, he must have also agonised over their fate. But he soon collected himself and continued.

"I am no man of letters; too busy tilling the soil and draining the marshes. But I still remember a few lines from Goethe's *Faust*. Do you recall how Satan Mephistopheles defines himself: '*Ich bin ein Teil von jener Kraft, die stets das Böse will und doch das Gute schafft*'? In my amateur translation it sounds like this: 'Of evil part am I and still I bring forth good against my will' - that fits Hitler like a glove."

Henry was sad because he could not soar high enough to join Shulman in his vision. To him a Jewish Homeland was only a dream, a Utopia never to be fulfilled. Perhaps in calling him a ghetto-Jew, Shulman was right after all. Although he had not actually been shut in one, maybe he had lived too long in a spiritual ghetto.

Chapter 28

Addio Ferramonti!

The day before departure from Ferramonti, his friends
gave Henry a farewell party. It was a quiet affair,
hardly a celebration, for so many uncertainties lay before them still. The war, which clearly had taken a dramatic
turn for the better, was still far from over.

"Where will you go?" asked Batyushka Borstyn, uncorking
a bottle of wine from his seemingly limitless supply.

"I'd like to go to Taranto."

"Why Taranto?" enquired Borstyn.

"I don't really know. But there is an army base there.
Maybe I can find work."

"Dr Raupner wants to dance the Tarantella," said Szafran,
who rarely missed the opportunity for a flippant riposte.

"What about yourself, Mr Borstyn? Don't you want to leave
the camp?" asked Henry with warmth in his voice, as he beheld the gaunt figure of that most humane elderly gentlemen,
seated on his four-poster bed.

"Where would I go? My home is up north in Milan. The
war isn't over yet."

"Mr Borstyn is right," remarked Linzer. "The Germans will
hold on to the north of Italy as long as they can. Until Genoa is
freed, I'll stay put too."

"He has to stay here," said Moishele with a twinkle in his
eyes. "How could AMGOT run the camp without Linzer? He's
such a great interpreter!"

"Shut up, Moishele!" replied Linzer, grinning and turning
to Henry he asked, "and why are you in such a hurry?"

"I'm sick of Ferramonti, sick to my back teeth!"

"Are you going to join the Springers?" Linzer enquired
with a glint in his eye.

"No! I'm not. They are in Bari."

Borstyn had a pensive, almost dreamy air about him.
"When you look at it," he said, "Ferramonti is not such a bad
place after all; not the place you'd choose of course, but with
all the horror and madness in the world, it's a little island of

sanity. Besides, where else would you have had the privilege of such good companionship?"

"True," thought Henry, looking at Moishele, the clown with the sad spaniel eyes, the big mouth, and the heart of gold.

A young woman opened the door but remained on the threshold, scanning the *camerata*. Little Wolf, leaned on his broom. He didn't like intruders who only brought dirt into the *camerata*.

"Looking for someone, Miss?" he asked with a glower.

"Thank you. I think I've found him." She came up to Henry, smiling. It was Verushka. "I hear you are leaving to-morrow."

Henry nodded and invited her to sit down.

"I cannot stay, but I've brought you something."

Henry looked startled.

"Really it is not mine to give. It belonged to the Master," and handing over a roll of paper she explained, "Do you re-member one special painting, 'Mother and Child'? I recall how much you admired it. I thought as a token of his friendship, and a souvenir from Ferramonti—if you need one—you might like it?"

She shook Henry's hand with a firm grip, clasping his hand in both of hers.

"I wish you the best of luck."

Next morning Henry got up very early and made his way to the cemetery in Tarsia. He felt the need to say farewell to Ossi and all the others who had not made it. There was by now a ring of Jewish graves close to the wall. Ossi, Meiersohn and Pryzbylewski lay side by side, and a little farther away rested the five air raid victims; still further was the newly dug grave of 15 year old Heidi Kreisler whose chance to blossom had been so tragically cut short. Henry stopped at each grave, trying to evoke an image of them in life. He saw Mr Meiersohn in his prayer shawl and phylacteries, swaying rhythmically in his dialogue with God. Przebylewski he recalled leaning against a tree, staring into space. He imagined the little watch-mender standing under the marriage canopy, flanked by his overbearing bride, looking timidly at the disapproving, hostile gathering. And there again, sprawled on the ground, lay the young woman, in a pool of blood. Other air raid victims he did not know not even by sight. They were the anonymous victims of Ferramonti. When he came to the last grave in the ring, to the explosion victims, he recalled that glorious morning in the spring, when on his walk with Su he had encountered that timid pair, the radiant Heidi and her newly found beau. Henry stayed longer at Ossi's grave. He could evoke many images of him, but mostly he saw him sitting with that intense look in his black eyes, spinning his little chain round his finger. He murmured a farewell to him, threw a handful of earth on the grave, and went away with a heavy heart.

Later in the afternoon his friends escorted him to the military truck that was to take him to Taranto. Among the many acquaintances, well-wishers and close friends was Yadranka, with her baby son clutched to her chest, and Sigmund, who wore an unspeakably sad expression in his eyes. Myra did not have the courage to come with him. They all shook hands, hugged and embraced him, little Wolf most of all. Henry was choked with emotion as the truck began to move. The only civilian among soldiers, he tried not to get in their way. Huddled in a corner, he clutched the battered suitcase containing all his earthly possessions. He felt sad and utterly lonely. Had he been wise to leave his friends and the relative safety of Ferramonti? What would he do in Taranto? Where could he stay? Doubts and depressing thoughts began to assail him. He would have to start life again all on his own, for most likely his family in Poland were dead.

As the truck passed the marshes, Henry was surprised to see so many flowers despite the wintry chill in the air. Somehow the sight of this multitude of colours had a soothing and invigorating effect. The soldiers broke into song and Henry smiled at the saucy refrain. He made a heroic effort to shake off his gloom. Why moan? He was free, wasn't he? Life would go on in all its customary ambivalence, with both grief and joy at every turn. Life's eternal Janus Head! He sought for words to express the way he felt and suddenly young Heine's outpourings came to him:

'Oh God! I feel the bitter-sweet pain of existence.'

The truck sped on, whirling up clouds of reddish dust.

THE END

Henry's Farewell Poem

In Hoffen und in Sehnen läuft ab die Lebensspende

Man greift um sich verlangend, doch bleiben leer die Hände

Und hast du schon das Glück gefunden

Kannst du vom Schmerz nie mehr gesunden.

D H Ropschitz, Ferramonti, 18 October 1943

The gift of life is spent in hopes and dreams

We reach out yearning, but our hands remain empty

And if by chance your dreams come true

The pain will never leave you.

EPILOGUE

by Henry's daughter, Yolanda Ropschitz-Bentham

What happened to my father immediately after leaving Ferramonti has been hard to ascertain; he didn't volunteer much information about those dark days and children often fail to ask the necessary questions until it is too late.

Military records show that he joined the Royal Army Medical Corps (RAMC) in Italy in 1944, finding work in Taranto and later Treviso, firstly as an interpreter then as a Captain, serving in the North Africa Section.

As he had feared, his elderly parents, (my grandparents), Jacob and Sophia Ropschitz, had perished at the hands of the Nazis, along with their four married children and their families. Henry's niece, Stenya, daughter of his sister Amalia (Malka) and husband Ludwig Merkel, escaped Auschwitz by jumping off the train taking her parents and grand-parents to their deaths. Stenya returned to Lvov after the war, married Arkadi Korostishevski. They had a son Anatoly and daughter Marina who I would dearly love to trace.

His siblings, Leon, Izhio and Helena had found refuge in America, Australia and South Africa before the outbreak of war. Anna and husband Dr Frederick Nussenblatt survived the war and lived out their lives in Nervi, on the beautiful Liguria with their sons, Enrico and Emanuele.

In 1947 my father was released from the RAMC and came to England which became his permanent home. He met my mother, a former Lucy Clayton mannequin, soon after and they married in 1949. At first he worked in general practice, in London, but inspired by Dr Ernst Bernhard in Ferramonti he pursued a career in Psychiatry, receiving his DPM in 1954 and MRC Psych in 1971. His area of specialism was suicide prevention and psycho-social welfare within mental health; this inspired his research into the "Gold Watch Syndrome." (1968)

His career took him to Liverpool, Derby, Huddersfield and Halifax where he practised as a consultant psychiatrist until retirement from the NHS in 1978. After a period in private practice, and in spite of understandable reluctance, he took up a psychiatric post in Germany at the Rhön-Klinikum, Bad

Neustadt, specialising in Psychosomatic Disorders. Contrary to his expectations, he found his colleagues delightful, welcoming people with whom he established an easy and enduring rapport. I recall my father's difficulty in reconciling these conflicting emotions and the intellectual challenge it presented.

My father continued his love affair with Italy, instilling a deep affection for the country in all our family. We have treasured memories of the pineta in Viareggio, the beaches of the Liguria and visits to our relatives, the Nussenblatts, in Nervi. As children, we didn't appreciate the significance of those places in our father's heart, but all became clear after his death and with his memoir. I continue to carry that torch in his name.

In 1982 he completed this autobiographical novel, but his declining health hindered his efforts to find a publisher. A planned return visit to Ferramonti with his friend Albert Goldfield had to be shelved and he died in 1986. He is survived by his former wife Violet, (my mother) and his two sons, my brothers, Manfred and Gordon.

So what became of some of the characters in this book?

Dino Fuhrman (Dr Isaaco Friedmann) was moved several times during the war from Ferramonti to Lungro and then Santo Stefano. He returned to Genoa after the war, married Ingeborg in 1973 and at age 60 was blessed with a son, Ruben. Isaaco (Iso) continued his friendship with my father and practised medicine until age 84, much beloved by his patients and all who knew him. He enjoyed good health, a lively intellect and a strong will until the end. He died just before his 103rd birthday. I was blessed beyond words to meet him and Inge in 2016 when he shared his many memories of Ferramonti with humour and clarity.

Ossi Gerber (Dr Stefan Greiwer) was an only child; his family perished at the hands of the Nazis in Poland. Stefan is survived by one distant relative in Israel who never knew him. I have been unable to identify the young woman, presumably his girlfriend, who appears in many of his photos (one in this book) in my father's possession, to know her fate.

Albert Goldfarb (Albert Goldfield) resumed his medical studies in Florence after leaving Ferramonti; he married and had a son, Norbert. The family moved to the United States where daughter Jane was born. Albert worked as a pathologist until 1980 and died in 2004 aged 91. He and my father remained friends to the end with a reunion in England in the 1980s. I am continuing the connection with Albert through his son Norbert, a practising internist who works to improve the health of marginalized Israelis and Palestinians. He is married and has two children.

Linzer (Enrico Insler) continued his friendship with my father, becoming "Uncle Henry" to me and my two brothers. He remained a bachelor, eventually joining his sister in Sao Paolo, Brazil. He died in 1971 at the age of 72.

Mendelsen (Michel Fingesten) was a well-known artist at the time of his internment in Ferramonti, prolific in graphic art, bookplates and works of a political and erotic nature. His death in the military hospital on October 8, 1943 at the age of 57 cut short a brilliant career. He is buried in Cerisano, near Cosenza. His Mother and Child painting is a constant and poignant reminder of Ferramonti, in my home today.

PHOTOS

The following photos, although not always of the best quality, have been included for two reasons; firstly to bring alive the realities of life in Ferramonti and Notaresco and secondly, in the hope that some of the characters in the photos might one day be identified.

Young Henry

Early 1920s: Ropschitz family. Young Henry (L) sisters Roza or Klara, Anna, Helena and Amalia with mother, Sophia Ropschitz (centre)

Parents Jacob and Sophia Ropschitz

Henry and school chums in Vienna 1924-1930

Henry (L) with Willy Klughaupt

Front: Willy (L) Henry and Albert Goldfarb (R)

Brother Mundek, sisters Helena and Anna in Venice late 1920s

Henry the medical student in Italy 1931-1937

Henry in his beloved Alassio

Mona and Henry, Alassio

Sister Helena and Henry, Bordighera late 1930s

The arrest 5.7.40

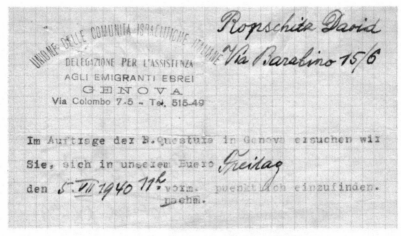

The summons to the Genova police, 5th July 1940, 11.00 sharp

Henry with Linzer on Via XX Settembre, Genova, July 5 1940

Before Ferramonti: Ossi and Dino

Ossi

Ossi In Nice

*Ossi and lady friend Piazza de
Ferrari, Genova*

Dino the sportsman

Dino and Ossi

Daily Life around Ferramonti

1940: Henry and friends amid construction

No luxuries in Ferramonti

A dip in the canal, Dino (R) sitting

Triumvirate and friends of Camerata 3

Ossi helps with the chores

Henry (R) plays chess while 'Kibitzes' look on

Ossi (L) and Henry on their palliasses

Dino plays accordion in Camerata 3

1941: Henry with school friend Dr Isaac Klein and Dino in Ferramonti

Note sentry in background

Henry (Centre) with friends

Camerata 3. Henry (Centre) Ossi and Moishele

Notaresco October 1941 — May 1942

Albert Goldfarb (L) and friend

Lapidus plays his Notarescana

Henry (2nd L) with Finzi and friends

The view from Henry's balcony, winter 1941

Henry on his balcony

Henry with Baumgart's Christmas visitors

Winter 1941

Henry (3rd L), Lapidus and others

Return to Ferramonti May 1942

Henry (2nd L) and friends

Group in Synagogue

Henry and Su Springer

Arnold and Sue Springer with Henry

Henry (2nd from R) with friends at the camp limits

Henry (2nd from L) with friends

Henry with friend

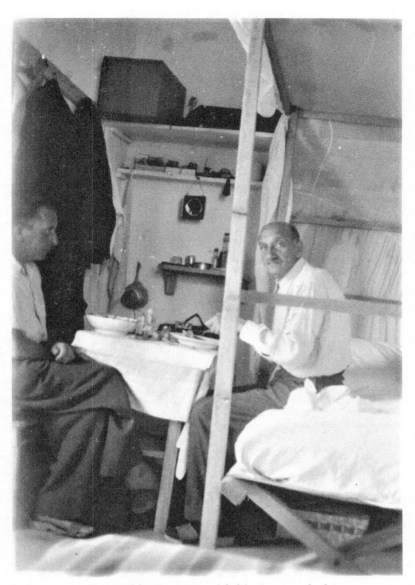

Batyushka Borstyn with his 4 poster bed

Mendelsen the artist (Michel Fingesten)

Mother and Child painting

Escape to the hills, August 1943

The Springers and Henry make for the hills

Santa Sofia d'Epiro, the Arbëreshë village

Leaving Ferramonti and later

In Taranto army base

Capt. D H Ropschitz, RAMC 1944

Capt. D H Ropschitz

Capt. Ropschitz and his men

Henry with wife Violet, Alassio 1954

Henry with wife Violet, Alassio 1954

Henry with Violet and children, Alassio, 1962

Henry with Dr Iso Friedmann (Dino) Genova, 1970s

ACKNOWLEDGEMENTS

I could not have completed this book without the help and support of the following people:

ITALY

TARSIA

Simona Celiberti, whose magnificent and selfless devotion to the Ferramonti Museum and its visitors is without parallel: the families of the internees can never repay you. Prof Mario Rende, for his encyclopaedic knowledge of Ferramonti, shared with good humour and patience, Maria Lavorato for her dedication and warmth towards the 'Ferramonti Family', to all the other wonderful volunteers without whom the Ferramonti Museum could not function, Ines Kant for translation advice, friendship and hospitality, the Municipality of Tarsia, for their generosity and continuing interest in my father's story, especially Roberto Ameruso and Roberto Cannizzaro, Angelo Paldino for identifying the Arbëreshë community of Santa Sofia d'Epiro.

NOTARESCO

The Municipality of Notaresco for their hospitality and kindness, Diego di Bonaventura, Mimmo Cusano, Marco Rapone, Stefano Pavone, Vincenzo de Sanctis.

GENOA

Cinzia Robbiano and Cesare Torre for finding the real 'Dino' in Genoa, sharing my first meeting with him and Ingeborg in 2016 and for translation help, Ingeborg Friedmann for being a vital link in the 'Ferramonti Family', my cousin Dr Emanuele Nussenblatt, son of my father's sister Anna and her husband, Dr Frederick Nussenblatt, for hospitality, generosity and kindness.

MILAN

Simonetta Heger, for our second generation friendship through our fathers, her hospitality and the wonderful musicianship she brings to Ferramonti to preserve the music and spirit of the internees. My cousins Fabio and Silvia Nussenblatt for supplying the details of my two murdered aunts Roza and Klara, who had, until recently, remained nameless, Natasha Nussenblatt for being the Milan social messenger, CDEC for permission to use the sketch of Ferramonti from the Israel Kalk Archives.

ROME

Film director Cristian Calabretta for *Ferramonti: Il Campo Sospeso*, his remarkable film which inspired me to finally publish my father's story. Anna Pizzuti, for her dedication to the Foreign Jewish Internees in Italy during the war; her database has proved invaluable to me and to Jews all over the world still searching for their lost families. Thank you for your spirit of humanity. We owe you so much.

ISRAEL

Dina Smadar for her pioneering work within the Ferramonti Museum, for helping create a wall of remembrance for my father and his friends in the camp, Eva Porcilan for friendship and supplying vital research data.

URUGUAY

Susannah Margoniner, granddaughter of Siegfried Margoniner who died in Ferramonti in 1940 and is buried in Tarsia cemetery, for her second generation Ferramonti friendship, her wonderful hospitality in Montevideo, her company on our South American travels and for her encouragement after reading the first draft.

AUSTRIA

Roswitha Klingemann, for accompanying me to the grave of Emanuel Ropschitz (Mundek) in the Vienna Central Jewish Cemetery, Eleonore Fischer for help with translations from the Jewish Community Archives, and for visiting my father's favourite Viennese haunts with me.

BELGIUM

My cousin in Brussels, daughter of my father's sister Helena, for help in identifying family photos over the last 5 years, for sharing a wonderful holiday with me in Bordighera, helping recreate the joy of the Liguria our parents loved so much.

AUSTRALIA

My cousin Lesley Roxon in Melbourne for help in identifying photos of my uncle, Dr Isydor (Izhio) Ropschitz.

USA

Norbert Goldfield, for being the son of Albert and therefore a second generation 'Ferramonti Family' member, for the details of his father Albert, Diane St Clair in Vermont for help in identifying old family photos of her grandfather, my uncle, Dr Leon (Lonek) Ropschutz.

ENGLAND

My mother Violet Harrington (Ropschitz) for essential post-war information about my father and support over the last four years, Colin Goodhind for his indispensable handiwork in Ferramonti Museum and loving kindness elsewhere, Dr Hilary Fraser for her encouragement and advice, my brother Manfred Ropschitz for his initial work on our father's story, Gordon Roxon for being my brother, Doreen Meal for her moral support to my father and his writing in those autumn years, all my friends for sustaining me along this journey of exploration. Peter Wright of 'Less Negative' for restoring old photos. Those unknown photographers whose work appears in this book.

Finally, my late father for helping me to understand him posthumously; better late than never, eh Dad?

Made in the USA
Las Vegas, NV
08 May 2024

89693767R00322